HOPE COTTAGE

HOPE COTTAGE

*The Journal of the Twelve Months spent
by Hugo and Gemma Loftus at Eastover in
Lewes in Sussex*

A NOVEL

BY

JULIAN FANE

Julian Fane

Hamish Hamilton and St George's Press

HAMISH HAMILTON LTD

Published by the Penguin Group
27 Wrights Lane, London W8 5TZ, England
Viking Penguin Inc., 40 West 23rd Street, New York, New York 10010, USA
Penguin Books Australia Ltd, Ringwood, Victoria, Australia
Penguin Books Canada Ltd, 2801 John Street, Markham, Ontario, Canada L3R 1B4
Penguin Books (NZ) Ltd, 182–190 Wairau Road, Auckland 10, New Zealand

Penguin Books Ltd, Registered Offices: Harmondsworth, Middlesex, England

First published in Great Britain by
Hamish Hamilton Ltd and St George's Press 1990

Copyright © Julian Fane, 1990

Filmset in Bembo

Printed in Great Britain by Butler & Tanner Ltd, Frome and London

A CIP catalogue record for this book is available from the British Library

ISBN 0–241–12871–4

To

CHRISTOPHER SINCLAIR-STEVENSON

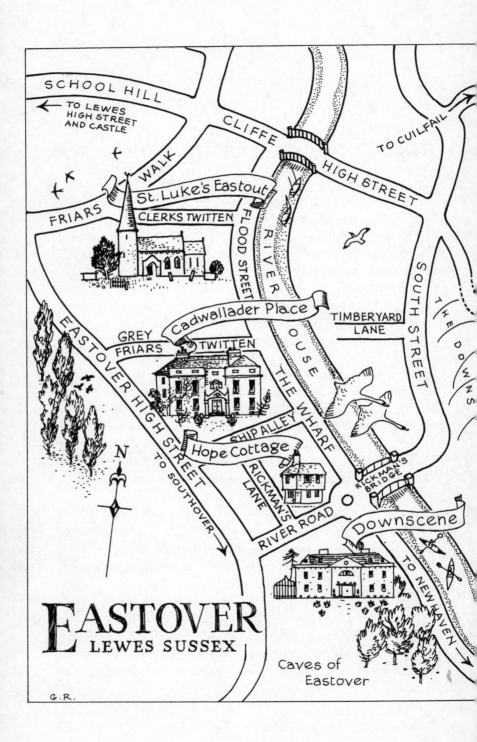

SCHOOL HILL

TO LEWES
HIGH STREET
AND CASTLE

CLIFFE

HIGH STREET

TO CUILFAIL

FRIARS

WALK

St. Luke's Eastout

CLERKS TWITTEN

FLOOD STREET

RIVER

OUSE

TO CUILFAIL

THE DOWNS

SOUTH STREET

Cadwallader Place

TIMBERYARD
LANE

GREY
FRIARS

TWITTEN

THE WHARF

EASTOVER HIGH STREET

To SOUTHOVER

N

SHIP ALLEY

Hope Cottage

RICKMANS
LANE

RICKMAN'S
BRIDGE

Downscene

RIVER ROAD

TO NEW HAVEN

EASTOVER
LEWES SUSSEX

Caves of
Eastover

G.R.

AUGUST

W ELL, HERE we are, thank God!
We arrived last Friday – it is now Tuesday – and
Lewes seems to be an even nicer place, and Hope Cottage is
definitely prettier and cosier, than we remembered.

Our village – I mean our part of the town – is called
Eastover. Looking towards Newhaven and the sea, Eastover
stretches along the right bank of the River Ouse.

The weather has been perfect so far – seasonable tem-
peratures, clear skies. We are reminded that Lewes is a mere
dozen miles from Eastbourne, which has more sunshine than
anywhere else in the British Isles. And it must have rained
overnight and refreshed the flowers in the garden. This
morning I followed Cindy out of doors and we stood and
savoured the aromatic air: the combination of the scents of
flowers and greenery and moist earth, and ozone from the
sea, and, emanating from some neighbour's kitchen, coffee
and frying bacon.

Cindy is our dog, a Cairn terrier, the grey kind, which
partly explains her fuller name, Cinders. Her fullest Scottish
pedigree name is Sweet Cinderella of Lomondside.

The Hope Cottage garden is actually a glorified backyard.
The space formed by several such backyards is almost completely surrounded by the rear elevations of other old dwellings and a modern block of flats. Alien roses and late clematis
intrude upon our privacy, and our vine sneaks through the
wattle hurdle of whoever lives nextdoor. The flint-white
antiquity of Lewes Castle, rearing up and commanding the

1

countryside, can be seen over the low roof of a line of garages.

Hope Cottage is 1 River Road, but could well be 25 Rickman's Lane. Our front door, guarded by a six-foot hollyhock growing out of the pavement, is on the corner – a diagonal cutting across a right angle. It opens into a dining-hall, which connects with the sitting-room, which contains the steep staircase. The kitchen is behind these two rooms and has a brick floor and a french window into the garden.

The upper storey boasts two bedrooms, a bathroom, and the dim slip of a study meant to be the scene of my literary labours: where I now sit in the easy chair jotting down these notes.

But the sunshine and the bright clear coastal light are again too much for me. Gem will soon be summoning Cindy for their stroll through the morning; and I want to be with them, and see the sights, and recruit my physical and mental forces – weakness overpowers me when I think of really writing my first book. I seem to need a holiday more than to get down to work. Besides, winter is on the way and bound to keep me indoors and my nose to the grindstone.

I wonder if I shall ever persuade Rachel to come and stay here. I feel sure it would do her good, and she would so love to explore the place.

Of course my dear sister's company would be yet another excuse to write nothing; and postponement in one's sixtieth year can easily look like an error of optimism.

WE WALKED to the top of Mount Caburn yesterday afternoon. Starting from the hamlet of Glynde, it took us about half an hour to reach the remains of the pre-Roman camp on the summit, where we sat on the sprung turf and looked down on the landscape.

The erstwhile defensive advantages of the site are obvious.

A hostile force would have had to attack it either up hill or along a narrow ridge.

We had approached by way of the ridge and a cart-track white with chalk, just as those even more ancient Britons must have done in peace and war.

The sea and the harbour wall at Newhaven were visible. A breeze wafted in – I swore I could taste salt. Swallows skimmed over the hilltop and soared and floated on the rising currents of air, and singing larks practised their diminuendos as they fluttered higher into the sky.

Cindy leant against Gem's knee. When Cairns feel like resting, they seem to want to make contact with their human friends: some will sleep on any available lap, others lean. Cindy sat with half-closed eyes, now panting with her tongue out, now shutting her mouth and twitching her black nose the better to partake of the cornucopia of smells.

'I think she thinks she's died and gone to heaven, what with country walks off the lead and always the chance of something to hunt,' Gem said.

We had brought a map with us, and we identified landmarks. Quaint old names tickled our fancy, Narroway Buildings, Pookhill Barn, and the Bottoms, Caburn Bottom, Oxteddle Bottom, Bible Bottom. Mount Caburn is a Down, which should have been called an Up, part of the South Downs, the range of chalk hills meandering from Eastbourne to Winchester. It is also one of the two sentinels at the eastern exit from the great plain in which Lewes is situated, the other being Firle Beacon, directly opposite us yesterday.

Firle Beacon is reminiscent of the shape of a whale, blunt-headed at its Eastbourne end and sloping more gently towards Newhaven.

The scenery round here amazes us, although we were taken on scenic tours when we stayed with Toby and Jane Whitaker. We approved as visitors of Lewes and its environs: whence the suggestion of a swap of our flat in London for their Hope Cottage. The big idea was that the Whitakers could have a year of metropolitan thrills and spills, while I would write my book and, with Gem and Cindy, revel in rustic pursuits – we three having been homesick for country as distinct from town. Anyway, now I can comment on the topography of East Sussex with all the assurance of a new resident. The Downs are more extraordinary than we knew, more beautiful, and mysteriously wild and unspoilt considering the crowds of people living and wanting to live in this particular region of the sunny south.

We offered up thanks to the local landowners and asked ourselves rhetorical questions as we gazed at the sequestered sunburned hillsides. Is downland so smooth because of sheep safely grazing? Are the hills bare because nothing much grows in chalk, or because saline zephyrs nip vegetation in the bud, or for esoteric agricultural reasons? What is the secret of the satisfaction afforded by a view of the shadows of the undulations, clefts, scoops and minor ravines of a downy panorama?

We lolled and looked at trains creeping along the Lewes-Eastbourne and Lewes-Newhaven lines like caterpillars, and cars catching the sun on their windscreens on the road to Brighton. An occasional dinghy braved the tides on the River Ouse, which writhed towards the misty sparkle of the open sea. From our vantage point Lewes was a molehill: in low-lying Eastover it seems to be a mountain.

Walking back I told Gem I had started to keep a sort of journal.

In her fond encouraging way she immediately compared it with books about writing books written by Proust, for instance, and Thomas Mann.

I had to warn her that if it was ever finished it would be more like *The Diary of a Nobody* without such good jokes.

THE VILLAGES that have been tacked on to Lewes in the last few centuries are Malling, Cliffe, Southover and Eastover –

4

or so I understand from the guidebooks I have read. There are also modern housing estates, Cuilfail, Landport, Nevill, Cranedown.

The centre of the town is almost literally as old as the circumambient hills. People have always liked to live in this pleasant place with its pleasant climate. The Romans planted vines here. The Normans built or rebuilt the Castle. And then the monks moved in.

The twin glories of Lewes following the Norman invasion were the Cluniac Priory in Southover, and the Grey Friars' establishment in Eastover. Monks for all their unworldliness are never slow to recognise, and develop, a prime piece of property. Both religious foundations were dissolved – or, to cut the euphemistic cackle, robbed and demolished – by that hooligan Henry VIII: who, by the way, granted one of his luckier wives both life after marriage and Anne of Cleves' House in Southover.

The more things change the more they are the same: Southover and Eastover have again become – in the lingo of estate agents – the more desirable residential areas. Some classic houses in Lewes High Street were grander – they now belong to bureaucrats; Victorian and Edwardian houses in the Wallands, The Avenue and Cuilfail have been fashionable; and at present the detached thirties-style houses in Houndean Rise are popular. Nevertheless, at least according to Toby and Jane Whitaker, persons of taste and discrimination still gravitate to Eastover in particular.

The Whitakers have a vested interest in publicising and promoting the location of their home, Hope Cottage, which is temporarily ours. But that is not to say they are wrong.

Eastover's picturesque muddle of streets and lanes, cobbled or paved with bricks, and often bordered by flowers, remind us of Rye, another hill town in Sussex. Narrow walled alleys separating back gardens are here called Twittens – an elided unification of the two words betwixt and between. Clerks' Twitten, connecting The Wharf with St Luke's Church and the churchyard, is delightful with the branches of trees reaching across its flint walls and shading it, and somebody's honeysuckle cascading down.

Flood Street and The Wharf are a modest equivalent of the part of Chelsea alongside the Embankment in London. Flood Street is about a hundred yards of Queen Anne and then Regency terraced houses overlooking the road and river. Its continuation, The Wharf, is dominated by a couple of mansions. The first, and the biggest, is Georgian, porticoed, in a bad state of repair, and stands behind an in-and-out drive. Each of its dilapidated stuccoed gateposts bears the legend in faded lettering: Cadwallader Place. It appears to be occupied, perhaps by a Cadwallader, whoever or whatever he, she or it may be.

The other must have been built in the 1950s; and the greenness of the semicircle of grass lawn in front, and the blackness of the tarmac of its drive on which pricey cars are usually parked, and the redness of its brick and the whiteness of the mortar and woodwork, make it look like a picture painted by an artist of the brutalist school. Gilded metal letters in twin arches above pairs of wrought-iron gates proudly and loudly spell out the mongrel name of this edifice: Downscene.

Not only the front elevation of Cadwallader Place and the pretentious embrasure of Downscene's front door, but humbler dwellings in the vicinity, hovels almost, sport blocks of stone expertly cut, shaped and sometimes carved. The Grey Friars' loss of their Friary in the sixteenth century has been the gain of their neighbours ever since. The same applies in Southover, where the majority of houses show more or less stone pinched from the Cluniac Priory.

Beyond Downscene is the third of the bridges of Lewes over the River Ouse, Rickman's Bridge, the others being Cliffe Bridge and the one known as the Phoenix Causeway. And still farther on is the roundabout on the main Eastbourne-Brighton road, which runs parallel to the sea.

The Wharf eventually links up with Cockshut Lane and Mountfield Road in Southover. The houses and bungalows in this southern suburb are poorer, although I believe they too sell for princely sums: condescension calls them the Caves. The porches of jerrybuilt villas are apt to contain six doorbells, and mattresses and prams to grow in front gardens.

Our River Road with Hope Cottage on its corner crosses the Wharf and Rickman's Bridge and joins South Street on the opposite bank of the Ouse.

What Eastover and Southover were originally over was a tributary of the river, the Winterbourne Stream, which has been canalised and re-directed via an underground drain.

BERTHA PRIOR is a study, as they say, meaning a character, which means an eccentric or interesting personality.

She is or was the Whitakers' daily lady, and has consented to look after us. She comes in not daily but for an hour on three mornings a week, and is the proverbial treasure, a real professional able to create order out of chaos with a flick of her feather duster.

She looks sixtyish and makes no secret of her eighty-odd years. Although rather heavily built, she is light on her feet – she still goes Old Tyme Dancing. She has a clear brown skin, fierce blue eyes behind rimless glasses, thick flat lips – they are positively Polynesian and would have appealed to Gauguin – and pretty iron-grey hair. She dresses well and seems to have an inexhaustible supply of frocks, skirts and twin-sets, not to mention pinafores. She was born and bred in Lewes. Her marital status is uncertain: she refers to a late husband – 'I buried that one' – suggesting other husbands, alive or dead. She owns a cottage along Rickman's Lane and a pair of Papillon dogs, confusingly called Minnie and Winnie. And she is an egoist on the grandest scale.

She does not converse: she voices paeans of praise of

herself. She is too clever to be exactly boring, she is more hypnotic. And she jolts her audience every now and then with an unsolicited insult.

For instance, she pats our dog and declares: 'Cinders is quite a nice little thing, but not as nice as my Minnie and my Winnie. They're beauties! They're properly exercised and fed. I've always had a way with animals – and people, for that matter. Some say it's men I have the best way with – which is only spite and jealousy. But I take no notice! I get up with the birds in the morning and let the birds sing me to sleep at night. I'm healthy! I go to bed with the sun nowadays – you can keep your telly! And I walk with my girls – we're street-walkers with a difference – we see everything and say nothing – my dogs are trained not to bark or be a nuisance.'

Gem and I were honoured with an invitation to call on Bertha yesterday evening. We arrived minus dog, evidently disappointing our hostess: she had groomed her two within an inch of their lives and tied pink satin ribbon round their necks in floppy bows. Against my better judgment I therefore fetched Cindy, who at once set on Minnie and Winnie, snarling and snapping at their pink bows. Our dainty darling was transformed into a shaggy wild beast lusting for blood in comparison with the Papillons, got up to look more than ever like butterflies, and social butterflies at that, and now trying to hide behind the furniture, moaning with terror. I had to shift the sofa to catch Cindy, Gem had to administer corporal punishment; but the savage breast of our pet was unsoothed, and we all departed in a hurry and in disgrace, while Bertha comforted older Minnie and younger Winnie, no doubt taking credit for their peaceable if somewhat craven behaviour.

Gem laughed off the incident, and drew my attention to the classless charm of the interior decoration of Bertha's home, the white paint and Cecil Aldin prints and chintz curtains and pots of geraniums on the window-sill.

Gem's romanticism is convinced by Bertha's distinctive attributes that she must be the illegitimate daughter of some superior local Don Juan.

If so, Bertha herself does not know it. This morning, having had the satisfaction of telling us that Minnie and Winnie had been sick all through the night, she was in a reminiscent mood. Her father was a boatman – or so she said and seemed to believe; he had worked on the barges that used to carry goods from Lewes to Newhaven and back again. Her mother had been a housemaid at Cadwallader Place: this admission was the cue for Gem to throw me a meaningful glance. Yes, Mr and Mrs Guy Cadwallader still lived at the Place, she replied to our questioning. What were they like? Oh – old-fashioned – at least he was – lord of the manor – that type. Cadwalladers had always been in Eastover, and probably always would be, she said: yes, Mr and Mrs Guy had a child, an only one, a boy, or rather the fully grown man he had become, Mr Peter. Bertha spoke Mr Peter's name with an unsuitable simper: surely she should be past half-smacking those lips of hers over the full growth of a member of the opposite sex.

Who lives at Downscene?

George and Madge Drewett, and Monica and that Reggie Drewett, she told us: they had business in Brighton, and were rich as you please, and had bought Cadwallader cottages cheap and knocked them down and built expensive to get the view of the river. Monica was the daughter of the house and had just come of age, and Reggie the son was twenty-five, Mr Peter's contemporary and crony.

We asked about our immediate neighbours, whose back-yards march with ours.

The occupant of 2 River Road is poor Mrs Aylward, Wendy Aylward, who, in Bertha's words, has never managed since her hubby ran off with his piece of fluff. The house round the corner, 24 Rickman's Lane, belongs to the Spedding woman, a widowed crippled pensioner losing the use of her legs – no wonder after making free with them for so long, Bertha added cattily.

BERTHA'S GOSSIP carries me back to Boltbrige, the village, our friends in the village, whose conversation was treasure-trove for students of snobbery.

I am thinking of the nomenclature employed not so much by snobs as by practical sociologists, exemplified equally by Bertha and the rude mechanicals of the Somerset of my youth. The answer to the question, 'What's in a name?' is or ought to be, for anyone interested in the class system, 'Everything!'

Bertha separated Cadwallader sheep from Drewett goats by means of nominal addition and subtraction. By putting in the Mister and leaving out the Cadwallader, she indicated she was on affectionately intimate terms with Mr Guy and Mr Peter, whose pedigree nonetheless entitled them to her respect. George Drewett without benefit of prefix was different: she scorned his filthy lucre. She would certainly not dare to call the Drewetts of Downscene George and Madge to their faces: all the more reason to do so behind their backs, in order to establish the fact that she never would kowtow to common or garden millionaires and social climbers.

Again, she called Reginald Drewett 'that Reggie': from which I deduce that he does not know his place or how to keep it, and, unlike his fully grown friend Mr Peter, lacks the passport of sex-appeal which facilitates the crossing of class frontiers.

The epithet 'poor' is pejorative in the popular vernacular: witness poor fool, poor cow, etc. It describes neither poverty nor suffering, subjects too humdrum for underdogs to dwell upon, but ineffectiveness. Mrs Aylward would be poor in Bertha's estimation because she let a piece of fluff get the better of her.

As for Mrs Spedding, what can she have done, how low can she have sunk, to merit the serious charge that she is a woman?

Incidentally, although Mrs Spedding's legs are alleged to have been liberal, I get the impression that Bertha's were not exactly conservative.

But the class distinctions of Lewes remind me not only of those of my birthplace, and the happy childhood and youth that my sister and I spent there once upon a time; also of Rachel now, not well, unhappy, and at the mercy of her marriage since Mama died and we sold Boltbridge Manor.

I shrink from writing about Rachel and her predicament. And I am well aware of the risks of advocating any sort of radical upheaval. Yet I cannot help wondering whether staying with us in Sussex might not be better for her than staying with Jim Claughton in Creedwell.

Boltbridge is not what it was – I am no longer its squire. Joking apart, our family home used to be in Somerset; but the part of Somerset that included the land of my fathers was amalgamated with a chunk of Gloucestershire some years ago. We went to sleep in one county, and bureaucracy waved its magic wand and behold, we woke up in another, Creedwell by name.

Somerset was lovely, but Sussex is preferable to Creedwell in my opinion, which Rachel would probably share. The South Downs are more dramatic than the foothills of the Mendips, and the proximity of the sea is a thrill. Moreover this county town in the prosperous south-east seems to be outgoing and friendly, whereas perhaps that agricultural community in the back of beyond in the south-west, just earning its keep from miserly soil, never was. And the political atmosphere as well as the air in Sussex is salubrious.

Gem and I particularly appreciate the friendliness of the shopkeepers of Lewes. We are used to London and getting kicked in the teeth in return for our custom, and are astonished to be greeted with smiles and polite offers of assistance.

In the Eastover Stores in Eastover High Street our bacon is even cut deliciously thin. The only other shop in Eastover is a newsagency selling sweets and cigarettes, presided over by two immigrants from Pakistan. The proprietor, Jahendra Patel, is thirtyish, handsome and with a twinkle in his eye; but the one who does most of the work is his uncle, a slight fifty-year-old in tinted spectacles, aquiver with sensibility and solicitude. I have shaken the latter's hand: it was like a tiny warm brown creature feigning death – its inoffensive passivity another outward sign of his inner conviction that the customer is always right.

At five o'clock every day I go to fetch my copy of *The Clarion*, the Lewes evening paper, and Jahendra's uncle hails me with grave courtesy.

'Mr Loftus, how are you, sir?'

'Not bad, thanks.'

'I am very glad, sir! And how is Madam?'

'She's well, thank you. I hope you are too.'

'Oh yes, sir. It is most kind of you to ask.'

'Could I have a *Clarion*, please?'

'Certainly, Mr Loftus. Will there be anything else, sir?'

'Not today.'

'Thank you, sir. No, no, sir – allow me to make a note of the money – nothing to pay. Good night, Mr Loftus.'

The fly – the gnat – in the ointment of our relationship is that I have not yet discovered how to address him. Is he another Mr Patel? Should I follow his example and simply call him sir?

Just a footnote: we are already addicted to *The Clarion* with its disastrous headlines. Yesterday's front page story was: 'Toddler casualty of catapult attack,' and today's: 'Triple tragedy for Lewes family.' The three tragedies were a son's motorbike accident that broke his leg, and the consequences of his father's heart attack, and his mother's additional distress because she had run over the family cat on the way to the hospital.

WE HAVE entertained our first guest in Hope Cottage.

Yesterday evening Mrs Aylward from 2 River Road, or Wendy since we are now on Christian name terms, knocked on our door at the cocktail hour, bearing a posy of flowers. She was effusively apologetic, so sorry not to have been around when we arrived, but had been away, staying with the Frobisher-Halyards: the flowers were an olive branch, she giggled. She seemed to take it for granted that we are members of the Frobisher-Halyards' social circle. Do we know them? Do they know us?

Wendy Aylward is about fifty, plump to the point of pudginess. She had a shiny silk scarf with a design of horses' heads loosely knotted round her neck. Her features were almost buried in whiteish face powder. She said she was devoted to the Whitakers and sure that any friend of theirs would be her friend: which reminded me that Toby and Jane, for reasons temporarily forgotten, regarded her as something of an enemy, or at least a liability.

We offered her liquid refreshment. She bridled; protested that she had come round to give, not to get; promised that alcohol was the very last thing on her mind; and asked for whisky with a splash of water. She had four between six-thirty and eight o'clock. There is nothing ineffective about her disposal of drink.

She told us she is an usher at Glyndebourne, which is only a few miles from Lewes: could she have meant an usherette? She told us her maiden name was Wilson-Firth. She told us about a certain Betsy Hooke, who lives in Flood Street, is frightfully clever and married to an unfaithful university don: Wendy acknowledged no connection between the frightful cleverness and the infidelity. She revealed rather more than friendship for a Graham Phipps-Hullett, gentle bachelor, retired and retiring, and resident in Lewes High Street. She probably yearns to regain in the Registry Office full membership of the double-barrelled club of Wilson-Firths and Frobisher-Halyards.

She grew increasingly confidential: the senior Cadwalladers were funny philistines; George and Madge Drewett were not out of the top drawer; Peter Cadwallader was cuddly and Reggie Drewett a scream. She mentioned a merry widow, Marian Travers, and made the annoying suggestion that I was bound to fall in love with her. She referred to Octavia Pritchett of Beggar's Roost, and to a couple of co-habiting men, Gregory Leplay and Charles Hart: she called them cave-dwellers – they live in or among the Caves of Eastover.

She declared she was bright green with jealousy when she thought of Toby and Jane in our glamorous flat in London, getting to concerts and art galleries and having the time of their lives. We corrected her. Gem said that our flat in the proletarian borough of Harrington was far from glamorous, and I that to get from there to concerts and galleries in the West End was both difficult and dangerous.

Wendy reverted to the subject of Betsy Hooke.

'I used to be Betsy's nextdoor neighbour. My married home was in Flood Street. You know my naughty old boy left me?'

She mistook our expressions of sympathy for interest in her marital problems. She therefore continued: her husband Derek, a solicitor, was keen on amateur theatricals, directed plays for the Eastover Thespians, cast Glenys Calthrop in *A Streetcar Named Desire*, and eloped with her after the dress rehearsal.

Wendy pronounced the name of Glenys Calthrop with satirical derision, then complained frivolously: 'It was so embarrassing on the first night – I mean for me, not for them – having to return money to people who had paid for their seats in advance, and tell everyone why the performance was cancelled.'

She giggled: 'Brian Hooke says Derek didn't only direct *A Streetcar Named Desire*, he took it. But Derek always was a one – and as a matter of fact Brian's another.' And she may have put the tragical comedy of her marriage in a nutshell: 'Derek bought me blue videos for Christmas. Naturally I wouldn't watch the dirty things – while he watched I did my knitting. Glenys was a physiotherapist, her business was bodies, she was quite at home with the seamy side of life. I was more romantic. From the word go, men in their shirt-tails and socks looked peculiar to me, and even more peculiar without them.'

She then spared our blushes by mounting the hobby-horse of divorcees. Derek with his legal training had been able to add injury to insult by robbing and ruining her, she said. Granted, he now had two wives to keep, and a big house in Brighton, and a litter of twins by Glenys – he was having to pay for his pleasure. But so far as alimony was concerned, he had wriggled off into the undergrowth pretty well scot-free.

'When I was young, I never knew what money was for. We had hordes of sweet family retainers who seemed to look after us for love. Marrying Derek was quite a come-down for me. I had to learn to be a humble housewife. Please don't think I'm bitter. I made a resolution not to be bitter when he chucked me out of Flood Street and dumped me in River Road. I thank my lucky stars every day that I've got the tiniest cottage of my own and two pennies to rub together. And Glyndebourne's a bonus, and so is having nice hospitable neighbours. But I shall have to love them and leave them – look at the time – I was brought up never to overstay my welcome. No, honestly, I must fly. Goodbye!'

After Wendy had gone, giggling pluckily and blowing coy kisses, we remembered that Toby and Jane had warned us she was a good sort but thirsty, and a paid-up member of that imaginary organisation The I.W.A., The Injured Wives Association.

TWO NOTEWORTHY occurrences: we have received an invitation to drinks on Sunday morning at Downscene, and a beautiful girl passed Hope Cottage at five-thirty yesterday afternoon.

Wendy Aylward must have given our names to Mrs George Drewett, who, according to her gilt-edged invitation card, will be at home to us next Sunday between 12 a.m. and 1.30 p.m.

The beauty passed the Rickman's Lane window and then the River Road window of our front-cum-dining-hall, where we were having a cup of tea. She is sweet sixteen or seventeen, blonde, at once slender and shapely, slightly sunburned, glowing, and was dressed for tennis and carrying a tennis racket. She was charmingly and ridiculously self-conscious, smiling at nothing and showing the pearliest teeth, brandishing her racket and attitudinising and glancing round, blue-eyed and blushing, vanity and modesty combined, trying to look grown-up without much success — as loose-limbed as a puppy, yet as ripe as summer fruit.

Who can she be?

Shortly after this vision had faded we paid a visit to Mrs Spedding, our neighbour in the other house adjoining ours. We knocked on the front door in Rickman's Lane, received no answer, found it was unlocked and walked in. There are two ground-floor rooms. In the farther one a television blared. I opened the door and poked my head round and saw an old woman slumped in an armchair with a budgerigar on her shoulder.

She was watching television, but suddenly caught sight of me and shrieked in a Cockney-ish accent: 'What do you want? You've come to mug me, haven't you? Don't you dare mug me, please!'

The budgerigar, also startled, made a mess on her cardigan and fluttered up to take refuge in his cage.

'No, no, we're from Hope Cottage,' I told her: but what with the television and her deafness she did not hear.

By now Gem too had edged into the room.

16

Mrs Spedding screamed at her: 'Oh you wicked witch, come to help him mug me at my age, you should be ashamed of yourself!'

At this point Gem proffered the pot of honey she had brought by way of a neighbourly gift.

'What's this? What is it, dear?' Mrs Spedding enquired in an expectedly mild tone of voice, then snapped with droll rage at the television set: 'Oh why can't you shut up?'

I asked her if she would like me to turn it off, and she uttered a heartfelt affirmative: 'Do, dear! they talk too much – I could chop their tongues in pieces!'

Explanations followed.

'Oh you did give me a fright, me and Timmy,' she said, referring to her budgerigar as Timmy and laughing. 'Mrs Whitaker told me you'd be at Hope Cottage – I should have guessed who you were.'

Timmy, apparently also reassured, fluttered back onto Mrs Spedding's shoulder and waddled towards his favourite position by her ear: her cardigan was patterned with his messes.

At her invitation we seated ourselves on hard chairs and chatted for half an hour. She is a clever humorous Lewesian of seventy-six, still pretty, a widow with a son called Bert, who, she claims, not only has a brain but knows how to use it. She gets a mid-day Meal-on-Wheels, has a Home-help, and receives an assortment of visitors, whence her unlocked front door.

'But,' she said, 'my legs have turned against me. They were my friends. Now I'd kill them if I could.'

She is sad not to be able to go upstairs to bed, or trot to the shops; and she is impatient to move into more convenient accommodation.

'I used to like this house, and having the garden and the lav out of doors. But it's getting awkward. The lav's most awkward. When I'm there, often I sit and think the journey was hardly worth it. And in cold weather it isn't half nippy.

Last winter I put Anti-freeze in the bowl.'

Is brainy Bert incapable of providing his mother with some form of indoor sanitation?

We kept that question to ourselves and asked aloud: when and where was she moving, and who was moving her?

'They are.' She jerked her head in the direction of County Hall and its Housing Department up on the hill. 'And soon, they promise. And into one of their central heated flats. But I've heard a few tall stories in my time.'

Who owned 24 Rickman's Lane?

She said she did.

Well – since it would be worth a small fortune, she could sell it and buy a flat for herself.

'Not I,' she retorted. 'Let them pay, if they're fool enough to do it.'

Evidently Mrs Spedding is still taking part in the national sport of obtaining something for nothing from the Welfare State.

She wanted to know if Bertha Didcomb was working for us.

Did she mean Bertha Prior?

'Prior, is it? She must have collared another husband while I wasn't looking. She always had more men than sense – and she wasn't married to every one of them neither. She lived with Diddy Didcomb along in the Caves – she practised her trade there. When he went for a drink in the pub, she waved from their first floor window at any fellow passing. I felt sorry for Diddy. I done him a good turn or two. And she can't forget it. What's the difference? We both had our share. And these days it's dogs for her and the bird for me – that's what we've come to. But once we could have got a cricket match going between us, her team against mine.'

She dismissed the shadow of her saucy smile and remembered herself, thanked graciously for the honey and asked us to pop in again.

Gem calls Mrs Spedding and Bertha, who were able to

mobilise twenty-two men to play cricket for love of them, the blest pair of sirens.

I HAD another unsatisfactory telephone conversation with Rachel. To start with I got through to James Claughton, commonly known as Jim, who held forth for a quarter of an hour on how the country should be run and he would run it. And when she was eventually allowed to speak, I could not hear too well because he kept interrupting her. She got angry with him, he got angrier, and my anger and anxiety made me speak sharply, which distressed her all the more – and, in turn, myself ditto.

She should ring me when Jim is out, or speak to me on a telephone in another room when he has nothing better to do than to curse her.

If only she felt well!

She was not very enthusiastic when I invited her to stay in Lewes. I suppose she knows she could not come alone: or perhaps she is nervous of being beyond the reach of Dr Ward. She wanted me to return to Boltbridge, and I vaguely agreed to. But the probability of trouble with the master of her house is a deterrent. I also dread the evidence of my own two eyes. She complains of various alarming aches and pains – she was born a hypochondriac.

We had a happier talk with the Whitakers. They rang to say they are as pleased with Thamesview Mansions as we are with Hope Cottage. We mentioned the invitation to Downscene and were urged to accept it: 'Study the wild life of Eastover while ye may,' Toby advised.

After supper on that telephonic evening we strolled into the town with Cinders. The weather was balmy – not a breath of wind – and the dusk was scented with the late summer flowers. We passed Cadwallader Place, where a dangling bulb under the portico shed a dim radiance on several cars of guests; then wondered in which house in

Flood Street Wendy Aylward had paid more attention to her knitting than to Derek Aylward's filthy pictures; and proceeded up School Hill, along Lewes High Street, and on and round and back by way of Rotten Row, Southover and Mountfield Road.

Twittens and the gaps between the houses on the ridge showed us views of the distant dip in the South Downs where the river flows into the ocean. The hills were a darker line of horizon; the dip was Newhaven, the lights of it twinkling and winking, strangely vari-coloured.

I said something about Lewes being too nice – more play than work – and not having begun my book – and the perennial distraction of worries in respect of Rachel.

We were in Rotten Row at the time, and had stopped to gaze over a garden wall and across the intervening three or four miles at the colourful winking lights.

Gem's advice was: 'Remember our address.'

SEPTEMBER

G EM LOVES autumn best. I love early spring, when twigs of trees are reddish and plants cautiously raise green heads to peep at the world. But the weather has been irresistible lately, and we spend our lives tramping round Lewes: spend, I insist, not waste. We wander and wonder, for the little we know of the history of the place invites speculation.

The site of the erstwhile Priory seems to magnetise us. The Mound in Southover, or Mount of Mountfield Road, was it part of the adjacent Priory? It is large, high, manmade, and a mystery: who were the men responsible for its making, and why did they make it? Is it connected with, is it the earth dug from, the sunken excavated area called The Dripping-Pan, now a football pitch? People say The Dripping Pan was something to do with the manufacture of salt. But why should anyone bother to manufacture salt by means of extensive earthworks, when the sea was and is a few miles away?

South of The Mount is a bowling-green. A ladies' match was in progress on the chequered lawn the other evening: a dozen stout matrons in white shirts and skirts and stiff-brimmed white hats solemnly competing. At a lower level is Convent Field, a huge recreation area stretching as far as the bypass, with the Tennis Club and the Priory Ruins on its western side.

Although the so-called Ruins are not much to look at, just some unconnected flint walls sprouting weeds, they give

21

an idea of the size of the buildings of the Priory. The monastic lavatory was one hundred and fifty-six feet in length, or fifty-two yards, or forty-seven and a half metres. The length of the church was four hundred and fifty feet, or one hundred and fifty yards, or one hundred and thirty-seven metres. I feel like asking: how long, O Lord, could the dormitory have been? And was there a convent in Convent Field, full of nuns to tantalise and be tantalised by the monks in close proximity?

On these September Saturdays the last games of the summer's cricket have been played there: it can accommodate three simultaneous games. The shadows of the players grow and elongate as the sun sets – the flannelled figures become heroes keeping winter at bay. We beat the bounds of Convent Field, dragged round by Cindy, who chokes on her lead in her eagerness to chase the cricket balls and generally join in. Groups of the members of batting sides, padding up, practising airshots, lying on the grass, clapping from time to time and idly chatting, summon bitter-sweet memories of my schooldays.

In the course of a circuit of Convent Field we caught another glimpse of that beautiful girl: she was using the tennis racket we had seen her carrying in Rickman's Lane. On one of the courts of the Southdown Tennis Club she was playing against, or perhaps it would be more accurate to say she was playing games with, a brown-faced black-haired broad-shouldered man in his mid-twenties, seven or eight years older than herself. His distinctive garment was a pair of red linen slacks. She wore a clinging pink T-shirt and abbreviated skirt – her figure is faultless, and its lissom fragility has a certain pathos as well as sex-appeal. And she glowed – her hair and her skin emitted a golden effulgence – and the flashing blue of her eyes and the pearliness of her teeth were thrown in for good measure.

I would defy feminism and denigrate her tennis by describing it as girlish: she had more style than energy – she

22

started well and finished weakly with hopeless cries and giggles.

They packed it in as we watched. After a flirtatious confabulation at the net, including her mock-chastisement with his racket, they collected their gear and walked towards the clubhouse. He had tied the sleeves of her pink sweater round her neck, and now he put an arm round her flexuous waist and she rested her head on his chunky shoulder. Then they separated, she ran ahead, nimble and feeble, he pursued and caught her, muscular and cocksure, and they embraced and laughed and progressed hand-in-hand, respectively yielding and assertive.

Gem's soft heart was touched by this show of romance, and she called me hard-boiled for saying the girl looked too innocent and her companion too experienced.

Gem's optimism complements my pessimism. In spite of having reached the age of discretion, she still hopes that journeys end in lovers meeting, and when lovers have met they will live happily ever after. And her feeling for the autumn is not clouded, as mine is, no doubt by having been responsible for the upkeep of Boltbridge Manor, by fear of the damage that the weather will shortly do to property and purse. Although she is my saving grace, she has not managed to exorcise the ghost of my apprehensiveness.

But after all apprehensiveness is the basis of the book I mean to write.

BERTHA INFORMS us that the tennis girl is Tracy Wilkins, only child, object of worship, and arbiter of the fate of Naomi and Bert Wilkins, who are our neighbours in Rickman's Lane and actually live nextdoor to Bertha herself in a house exactly the same as hers, but differentiated from it by the name Rookery Dene.

Bert Wilkins runs the Gentlemen's Outfitters in Lewes High Street founded by his wife's father, Caleb Hocking.

'Bert was the delivery boy. But he jumped over the counter of the shop straight into Naomi's arms – he married his boss's daughter – and she inherited everything from old Caleb. They're well suited, I will agree, because Naomi's as pushy as he is – calling their home Rookery Dene and hitching up their lace curtains – and making so much of young Tracy.'

Bertha piled competitiveness on egocentricity during our discussion of Tracy's charms.

'Funny, isn't it,' she simpered, 'but I can't see she's pretty. I still think of her with jam round her mouth. She was a mucky one and no mistake – they couldn't keep her clean when she was little for all their fussing. She's grown up better than anyone expected – you'd never guess how spoilt she is to look at her. I feel sorry for the girl, I do! That milk and water colouring won't last – she'll fade and wrinkle – and men won't pay her compliments or the bills – not any more. At her age I was called the prettiest thing in the whole wide world, so I know what I'm talking about. But I was luckier, having a lovely olive complexion, which never has let me down. Now I'm blowing my trumpet, aren't I? Well, I'd rather put it the Bible's way: I'm not hiding my light under a bushel for no one.'

Bertha was strangely stirred by our mention of the red slacks of Tracy's partner for tennis and so on.

'Red, were they? He's at her, is he? He doesn't let the grass grow! No wonder Naomi's nose is in the air.'

She explained to us that the legs inside the red slacks belonged to Mr Peter Cadwallader, son and heir of Mr Guy.

And she wagged a metaphorical finger at Tracy: 'Silly goose! She's hoping to march into Cadwallader Place through the front door in order to climb the stairs to the bedrooms. But unless I'm much mistaken, it'll be Tradesmen's Entrance for the Wilkins family, same as usual.'

We edged in a defensive word: Tracy had seemed to be in love, not eyeing the main chance.

Bertha snorted with cynical laughter: 'They're all after Mr Peter for one reason or another. As for love – well – I've had more than Tracy's ever likely to. They won't stop buzzing round for it, men won't – you should see them at Old Tyme Dancing – though nowadays they have to be satisfied by a Viennese waltz. No – love's nice, but it isn't a ring on your finger. It doesn't make an honest woman of you, let alone a lady. She'll rue the day, you mark my words.'

Later, when we were on our own, Gem advanced the theory that Bertha might be moved by filial pity to have a go at Tracy: since her mother had got nothing from the Cadwalladers except a baby, namely herself, why should Tracy get more?

I tried to bring my imaginative wife down to earth by explaining that Bertha is just typically British in wanting to put Tracy in her place in a class sense, and keep her there.

On the subject of earth and being brought down to it: Jane Whitaker has asked us to help to celebrate Toby's sixtieth birthday at a dinner party in London. Toby is almost my exact contemporary. I knew it, yet was shocked to be reminded of his age and mine, and of the shortness of the longest possible period in which – amongst other things – to realise my literary ambitions.

Gem agrees with me that we have neither the time nor the inclination to leave Lewes, and nowhere to spend a cost-free night in London, so we are going to wish Toby many happy returns from a distance, and stick in the mud.

WHEN MAMA was widowed, I assumed responsibility for her welfare, her material welfare at any rate.

But Father died thirty-five years ago, and Mama lived to be ninety-two, longer than either of us bargained for.

Materially, financially, most of the family fortune was confiscated by egalitarian collectivist politics. I marked time

25

in the army, and frittered it away teaching English to foreigners, and commuted from London to Somerset year in and year out, and presided over ruination. In fact, selfishly speaking, the major part of my adult life was a struggle with the sums that were meant to add up to my mother's peace of mind, and definitely subtracted from mine.

At last I travelled the hundred and fifty miles from Thamesview Mansions to Boltbridge Manor in hopes of burying my frustration and exhaustion and exasperation in her small grave.

Two years have elapsed since then. I miss her increasingly. And I have not begun my book.

Would-be writers who write nothing are as common as muck. But my literary or un-literary situation when I was looking after Mama, doing my duty and not much else, struck me as exceptional and excusable. Now I must not let concern for my sister come between me and the blank sheet of paper.

Rachel rang up yesterday evening – Jim had not returned from some race meeting. She began by being brightly imper-sonal. But although we have never been confidential friends, the blood we have in common cannot keep a secret, and I realised she was desperate.

I said: 'It's so nice, talking to you without interruptions. Couldn't you ring more often when Jim's out?'

Her reply was edgy and obliquely negative: 'You should be here on the day our telephone bill arrives.'

'Well – reverse the charges.'

'If he discovered you were paying for my calls, he'd think he was being patronised.'

I changed the subject, urging her to come and stay with us in Lewes.

Her inconsequential enquiry warned that Jim would have to tag along: 'When are Brighton Races?' – and was tan-tamount to a refusal.

'Well – what about us coming to see you? We could drive

26

over for a meal – it's not all that far – we could bring a picnic – if and when it suited.'

'Wouldn't that be fun?'

I was upset by her non-committal answers, and blurted out: 'How are you, Rach?'

Not good, she said – bad – did not know what was wrong with her – Dr Ward either could not or would not tell her – and it was impossible – her marriage – life – and she was so sorry – sorry to feel rotten and be miserable – sorry to unburden herself and burden me with her misery – sorry she had ever been born – sorry, sorry!

It was awful. She was crying, and I tried in vain to be philosophical.

Then she suddenly said she was quite okay, and goodbye.

I dared not ring back in case I got through to Jim. He must have arrived home, and I might have quarrelled with him and made matters worse.

I interrogated Gem as to what I should do, what anyone could do, and, once more, what Rachel had done.

The charm of Jim Claughton is not obvious. Ex-amateur jockeys, he-manikins with fire in their bellies and iron in their souls, are probably an acquired taste. I suppose he is a descendant of Surtees' heroes, a pint-sized grittier version of Mr Sponge, for instance, or the horsey character who was galvanised gristle.

Is it ungenerous to suggest that Rachel's circumstances at the relevant trysting-time would have lent enchantment to any suitor? She was getting on for forty, a childless widow, immured in a house that was too big for her, frightened and lonely. She seems to have knuckled under to Jim as soon as he strutted into her life in his cavalry twill and battered trilby. Yet she had had one unhappy marriage and ought to have been twice shy of a second. And however fit and well she then was, she should have taken into consideration the tough attitude of her intended to ill health.

Gem believes Rachel loved Jim in the first place, and that

her feelings for her husband, ambivalent as they are, may still in the main be loving.

Who knows?

The practical answer to that question and all the others boils down again to the stoical adage: what cannot be cured must be endured.

Like the Editor of *The Clarion*, we will have to find comfort in catastrophe. His banner headline yesterday was: 'Parson indecently assaulted by choirboys.'

THE SUNDAY of the Drewetts' party dawned pearly and dewy, as they say. The chill morning mist had cleared by nine o'clock, and the sun resumed its work of carving shadows in the hillsides.

We went to Matins at Eastover Parish Church, St Luke's, officially called St Luke's Eastout – Eastout meaning without or outside the ancient walls of the town in an easterly direction. It stands behind and above The Wharf, a simple flint-faced barn-like edifice, its flints not marvellously knapped and squared like those of St Michael's in Lewes High Street, but knobbly and blackened by time; and it has a round tower at its western end, housing bats and bells. We walked to it by way of Clerks' Twitten.

We have been to services there on several of these last Sundays: religious observance is so much easier in the country. The bells have succeeded in summoning us to worship, as they were always meant to. St Luke's seems to have only two, one with a higher note than the other. But there is a four-bell peal at St Thomas's, just across the river at Cliffe; and the tunes played by the ten bells of St John The Baptist's at Southover drift across, like echoes of the peal which must have rung out from the great medieval belfry of the Priory.

The bells of the churches of London provide more variety and volume. The bells of Rome and Venice are more melodious. Yet for some reason the bells of Lewes sound irresistibly sweet to me.

I hope the Almighty stretched a point and pardoned the even less religious reason for our churchgoing on the relevant Sunday: we were sneaking a preview of neighbours who might be at the Drewetts' do.

There were about twenty of us not quite gathered together for the service, but scattered in the pews, which could have held two hundred. Wendy Aylward made a friendly face at Gem from the recesses of a large gaudy headscarf. She was sitting with a long-nosed woman in a stiffly conventional tweed coat and skirt. The first lesson was read by a man of sixty or so with a purple complexion and insecure false teeth: we had heard him reading before, or rather not heard him, for he fluffed almost every word and mispronounced the proper names. At the end of it, having told us with difficulty that it endeth, he returned to what might have been a family pew with a tall wooden back, above which a female head of badly dyed black hair was visible – her body was hidden: we wondered if they were the Guy Cadwalladers. The second reader was a Falstaffian figure complete with paunch, double-chins and pop-eyes, wearing a glossy grey suit: surely our host to be, George Drewett.

The rector of St Luke's is the Reverend Crispin Peterson. He is middle-aged, married with brats galore, and has a shiny complexion, jutting chin, and thin fair hair ruthlessly flattened down and brushed back. He is a jogger, a moral as well as a physical jogger, so to speak, keeping in trim for God's sake. Although we are the more thankful to be his parishioners because he uses the good old English Bible and Prayerbook, we suspect he may turn out to be a wolf in sheep's clothing, or, in clerical terms, a modern evangelical in the vestments of a traditionalist, and at some embarrassing moment will put our Christian principles to the test by asking us to embrace a total stranger.

29

The subject of Mr Peterson's sermon was AIDS. His sermons seem to treat of matters not of consuming interest to his sleepy superannuated congregation, for instance abortion, or the politics of Nicaragua. He now exhorted us not to transmit our viruses sexually. If the males amongst us were to give in to our ungovernable lust, the least we could do would be to wear a condom, he argued, notwithstanding his cowlike wife and six children in the choir stalls.

Actually there was one member of the congregation who, if only because of his eighteen or nineteen years of age, might have derived benefit from these fulminations. He was standing at the back of the church. As we turned to leave, his appearance hit us in the eye. He was a punk with a cockscomb haircut, that is to say his skull was shorn except for an inch-wide strip of hair from forehead to nape of neck, which was somehow persuaded to stand on end, and was gold at its base, then orange, then pea-green. He had safety-pins in his visible ear, and was dressed in leather, studded jerkin, bandolier, belt, trousers, boots, and dangling straps between his legs. His countenance was contradictorily mild, pale and spotty.

I am sorry to say he activated my prejudices: I was convinced he had come to church to mock, was the next best thing to a Hell's Angel or the worst, a nihilist, an iconoclast in the fashionable brainless mould, and would probably make off with the silver candlesticks on the altar.

In the churchyard Wendy Aylward rushed and gushed at us, and introduced us first to her companion, Miss Pritchett, the Octavia Pritchett of the Cave of Eastover that rejoices humbly in the name Beggar's Roost; and secondly to Mrs Travers, Marian Travers, the lady she expects me to fall in love with.

Miss Pritchett is probably younger than me, but I hope she looks older. I would call her hard-bitten if I could imagine anyone daring to bite her. Her manner is as stiff as her tweeds, and she seems to parry friendly overtures with her long sharp nose. Instead of shaking hands she either bowed minimally, or tossed her head at us.

Marian Travers may be the exception to the rule that one cannot have too much of a good thing. There must be nearly six foot of her, and her hands are as big as flippers. To my way of thinking she is more a handsome grenadier than a femme fatale. She has the true-born Englishwoman's horse-face.

She is nonetheless attractive with her creamy colouring, blonde hair, which could be naturally curly, soft blue eyes, full mobile lips, gleaming teeth and maturely curvaceous outline: she is in her mid-thirties. She was wearing a showy black velour hat and a tight-fitting grey outfit. Was she in mourning? When and where did she lose Mr Travers? Grief was conspicuous by its absence from her phlegmatic small talk and composed smiles.

While it was being established that we were all heading for the Drewetts', the leather-bound punk passed by.

To my surprise Wendy greeted him: 'Good morning, Jeremiah' – at which he smirked shyly.

Miss Pritchett expressed her opinion loud enough for him to hear it: 'Ludicrous!'

I asked who he was.

'That's Betsy and Brian Hooke's little lad,' Miss Pritchett replied; 'and good luck to them,' she added with a malicious chortle, as we moved off towards Downscene through the sparkling mote-filled autumnal air and the smoke of weekend bonfires of fallen leaves.

GEM AND I lead such mercifully quiet lives that we were daunted by the crowd and the hubbub in the Drewetts' front hall.

Not only the company and the hall itself were large. Outsize flowers and branches of greenery were arranged in a sort of brass dustbin on a central table. In a massive fireplace a tree-trunk smouldered. Guests seemed to be sipping cock-tails out of vases.

A woman with steel-grey hair like a helmet, also armour-plated by an unmistakeable corset, heavily made up – every eyelash mascaraed, and wearing a smart silk dress, emerged from the throng to welcome us.

'Hullo! I'm Madge Drewett. So glad you're here! Come in, come in!'

She is roughly my age; laughs a lot; drawls her words with her mouth open; tacks a 'dear' on to almost every sentence, pronouncing it 'dar'; and is shamelessly repetitive.

'So glad you're here!' She pronounced it 'har'. 'Have you met the Drewett gang, dar? You must meet the Drewett gang. Whar are the Drewett gangsters? Follow me, dar, and help find the wicked ones.'

The gangster she introduced us to was George, her husband, who had indeed read the second lesson in church. His girth is decidedly Falstaffian, but at close quarters his pear-shaped face and sticking-out front teeth and quivering jowls are more reminiscent of an overgrown hamster. His grin is benevolent, although his pop-eyes manage to be beady and again remind me of some rodent.

George passed us on to Monica, the younger of the two Drewett children, who is dark-haired, brown-eyed, fleshy and fertile-looking, but cursed with her father's protruding front teeth. I thought she was a bit offhand: no doubt she was preoccupied by love. She had nothing much to say to us and vanished as soon as her brother hove into view.

Reggie, in a manner of speaking, is the skeleton in the cupboard of the Drewetts' social pretensions. He is the weak link – almost the missing link – between their old poor past and new rich present. Obviously he does not, and never could or would, belong in Wendy Aylward's top drawer with the Wilson-Firths and Frobisher-Halyards.

He approached us with empty glasses clipped between the fingers of one hand and a jugful – a ewer full – of iced liquid in the other, singing out in crude imitation of a Sussex accent: 'Make way for the marts! Them there marts do be coming!' By marts, he meant dry martinis.

Reggie has eyes which might be called Drewett-size, that is too big, and too blue and hot and disingenuous; thick straight hair parted in the middle and so greasy that the track of each tooth of his comb can be seen; a beetroot-coloured face and the chatty cheek of a door-to-door salesman. He wore a loud check suit with a sprig of honeysuckle in the buttonhole.

His greeting was poetic: 'Have no fear, Reginald's here!' He thrust glasses at us, sloshed marts into them, and wanted to know who the hell we were.

When our identity had been established, he asked in his Sussex accent: 'Met Squire yet?'

He explained to me: 'Squire Cadwallader, old boy, and his lady-wife – have you had the pleasure of their acquaintance?'

I said no, at which he yodelled through the flower arrangements: 'Foxy-poxy!'

We and the Cadwalladers had to introduce ourselves to one another: by the time we had edged round the table with the flowers on it, Reggie was dispensing marts elsewhere.

Foxy-poxy, otherwise Mrs Guy Cadwallader, has the dyed black hair with the henna-orange and the white roots showing through, which I had noticed in church. Her dress was a stained brown sack that had got hitched into her knickers behind: she must come out of a drawer even above the one containing Wendy's family, the Wilson-Firths, to dare to dress like that. She giggled loosely at Maurice's mode of addressing her – and loose is the right word, since her denture nearly fell out when she laughed, just as her husband's had when he read the lesson: they probably go to the same dentist.

We shook hands.

Guy Cadwallader said: 'Good health!' – dropping the aitch for comic effect. He is tall and tweedy, a genial and jovial OAP. Both Cadwalladers drained their glasses in our honour, or anyway drained their glasses, and held them out for more of the same from George Drewett, who happened to be passing with another ewer of the dry martini mixture: Maurice's suggestive recipe for which was that the gin should not be violated by the vermouth.

George's amusing accusation: 'Talk of the Ancient Mariner dying for a drink – you two are even thirstier!' – caused toothy laughter all round.

Mrs Cadwallader insisted on our calling her Foxy: 'I've forgotten my first name, I was christened so long ago.' Then she tugged at the coat-tail of an adjacent male, sniggering at the familiarity of her gesture. When he turned, we recognised the handsome beast who had played with Tracy Wilkins at the Southdown Tennis Club: 'our boy Peter,' as Foxy told us unnecessarily.

He is sun-tanned and square-jawed, and has flattish crinkly black hair. He now wore a charcoal-grey double-breasted flannel suit and suede chukka boots. He seems inarticulate to the point of dumbness, and to express himself largely by means of twitches, blinks and grimaces. He mouthed politely in our direction, and his eyebrows slanted and his shoulders heaved with humour in response to one of his mother's sallies; but, perhaps because of a late influx of guests and decibels, he might have been acting in a silent film so far as I was concerned.

Wendy Aylward, a proud smile on her powdery face, was dragging a woman towards us: I was reminded of a labrador wagging its tail as it retrieves a dead pheasant.

'I wanted you all to meet,' she panted. 'Here's Betsy Hooke.'

Mrs Hooke must have wanted something different: she smiled at us with reluctance – it was really more of a sickly snarl. She is extraordinarily colourless: someone said she ought to be hanging in a kosher butcher's shop. She is middle-aged, has lank hair and a pudding-basin haircut, and

34

was wearing no make-up and a sexless thick-knit beige pullover reaching almost to her knees.

I shook her limp hand: which made me feel like that madman in the Steinbeck story who does not know his own strength and strangles kittens by accident.

And I mentioned having caught a glimpse of her son Jeremiah at St Luke's.

'Poor Jeremiah!'

Her voice was crisp, but had a sighing dying fall. It sounded irritable as well as arrogant to me.

I assumed she was pitying Jeremiah – and herself as parent – on account of his appearance, and attempted to comfort and reassure her: 'Oh well – I'm sure I made myself look ridiculous at his age – I'm sure he'll grow out of that sort of nonsense.'

She retorted: 'I don't think he looks ridiculous,' laying emphasis on the 'I' and the 'he', thus implying that I was lagging behind the times, and I was the ridiculous one to look at.

She continued: 'I think he's beautiful. I think he dresses beautifully. I'm accustomed to the modern idiom, you see. I'm just sorry for Jeremiah, because he's under pressure from boring conventional people – and mainly because he was wasting his precious young life in church.'

WENDY GIGGLED uncomfortably and tried to remove the sting from Betsy's radical waspishness by saying: 'She's priceless, isn't she? She never lets one down.'

Betsy may never let Wendy down; but down is where she had tried to put me.

Brian Hooke joined our group. He teaches at Sussex University, which was founded and built not long ago between here and Brighton. He is an improbable Don Juan: stocky, bespectacled, desiccated, provocative: the last adjective refers both to his manner and manners.

'How are you liking our "Hlaew",' he demanded with spirited pedantry.

I begged his pardon.

'"Hlaew" – Old English for town – whence Lewes – are you liking it?'

'Very much,' I replied.

'Ah – but autumn has come, so winter cannot be far behind,' he warned, allowing himself a self-congratulatory smile at his revised version of the quote. 'Our maritime climate in winter is apt to play rough.'

He then scraped almost the bottom of the conversational barrel by asking what I did and was doing in Lewes.

My answer was no more sophisticated than his question.

I said: 'I'm a gentleman of leisure at present.' I was trying to protect the tender shoots of my literary aspirations from the lethal rays of academic scrutiny.

'Oh but how refreshing!' he exclaimed, his horn-rims glinting with egalitarian satire. 'It's many a moon since I've met a genuine gent. I can't say I've ever met a gent who was genuine. Gentlemen lived hereabouts once upon a time, even the odd duke, suchlike odds and so-and-sos of the older school, who ground the faces of the poor in the approved fashion; alas, no more, no longer – gentlemen have gone the way of the bustard – the bustards and the bastards, if you'll excuse the alliteration, have ceased to be – and we're left to sink or swim without a single gent to pull our forelocks to. But now you claim to be one! Betsy, my dearest, we have a rara avis in our midst. Or should I say something less avian and more fishy? Has the equivalent of the coelacanth propelled itself into our backwater? It's a real live gentleman, my love!'

Gem rescued me by plucking at my sleeve. She had been talking to a couple of male guests – far be it from me to expose them to verbal assault and battery by calling them gentlemen. One was tall and elegant with wings of grey hair and sideburns, the other bright red – the little hair he had

36

was red, and he was red–skinned, red–handed and seemed to be red–eyed.

Gem said to them: 'I'd introduce you to my husband, but I'm afraid I didn't catch your names.'

The taller of the two was Gregory Leplay, and the short red one Charles Hart.

Charles asked me: 'You're the new boy, aren't you?' – with an absurdly flirtatious leer.

Reggie Drewett approached, his hands full of marts and Marian Travers.

'Drink up or for ever hold your peace,' he proclaimed, mispronouncing the last word: he was scolded for his smutty catch-phrase.

Marian and Gregory exchanged pecks on the cheek.

He said: 'La belle Marianne!' and she: 'Hullo, Grégoire!'

Reggie commented: 'Mind out, you frogs, mind out for your legs!' and moved on, having charged our glasses unsteadily.

The talk turned to Glyndebourne, the operatic Festival there. I amused the three locals, Marian and Gregory and Charles, by saying we might buy some seats or drop in to see the fun. They corrected me. They informed me that I had missed the boat, the Festival finished in early August after starting in late May, and that the opera house was small, and seats were in short supply, extremely expensive, and by no means easy to obtain even if I could afford them: long-term supporters of the establishment at Glyndebourne, amateurs of opera and professionals, corporate members and sponsors crammed in for every performance.

Had they themselves been to Glyndebourne? What was it like, was it worth going, was it worth the money it cost to go, I asked.

Further polite mirth was the reaction to my clearly ignorant queries.

Marian admitted that she wangled seats by hook or by crook every year.

Charles wagged a red finger at me: 'Don't you take tickets if you don't want them – they might be the very ones I would have got!'

Gregory Leplay was more explanatory. He is some sort of designer, businesslike and dignified. He said: 'Glyndebourne's a country house in the Sussex Downs. John Christie, whose family had owned it for donkey's years, married an opera singer; and they built their theatre for opera behind the old house in 1934, and employed all the best musicians and producers who were fleeing from Hitler. The highest standards were set, and, strange to relate, have been maintained ever since. The performances and the place, and the whole idea for that matter, are remarkable: how would you persuade mostly English people to travel miles in their evening clothes to pay a packet to see an opera – even if tickets here are a bargain compared with Salzburg? The Festival's over for this year, but there are previews of the operas that are taken on tour in October. Seats for the previews are reasonably priced, and you might be lucky if you applied for some without delay. Although October evenings can be dark and nasty, and you won't get the Glyndebourne garden, you'll find the productions first-rate.'

Madge Drewett barged in vocally, drawling in the style of a music-hall comedian: 'I say, I say, you rotters – show respect for my Dadda!'

This incomprehensible injunction referred to the bald-headed bottle-nosed dog-collared clergyman she was shunting into our circle.

Madge greeted Gregory and Charles, translating the name of the former into French as Marian had done, but so mangling it in the process that it would have to be spelt thus: Grogwour.

'Hullo, Grogwour dar! Hullo, dar Charles!'

She turned to Gem and me, laying a plump hand heavy with rings on my shoulder: 'You two dars must meet Dadda Byrne. He's a Roman from Dublin – such good value –

aren't you, dar? I don't call him Father – he's Dadda to me, because I love him so. Now, Grogwour, and you, Charles dar, you're not to tease my own Dadda!'

By this time I had gathered that Father Byrne was the priest in charge of the Roman Catholic Church in Eastover High Street.

He grinned at us benignly, showing teeth either blackened or missing. Madge removed herself, and Gregory told the new arrival on the scene that we had been discussing Glyndebourne.

'Well, here's a funny thing,' Father Byrne began, somewhat overdoing the soft Irish brogue and the fey Celtic charm: 'Lewes has several thousand houses, whereas Glyndebourne has only the one house, plus a few cottages. But Glyndebourne's bigger than Lewes in the eyes of the world. Lewes is Glyndebourne's satellite. It's Glyndebourne's dormitory. Take the company here present: Marian rents out her top-floor flat to singers in the summer. Gregory's done work for the Programme Book. Wendy Aylward's not the only Usher in this room. Peter Cadwallader and Reggie Drewett both shifted scenery when they were teenagers. And I live in hopes of a Prima Donna coming to glorify God in my church and draw a larger congregation. We're all just extras in a Glyndebourne opera. We're the chorus of peasants.'

Guests were departing with more of a bang than a whimper: it was already half-past one. Over by the door the laughter was tipsily loud, kisses were smacking and goodbyes on the maudlin side.

Not many of us were as sober as we had been. I should have known that my weak head would be no match for the strength of Reggie's marts. I hope I did not shake the hands of Gregory and Charles with a warmth that could be misinterpreted.

We made for the exit and found ourselves face to face with Jeremiah Hooke.

According to Gem, I startled the wretched youth by addressing him in a censorious and oppressive tone of voice: 'How do you do, Jeremiah! I'm Hugo Loftus and this is my wife Gemma. We're from Hope Cottage, where you wouldn't be able to stand up straight – your cockscomb would hit the ceiling!'

Luckily Gem pushed and pulled me towards our host and hostess, from whom we parted – or I did – with expressions of deepest gratitude and undying friendship.

Reggie Drewett and Peter Cadwallader, thick as thieves, and Foxy and Father Byrne, arm–in–arm and perhaps supporting each other, were ranged round Guy Cadwallader, who was offering cigarettes from his cigarette case. The case was either old-fashioned or new-fangled, but at any rate a novelty in the sense that it was unusual. It had a sliding top, which, on being slid back, allowed one cigarette at a time to pop up – the cigarettes in it must have been in spring-loaded compartments. Guy was releasing them and pretending to be astonished when they popped, exaggerating his astonishment and clowning, while his companions laughed and laughed as if at the very best joke that ever was cracked.

DRINKS BEFORE lunch impale me on the horns of a dilemma. If I do not partake of the alcohol on offer, I bore everybody – small talk on an empty stomach is impossible. If I do partake of alcohol, even in moderation, I might as well go to bed until the next morning, since the rest of the day is a washout and waste.

I communicated these reflections to my better half, who shot them down as it were with a left and a right. Moderate at Downscene I had not been, she said; and considering not only my weak head but also my jaundiced liver, I should either not go to parties, or not drink at parties, or, in any event, not complain because I had gone and had drunk more than was good for me.

I was forcibly reminded of that doctor who once prescribed the cure for my hypochondria: matrimony.

But Gem did sympathise with my headache and listlessness following the Drewetts' jamboree to the extent of admitting that the merest taste of one of Maurice's marts probably meted out instant death to several million brain-cells.

And at least we are agreed that we quite enjoyed the party while it was in progress, and have enjoyed it even more in retrospect.

We thank our stars for guiding us to discover a new world in Lewes, socially now as well as topographically, at our age.

Yesterday, Wednesday, was a complete contrast to last Sunday – I mean the weather was foul, and we were invited nowhere and had nothing to do. I scribbled in this journal in the morning; then we went shopping and got soaked through; then the rain bucketing down in the afternoon made us scrap plans for an expedition; and I felt idle and guilty.

After tea it cleared sufficiently for Cindy to drag me out on my lead to fetch a copy of *The Clarion*.

There were no other customers in the Patels' paper shop. Only Jahendra's uncle was in attendance. And the following conversation ensued.

'Good evening, Mr Loftus. I hope you are well, sir.'

'Yes, thanks. And you?'

'Oh yes, sir. And Mrs Loftus is well, too?'

'Yes, thank you.'

'Here is your paper, sir.'

'Thank you.'

I paid and said: 'Can I ask you a question? What am I to call you? Are you a Mr Patel, like Jahendra? Or should I use your first name as I use his?'

'Please, sir, Uncle will do.'

'Plain Uncle?'

'I would prefer it.'

'All right. I'll start at once. Not a good evening, to tell the truth, Uncle!'

Although we both laughed bashfully, his swimming eyes behind his tinted glasses met mine without embarrassment.

'No, the weather is bad today, Mr Loftus. Winter is on the way. But the general climate of Lewes is temperate.'

'Don't you miss the hot sun of your homeland?'

'Oh no, sir! If the sun is hot or cold — it makes no difference. Where I came from we had troubles not like the weather, political troubles — ignorant bad men making troubles politically, you understand. We are so happy to be in Lewes. Britain is our homeland now.'

'Well, we have our share of ignorant politicians. And our troubles would be worse if some of them were in power.'

'Perhaps British people do not know how much trouble politics can be – they are fortunate not to have the experience, sir. They wish for change. Some wish for it. They have forgotten the difficulty of changing. Oh yes, changes must come, but slowly, a little at a time, not more than a little, and never with violence and sadness.'

'You're a philosopher, Uncle.'

'Thank you, Mr Loftus. Sometimes in my old homeland, philosophy was the difference between living and dying. You have to learn it to save life. Britain is still a very nice country. We are so happy to be British.'

At this point a man in a mackintosh entered to browse amongst the pornographic magazines, and we were interrupted.

Later on, after supper, I ventured out again: wife and dog and I went for one of our nocturnal strolls. The chill rain-washed air was pure and somehow purifying, even though it smelt of the rot of autumn. We did not go far, just across the river by Rickman's Bridge, along South Street, and back by Flood Street and The Wharf. I gave Gem an account of my chat with my Uncle, and promised to set to work on my book without any more mucking about – what he said has a bearing on what I want to say.

Cynicism might suggest I am rebounding temporarily from the fun and games at Downscene.

I know there is nothing like frivolity for making you feel serious.

OCTOBER

FATHER WAS pleased to believe our family figured in the Domesday Book, compiled in the eleventh century. I was never convinced that one of William the Conqueror's Servientes or King's Sergeants, a certain Tolfusse of Bolde's Hundreds in the West Country, was transformed at a later stage into a Loftus of Boltbridge.

But in Tudor times we were going strong enough to build the timber-framed edifice depicted in contemporary prints and apparently considered a model gentleman's residence in its day. The present Boltbridge Manor was built on the foundations of the Elizabethan house, which had burned down. According to the architectural plans and builders' receipts that I had to sell off, the work took some five years in the Georgian 1750s.

Father followed in his father's footsteps by enlisting in the Somersetshire Hussars in 1912. He got safely through the Great War, stayed on in the army and married my mother in 1922. He served in India in the twenties, then in various outposts of empire; commanded his regiment in France in 1939; was wounded and captured at Dunkirk, locked up in a prisoner-of-war camp, and repatriated and demobilised in 1945. Three years later, at Boltbridge, the tractor he had been driving on Hillside Acre toppled over and crushed him. He was fifty-five.

He was a kind man and a good soldier – he won the Military Cross. But his parents, my paternal grandparents, perished in the flu epidemic after the 1914 war. He therefore inherited Boltbridge Manor, the house, farm, tenants and responsibilities in 1920, and was an absentee landlord for twenty-five years. And he made his last will and testament during his engagement to Mama.

He was called Thomas Loftus. He was tall, broad-shouldered, very blue-eyed, and had that typically English colouring of reddish weather-beaten complexion and reddish thinning fair hair. He had big hands with cushioned fingertips, resembling the suction-pads of lizards that can walk on the ceiling. He enjoyed country pastimes and pursuits. His enjoyment of bloodsports once surprised me as much as his professional readiness to kill people, considering his compassionate and peaceable character. He smoked a pipe and read dull biographies. He wore old checked tweeds when he was out of uniform and at home.

I was born in 1927 and Rachel in 1930. We never knew him well: his leaves were short, our school terms seemed to be long, and then he was a POW. Besides, he was meant to be busy, and he was probably shy. But stored at the back of my mind are souvenirs – mental snapshots blurred and tinted by the passage of half a century. Here he sits on his horse Sultan in the stableyard, bowler-hatted and wearing breeches and leather leggings. There he is in the brushing-room at Boltbridge, preparing to take his ten-year-old son out shooting. He would hand me my gun, almost as if I had been his native bearer in India: he still tried to exercise control over when and how I pulled the trigger. Again, I see him fixing a fly on my fishing-line while I shiver in gumboots and overcast weather on the banks of the River Bolt. He monopolised the action, perhaps to spare me the blushes of inadequacy. On our fishing expeditions, in the unlikely event of anything interesting having to be done, such as baiting a hook or landing a fish, he was inclined to do it.

I remember his intent predatory expression, his normal mild benevolent one, and his moistly shining blue eyes and crisp military voice. I remember his sweet-tempered patience, and that willingness to listen, explain, render assistance and rectify error, which is often another advantage of physical health and strength. He tied his own fishing-flies, sitting at the card-table in the drawing-room on winter evenings, peering through a magnifying glass and performing intricate operations with his cushiony fingers. We children watched and interrupted and asked questions, and Mama kept on calling him, and he answered without a trace of exasperation.

He was really too kind. He had no grasp of money and gave away more than he could afford. And his officer-like habit of showing initiative and taking command misled me. I left things to him, assuming he knew best.

But tractors cannot be driven across the steepest slope of Hillside Acre. He should have recognised the danger, and would have, if he had paid more attention to his estate and my patrimony.

FAMILY HISTORY is like digging up nettles: which sting, and you never get to the end of their roots.

Was Mama in love with Father? Rachel and I doubted it, and Gem is equally sceptical. He was not her type, except superficially – inasmuch as he was a handsome young hero with a solid property behind him. She was one of those cool virtuous Englishwomen who like to flirt with jolly cads and bounders.

Father, who was no ladies' man, spoilt her. The fact that they had been married for five years before I came along may not signify – she was young enough to bide her time. On the other hand they were sleeping in separate bedrooms according to my earliest memories. Had Mama already begun to love her home – the bricks and mortar and garden and grounds of Boltbridge Manor – exclusively?

She was an only child, the daughter of a successful solicitor in Bristol and his superior short-lived wife. In 1921 she was invited to play in an amateur tennis tournament partly organised by Father, and decided there and then that Boltbridge was the best place in the whole world. She was pretty and dainty, and he was soon suing for her little long-fingered imperious hand. She was surely drawn to him for reasons other than his ancestral home. Their temperamental similarities, their unworldliness and lack of sensuality, would have been reassuring; and she was certainly not the first girl to surrender unconditionally at the sight of a martial uniform.

Later, in the 1930s, when I was beginning to make their acquaintance, they seemed to rub along well enough for the two or three months they were together out of every twelve: she had ceased to follow the drum – she kept the home fires burning.

The war changed things even at Boltbridge. A turning-point was the news that Father was in prison. Although a slight wound and loss of liberty were better than being killed, everyone was more or less upset to think of him suffering any kind of punishment, which in a civilian sense he did not deserve; and special sympathy was extended to Mama, who would now have to run the family show quite on her own.

Wisdom after the event rouses my suspicion that her biggest problem was guilt. She felt guilty to be pleased to have Boltbridge to herself. She therefore made more fuss of her husband in his absence than she had when he was present. She pretended to miss him and grieved publicly; and her gratitude to him for being no bother must have fanned the embers of love.

Her fond proud attitude, combining with my sentimentally jejune idea of his predicament, exerted a dominating influence on my teenage self. As he was translated into Mama's lost lover, the Ulysses for whom she waited like some latter-day Penelope, if with mixed feelings, so my idealism glorified his unassuming person, and I could hardly wait to join the army, and liberate and avenge him.

I had been a soldier for a year when he returned to Boltbridge. He looked roughly as I remembered him: his patience had clearly stood him in good stead in his four wasted years. But he was more impersonal, detached to the point of inattentiveness, and expressed his relief at coming home by means of a sort of philanthropic spending spree. He built cottages for two ex-warrant officers of our regiment, Hussar-Sergeants Bright and Marston, who had been in prison with him. He seemed to have lost the knack of saying no, and acceded to every request for financial assistance.

He had little else to do. The exercise of his manorial rights would have interfered with Mama's managerial plans and pleasures, and he deferred to her as usual. He could not settle to his former sporting ploys – he was loth to kill a fly. He reminisced with Bright and Marston, and pumped me for regimental gossip when he got the chance, and occupied himself increasingly with simple physical labour.

I was not very often at Boltbridge at this period. I expected to inherit the place one day, and in the meanwhile, although not especially keen on the army, I tried to make the most of the leave and leisure it allowed me by indulging a young man's fancy in London and elsewhere. Besides, I relied on Father to look after everything.

Retrospectively I continue to be amazed that he never mentioned business to me, and to my knowledge had no money worries.

His death was shocking not only for the obvious reasons. His will had been made years before I and then Rachel were born, and his widow was his sole heir.

MY CHILDHOOD might seem too good to be true – but it was true.

The scene and the scope of it were a large cosy house with

attics and box-rooms to play and hide in; blue wisteria against golden dressed Bath stone; thirty acres of parkland grazed by sheep; a rookery in a grove of trees on one side of the drive and a garden walled with mellowest red brick on the other; an adjacent farmyard; fields and woods; and a village, a sweetshop, and cottages full of hospitable friends within walking distance.

My good luck, again, was that my parents were more traditional than original: originality – unpredictability – is as bad for children as for dogs.

Reveille and lights-out were observed in no military establishment more strictly than in my nursery. And four tasty meals appeared on the dot. Exercise and lessons were slotted in to the schedule. Regular habits were considered to be the basis of health and happiness by the generation that brought me up.

Dragooned as in one sense I was, the extent of my freedom in another sense would surprise modern children, who are relentlessly studied and circumscribed, and especially town children, restricted by terror of the traffic and the sex maniacs of the permissive age. Although my wishes were sub-ordinated to those of my elders and betters, I had the run of the farmyard as soon as I could toddle into it, and mixed with poultry, including hostile cockerels and hissing geese, cows, pigs and carthorses. Before I was in my teens I was allowed to roam the countryside, birdsnesting, and then bicycling miles on my own. When father stopped showing me how to use my gun, that is to say commandeering and using it himself, I went shooting alone. From my twelfth year onwards, I shot or shot at everything, barring human beings; also ratted enthusiastically when the ricks of corn were threshed in the autumn; also rabbited with ferrets and nets belonging to our cowman George Barrett, better known as Juggy Barrett because of his way with beer; and killed sparrows in the hedgerows, or tried to, with the catapult that Mr Wickes our gardener helped me to make.

Squeamish city-dwellers would not approve of my boyish savagery. My sport would come into conflict with theirs, which is throwing stones from inside glass houses. Generally speaking, they eat their dumb friends, and dress in their skins, and, in short, live on the premature deaths of equally animate objects. Their consciences remain unsullied by virtue of their ignorance.

Down on the farm, the veil of civilisation is rent. To tell the truth, I have known twinges of regret for my blood-thirsty youth. But nature would raise no objections. Nature's not so secret stock-in-trade is blood, blood and tears, however and by whomsoever shed; and farmers, and even their children learning the business, are merely some of its accomplices – and indeed the delegates of our species.

Gentler joys figure in my recollections. I was extremely fond of our nursemaid, Rachel's and mine, a beautiful girl with the suitable name of Bella. When I was five or six, Bella and I bought baby ducklings with our savings, reared them, sold them and shared the profits. Nature, notwithstanding its cruelty, was kind enough to give us money for jam.

Bella soon married; and then I would escort Rachel to tea with – say – Mrs Barrett or Mrs Wickes. At about four-thirty in the afternoon of the day of such tea parties, we would collect a basket of eatables covered with a linen napkin from the Boltbridge pantry, trip down the drive and knock on the front door of a cottage in the village, guarded by some sleepily barking geriatric mongrel. I remember dark hot kitchens with clothes airing before the range, and our basket being unpacked with cries of grateful astonishment, and parlours smelling of damp and furniture polish and strong tobacco, where two tablecloths covered the festive board, lacy white over puce chenille.

Etiquette demanded that our hostess should pretend to be overwhelmed by the generosity of the contents of the basket,

51

although the custom was that we gave more than we were about to receive.

But those layered triangles of new crusty brown bread thickly spread with moist farm butter, those almost fresh strawberries preserved in sweetly glutinous liquid, and the hunks of crisply baked fruit cake seemed to us a cut above, and infinitely preferable to, the mingy cucumber sandwiches and light sponge fingers on offer at home.

Usually the master of the house would take his place at the head of the tea-table, George Barrett – Juggy – with his great globe of a face and hands like agricultural implements, or Mr Wickes complete with horn-rims and bristling moustache; and their appetites put an even sharper edge on ours. And conversation never flagged. They were at least as interested in our goings-on as we were in theirs – probably more so, considering we represented power whereas they only represented difference.

The Barretts and the Wickeses were incredibly old, judged by our juvenile criteria: in fact they were younger than I am today. Their offspring had grown up and flown the nest; and I do believe Mrs Barrett and Mrs Wickes entertained us not to curry favour with our parents, their husbands' employers, but because they liked children and missed their own, and because we liked them so much. They must have been somewhat gratified, motherly Mrs Barrett by our responsiveness to her hugs and kisses, and our unmistakable delight in helping her pick her garden fruit or feed Juggy's red-eyed ferrets, and diminutive Mrs Wickes, of whom it was said that her brain was bigger than her body, by the wonder and admiration in our eyes as we watched her catch a chicken, tuck its angry head under its wing, and rock it to sleep.

Our goodbyes were the measure of our appreciation and affection.

'Thank you, Mrs Barrett, thanks awfully, we've loved it, can we come again, please let us, we really have loved it . . .

Goodbye, Juggy! Goodbye, Mrs Wickes, it's been such fun, we've never had such a nice time ... Goodbye, Mr Wickes, goodbye, Mrs Wickes! Goodbye! Thank you, thank you!'

We would walk backwards in order to wave at our hosts and hostesses by their garden gates, and as it were roll home, full of food and friendliness, and giggling at two of our private jokes. It amused us, first, that Juggy and Mr Wickes called their spouses Mother, and secondly that Juggy stank of either the milk or the dung of the cows he tended – needless to say we were more amused by the notion of the dung.

The hour would be six o'clock or so. On summer evenings bees and flies buzzed in the high beech trees on either side of the drive, and wood pigeons flapped and cooed in the grove. In the frosty gloaming of autumn or spring the chimes of the church clock in the village of Boltbridge had a vibrant echo. We played games with the empty basket and got mud on the white napkin, and everything seemed funny.

RACHEL WAS fair, fairy-like, light on her feet. Most children are bores: she not only touched this world lightly in a physical sense, she had a light touch – she was never anecdotal and long-winded.

Yesterday's grown-ups called her highly strung. I suppose today's would use that more pejorative term, neurotic. She had a passion for Worcester Sauce and sprinkled it on bread and butter – her taste was viciously savoury. She was mad about her mother until she was six years old, then inexplicably turned against her, shunned and refused to kiss her. And her hypochondria was already chronic. If she should hear of a disease she would be sure she had it, and she disturbed many of Bella's nights with her fears and tears.

I hate the harsh law which apparently lays down that fear somehow attracts whatever we are afraid of. Our fearful groans are all too apt to reach the ears and put ideas in the head of fate.

Rachel could be a nuisance when she was panicky and stubbornly un-cooperative: such was the consensus of opinion. But my conviction for most of the time was that my little sister was the best of eggs. Although bad at her books, she was clever enough – quick enough – for me. She was trustworthy and fiercely loyal. And she had the quality which compensates for many defects, and may well be the most envied of assets: she was lovable.

My initial response to her niceness, gaiety and warmth, in a word her lovability, was at least as odd as I have accused her of being. I hid behind doors and under beds, stalked her in the house and garden, pounced out upon, and also unnerved her with ghastly grimaces, imitations of deformity, sinister footsteps and blood-curdling yells. I was like the Fat Boy in Pickwick Papers: I wanted to make her flesh creep – and succeeded – but I hope she enjoyed playing the mouse's part in the game as much as I enjoyed the cat's. She called me Huge with a soft G, short for Hugo, and may thus have been commenting on my ability to alarm her by the additional means of my size. We were Rach and Huge to each other.

How different nowadays!

Now I have to try to remove her terrors and reassure her.

Anyway – my schooling spared her unorthodox expressions of brotherly love – I consorted with other schoolboys if I could, and suddenly saw the point of girls who were not my sister.

When I joined the army in 1944, Rachel was fifteen and flat-chested.

Yet in 1947 she was married.

Her first husband was Bayle Howard from Howardsville in Virginia, U.S.A. He was the scion of an erstwhile colonial family, the proprietor of a small-scale stud farm, a divorcee, a chain-smoker, and thirty years older than she was. He was

54

blue-eyed and clear-complexioned – along with every white male American of that era he had a look of Bing Crosby. Notwithstanding his relaxed flippant sort of charm, he rushed her to the altar or rather the Registry Office in three short weeks.

I was informed of the romance by means of an invitation to the wedding. I was serving with the Army of Occupation in Germany, had difficulty in obtaining leave at such short notice, and only just made it to the ceremony.

Rachel had had overdue second thoughts, but steadfastly refused to jilt Bayle. I remember her pinched grim countenance and excess of make-up. Her hand shook so much that the bridegroom could scarcely get the ring on her finger. Mama was in tears and Father vaguely unhappy: they were losing a daughter and not in any comfortable sense gaining a son. And no one could have been comforted by the scowling face of their step-grandson-in-law, Rachel's stepson, Bayle's son by a previous marriage, Garth by name, a twenty-five-year-old six-footer with crew-cut and crushing handshake.

The following year Rachel was unable to attend Father's funeral – she was in the act of miscarrying and losing her chance of having other children. She returned to Boltbridge for brief bi-annual visits thereafter, in the course of which, in spite of or perhaps because of the conspicuous absence of her husband, she appeared to be all right.

But Bayle died of lung cancer in 1965 and his widow hurried home. She was too relieved to be reserved. She was past suffering in loyal silence. Her marriage had been cheap melodrama from beginning to end. Howardsville was nothing but the dilapidated and decaying house, stables, barns and sheds of the Howard estate: there was no ville or village. The nearest neighbours were some black people twenty miles away. The township of Degas, where Rachel had to shop, was thirty miles farther on. She had been put in a menial position by Bayle and Garth, made to skivvy for them and muck out their horses, while they smoked and drank together in the so-called office, or drove into Degas to play pool with their cronies. She was blackmailed into doing their bidding, and keeping quiet, not complaining, and not bolting to Boltbridge, except for ten days every two years, by Bayle's threats that he was ready and willing to drag her through the divorce courts, and Garth's that he would break her neck. Darling Rachel! She never was slow to say, or imply, what most of us think: that others are to blame for our tribulations. She told Mama and me in tones of near-reproach that she had been homesick and unhappy throughout.

But her harrowing vigil by Bayle's death-bed, let alone the events leading up to it, entitled her to sympathy; and the fact that she retained many of her lovable characteristics, somehow her delicate grace and innocence and vulnerability, ensured that she got it.

Her better luck − or was it worse luck? − was that she sharedwith Bayle's other wife the proceeds of a Trust Fund created by a Howard forefather. She was able to buy Tillers Grange in Boltbridge. Her feelings for the ambience of her childhood, and delight at being back amongst her family and friends, also touched hearts.

Tillers Grange is located at the eastern end of Boltbridge, alongside the road to East Boltbridge. It stands in its own grounds, and is large and isolated. Jim Claughton seemed to offer her company and security, and he may or may not have inspired love.

She married him; and then she fell ill.

RACHEL IN the backwoods of America was preoccupied with marital problems when she heard about Father's will. And she always was the opposite of mercenary. She was nonetheless wounded to know that he had not only failed to provide for her, as they say, but ignored her existence completely in a testamentary context.

The argument that he would have changed his will if he had not been crushed by that tractor was no consolation. He had had years to recognise his issue in the ultimate legal document before he went off to fight and possibly to die in the war. Why did he not re-make his will in 1939, as private soldiers on active service are instructed to? He was not vague in those days – he was in command of a regiment of men who had no doubt acted more responsibly towards their dependents than he had.

Of course my sister's wounds seemed to be scratches in comparison with mine.

Father had been an absentee landlord partly because he was a professional soldier, and partly because he disliked and was embarrassed by his squirearchical duties. He had no interest in agriculture, and cared nothing for possessions, even if he enjoyed the sporting amenities of his inheritance. Before I was in my teens he had led me to believe that he would hand over at least the management of the estate at the earliest opportunity.

I was in the army when he got out of it. He was released from his prisoner-of-war camp and returned to Boltbridge. But far from handing over any of his prerogatives or burdens, or persuading Mama to relinquish those which she had exercised or borne, he suggested I should sign on and become a regular peace-time soldier.

Accordingly I did so.

My private reasoning was that I could buy myself out, and regain civilian status, as soon as my assistance was required at home. Meanwhile I would await the summons at the expense of the War Office, which fed me and permitted me to travel and see sights and read books. In fact I was not yet ready to be buried in the depths of the country. Father's forgetfulness was more reprieve than disappointment.

The ability of the family to finance my eventual apprenticeship as farmer and landowner was taken for granted.

Although I had just about earned my living since leaving school, and Rachel had married without much of a parental blessing in cash or otherwise, we both assumed our parents were separately rich and jointly richer. They never referred to money, because, we believed, they had enough of it.

But Father died; and old Dick Harris of Harris Stourton and Harris, Solicitors of Wells in Somerset, disillusioned me.

He began with the will. The two of us were in the drawing-room on the morning in question – I was sitting at the card-table on which Father had tied his fishing-flies, Dick in the chair by the log fire with his bulging briefcase on his knee. Mama was arranging flowers for the funeral in Boltbridge Church.

Apparently Father had not intended to cut me off without even a shilling. But he was not prepared to try to evade the taxes on dying, he was depressed to the point of paralysis by forecasts of the duty payable, and death interrupted his deliberations.

However, Dick continued, the immediate problem was not who had inherited Boltbridge, sorry as he was to have told me that I had not, but how much of the estate could be rescued from the clutches of levelling legislation and the Inland Revenue.

I asked for his estimate of our liability, and he named a considerable sum.

Well, surely, said I, we could afford to pay up, settle the matter and have done with it.

Dick cleared his throat and replied that my father had been generous to a fault, that my mother was equally so, and their open-handedness was appreciated throughout the locality.

At last he spilled the beans: after paying up there would be £25,000 in the family kitty.

Twenty-five thousands of pounds may be a small fortune; but it was a drop or droplet in the ocean of the expenses of owning and maintaining three farms and sets of farm buildings, six hundred acres of land, two dozen cottages and a minor stately home with as many bedrooms, not to mention the wages of employees.

What had I counted on? – In the old-fashioned phrase, a modest sufficiency, or, in terms of my complacent ignorance, the wherewithal to carry on doing as we pleased.

I demanded: where had the money gone? – reeling from this second bombshell, and wondering how Mama would manage, and everyone else for that matter.

Dick's explanation was that our family was traditionally landed, not moneyed, and had lived by farming and renting out land; but Father had been a rotten farmer and had reduced rents, especially in the depressed thirties, when he should have raised them. He had never received anything like his dues, he gave instead of receiving, he scattered largesse in the form of tips, Christmas Boxes, interest-free loans, subsidies, donations, and indirectly, for instance by granting long cheap leases of cottages which he had re-roofed and modernised. He would spend five thousand pounds on property that he let for five shillings a week, the equivalent of today's 25p. He charged Hussar-Sergeants Bright and Marston nothing for their cottages. It was like a variation of the story of the rake's progress: he had squandered his sub-stance on others. As for Gaffer Wright and his son Joe, the tenants of Home Farm, and John Baldridge at New House Farm, and the Hebdens of Pinnock, they must have coined money virtually at his expense.

I prosecuted my enquiries: what had happened in the war, when, so to speak, Father was out of harm's way?

Dick said that Mama had been, and was, as good or as bad as Father – depending on how you viewed their prodigality.

But Mama was the heiress of her parents, my grand-parents – she was the daughter of a solicitor, I reminded him – she must have been well-to-do in her own right.

Dick permitted himself a wintry smile. Not all solicitors

were rich, he explained; and Mama's money, such as it was, had been pooled with her husband's and had gone down the same drain.

The family was not bankrupt, he added. Upon the security of its assets, financial institutions would be prepared to lend at a price. In other words, cash could be borrowed. But sooner or later, and despite father's will and wish that the estate should remain intact and his tenants should be protected, we were going to have to sell some hereditament.

Dick urged the grasping of the nettle without delay. Loans, mortgages and legal costs must not be allowed to complicate an already complex issue. He would propose the sale of Pinnock Farm, where the soil was thin, and the young Hebdens were always in trouble or making it.

He convinced me: we had reached our decision after several testing hours.

Mama joined us. She was wonderfully composed, poured out glasses of sherry, and hoped we had had a nice talk.

I recapitulated the latter part of it.

She responded as follows: 'What an extraordinary idea! Hebdens have farmed at Pinnock for three generations. Where else would Geoff Hebden scrape a livelihood for his silly wife and all those children? The place can't be sold over their heads. Our people come first, darling. But let's not talk business, please. Are you ready for your lunch, Dick?'

MAMA CHANGED the subject, leading us towards the dining room, and, in collusion with Father, the direction of my life.

I realised she was accepting the ownership of Boltbridge as she had accepted the loan of it in wartime: that is, gladly.

She loved her home with the passion of a woman not oriented towards men. But I was disinclined, too diffident or too proud, to allow the flicker of an eyelid to betray the fact that the new arrangements were bad and sad for me. Just as I had never revealed that my soldiering was a stop-gap, for fear of offending interested parties, so I never called in question the provisions of the will. Therefore Mama had reason to believe she was conferring a favour on her dear son, similar to that which she had conferred on her departed husband, by taking charge. She continued to do what she had done in the war, and during Father's last three unsatisfactory years; and enjoyed it the more by persuading herself that she was enabling me to realise my dreams of military glory.

It was not her fault. If I had spoken the unspeakable question – 'What about me?' – she would have answered it selflessly. If I had complained, she would have been horrified. But a trio of difficulties, like three witches, foretold my future. Politeness inhibited; I was loth to have my motives misunderstood; and how was modesty to say that I might do better at Boltbridge than she had or would?

Naturally I said nothing.

No – I encouraged her to rule the roost.

Moved by the pathos of that £25,000 in the bank, I also refrained from pointing out that Rachel and I had been disinherited in the monetary meaning of the word. Mama would have been pleased to give us every single penny she possessed. But I think she thought that for us, too, money grew on trees, and, optimistically, that we were thinking she was no more than the guardian of the resources of the whole family.

The result of these developments, or, to put it bluntly, of my lack of the necessary, was that I more or less had to remain in the army. What would I buy myself out with – and why? And alternative careers and employment exerted an appeal that diminished as I recognised my vocation to lead a quiet life with a little literary research and possibly a bit of scribbling thrown in.

In my early twenties I felt I was too old to go back to school at some university, supposing I could have afforded to. Since the ideal and hope of every Englishman – to be a country squire – had been frustrated in my case, I embraced the secondary objective of an Englishman's existence, which is to obtain maximum remuneration for the minimum of labour. Bearing it in mind, I concluded that nowhere else would I be sitting much prettier than I was at present.

Military life is said to be composed of intense boredom punctuated by acute fear. For various reasons, some connected with an erroneous medical opinion of my fitness, I am happy to report that the totality of my experience of it was boring. I killed no foe, I never heard a shot fired in anger; I was the officer in the office, an armchair warrior, pushing a pen for a few hours daily, and otherwise at liberty to recreate myself. Briefly – and brevity is indubitably wit in this context – I settled for and stayed on in the army until I was forty.

But the leisure thus afforded me was ever busier. The roost that Mama ruled was soon disturbed by the homecoming of the chickens she had released on that day in the drawing-room with Dick Harris. For example, less idiomatically, eighteen months after taking her decision in respect of Pinnock Farm she was forced to yield to mine. She had by then run up an overdraft of £50,000: my figures are approximate. She was in trouble, and had to be extricated from it.

I set the machinery in motion for the sale of Pinnock.

But while my back was turned the plot thickened. Father's fellow-POWs, co-regimentals and recipients of his bounty, bit the hand of the widow of their benefactor. Hussar-Sergeant Bright had turned out to be a violent drunkard who picked fights in the village, and Hussar-Sergeant Marston lured harder-working men into his cottage to watch racing on television, gamble and usually lose money. They frightened, injured, robbed and generally upset most of the members of the Boltbridge community, who begged Mama to get rid of them. Bravely, she took it on herself to summon Bright and Marston to the Manor. She apologised for having to abide by the verdict of the neighbourly democracy and asked them to look for alternative accommodation. They immediately invoked the law against landlords and land-ladies enacted by collectivist government: with which just law they so browbeat and blackmailed Mama as to extort from her the promise of £25,000 apiece in return for vacating their premises.

Her overdraft was thus multiplied by two: £100,000. But Pinnock Farm was worth £250,000. After it was sold, she would still be better off.

I had overruled her moral objections to selling it. Admittedly three generations of Hebdens had farmed the Pinnock land. On the other hand they had benefited from paying a ridiculously low rent. The bottom line – in the jargon of today – was that they owed us rather than vice versa.

Admittedly, too, the grandfather and father of the present incumbent had been upright conscientious men, contending as best they could against the handicap of the soil they tilled. But Geoff Hebden was stupid and idle, and good for nothing except breeding hungry kids and pleading poverty.

Somehow he heard tell of the sale. While I was trying to work out where the Hebdens would live and what they would live on, Geoff approached Mama and begged her to let him buy Pinnock at a bargain price. Perhaps he was not all that stupid. He got it for £125,000, and a year later, probably in association with whoever had provided the capital, sold it for £300,000.

Mama had no regrets. She was happy to have helped the Hebdens yet again. And she was no longer in debt, thank goodness. But she was back where she had started from, with only £25,000 to bless herself with. She had a smaller income – no rent from Pinnock – and larger outgoings: for the achievement of the egalitarian economics in vogue was that wages went up and the value of money and savings went down. Moreover she clung to the luxurious idea that she was responsible for the welfare of her tenants and dependents: our people, as she called them.

I am not pretending she was poor, except in relation to the expenses she chose to incur. That she and I lurched from this crisis to the next – to crises in the plural – is also beside the point.

No – our chapter of financial accidents – the account of Mama's philanthropy and impoverishment – is the background of my book and already a political statement.

AT THE age of thirty I inherited my half of the Railway Settlement, money put aside by our paternal grandfather – Rachel had the other half three years later.

A decade rushed by, and I resigned my commission in the army; bought a flat with the proceeds of the Railway Settlement in the respectable leafy suburb of Harrington in South London; taught English to foreign students at the school of languages run by my old friend Charles Hardy; and spent every third weekend at Boltbridge.

Maybe I should have tried to make enough money to finance the family instead of malingering in the army and taking the king's shilling; and now, even more urgently, I should have gone for more cash instead of less aggravation. But I had a retiring personality and no formal qualifications. My pessimistic attitude to reimbursement was that something was better than nothing. And working for Charles had three advantages by my standards: it was agreeable, my students interested me, and absenting myself to write a book if I were ever moved and could afford to do so would present no problems. By this time I had graduated from reading books to hoping to write one, although I was still short of a subject.

Additional pressure not to take too demanding a job was exerted by the requirements of Boltbridge, where things were going from bad to worse, and the emotional screw was turned by Rachel returning from America, by her unhappiness, her unhappiness matrimonial and then medical.

In my forty-fifth year I met and married Gemma: which turn of events represents as much luck as anyone can expect in a lifetime.

Gemma approved of Boltbridge; and my wife, mother and sister all took to one another; thus reinforcing my commitment to the causes of Mama and Rachel.

That chronic commitment to avert Mama's economic humiliation, and to protect Rachel, may be incommunicable. How would I, how did I, explain its obsessiveness? I just could not bear to imagine Mama's eviction from her old home and mine, and saw her in nightmares hobbling down the drive and casting tragic glances in my direction.

Gem's appreciation of my feelings cut both ways. I was grateful for her support, but worried by her relying on me to save the day for everyone. Her theory, meant to encourage me, was that her mother-in-law must continue to live as and where she pleased: to which my practicality retorted in increasingly agitated accents – yes, yes, but how?

The other two farms had been sold – New House and the Home Farm – and again, as in the case of Pinnock, at extravagantly favourable prices to the resident tenants. The only land owned was the thirty acres of the park, let for grazing at a peppercorn rent. The sale of cottages verged on the farcical; but I could not crack a smile at the performance. Repeatedly Mama spent more on buying another home for the cottager than she received by selling the old one. The Reynolds portraits of my forebears, and the furniture in the bedrooms along the North Passage, and a lot of silver and books had disappeared by now.

And Mama at seventy, eighty, ninety was frail but hale, if not hearty. Actuarial calculations puzzled me: which was going to win the race, death or insolvency – and would the prize be her body or her soul?

Her sorrow when Rachel was ill spilled over into being sorry for the state of affairs at Boltbridge.

She would put forward a plea of personal asceticism to justify her stewardship of the family fortune: she had spent nothing on clothes or travel, she had not had a holiday for half a century, she no longer centrally heated the house, and she ate like a small bird. She had maintained her best rooms, but in order to continue to provide a sort of community centre, where she could entertain the village to the customary dinners and dances at Christmas, Easter and Harvest Festival, and where meetings of the Women's Institute and the Parish Council, and wedding receptions and christening parties and the wakes after funerals could be held. And she kept up the garden to open it to the public in the summer and raise money for local charities.

She was sorry there was so little left for her to leave her children. It grieved her to have loved Boltbridge and lost most of it, and presided over the severance of its immemorial links with the Loftus family. But what should she have done?

Although too sophisticated to say so, she implied that we had been, were and would be honour bound to render assistance to those less fortunate than ourselves.

I really agreed with and admired her, even as I fought to keep our noses above the water of her philosophy in action. The answer to her rhetorical question was that neither of us could have done differently, given our characters and convictions. She was not to blame for being born with a streak of reckless benevolence, and because she became the heiress of more obligations than of funds with which to discharge them, and the victim of contemporary politics.

Her last years, anguish over her daughter, harsh treatment by her son-in-law, and physical decline – all this is another story.

The same applies to the difficulty of stripping more and more of the assets from our former estate, parkland and chattels, and the remaining cottages, without causing her tenants or herself too much distress.

But her victimisation by politics is the heart of the matter.

Collectivism, Socialism, egalitarianism, the politics of envy, guilt and squalid hypocrisy, the politics that penalises virtue and rewards vice, had dogged her footsteps and therefore mine, and by means of expropriatory taxation and inflation, and some help from ourselves, hunted us to a standstill.

Again, collectivist politics in its more extreme manifestations, Marxism, National Socialism, had dragged us into wars, imprisoned our dear ones, killed our friends and relations, infiltrated our institutions, attempted to undermine our social system, threatened us relentlessly, baited and bullied us – and in power, in countries where it wielded power, committed crimes without parallel and set terrifying examples.

Now, nearer home, the reform of local government not only translated our part of Somerset into Creedwell, but included in the body politic of Creedwell certain populous areas, industrialised, unionised, or simply disaffected. Rumour warned that the apostles of Collectivism were moving in and preaching their ungodly sermons; and the new atmosphere of bloody-mindedness in towns, businesses and shops confirmed it. Eventually the Creedwell District Council was ruled by a coalition of Marxists, Trotskyists, Maoists, and militants belonging to what sounded like pop groups, Red Dawn, Drumhead Justice: which had got elected in spite of multiple charges of vote-rigging and intimidation of voters.

The General Rate payable for Boltbridge Manor shot up by sixty per cent, and in the following year by another sixty, and Mama was harassed by official and officious letters directing her to lop trees overhanging public pathways, to replace old cesspits which might be a health hazard, to preserve her crumbling garden walls by re-pointing them, and, in short, to disburse moneys she did not possess: all she now had was a loan borrowed from the bank against the collateral of the house.

More than ever she insisted on subsidising poorer folk, who were hit hard – as they always are – by radical tampering with the economic order. But she realised that my efforts to look after her were finally being frustrated. She was inclined to apologise to me for living so long; and, I believe, to Rachel for her fairly good health.

Considering how healthy she was even in her ninety-third year, the suddenness of her death surprised everyone. She had expired in the act of attending to her morning mail, which included another exorbitant demand for Rates. But she was used to receiving such bills.

But scrawled across this one in red ink were the words: 'Rich bitches should and will pay more,' and the sign of the hammer and sickle.

Mama died – and my book was born – or almost.

I happened to read the autobiography of Kim Philby, which had an introduction by Graham Greene. Both authors contended that spying, lying, disloyalty, treachery, and condemning friends and colleagues and countless others to suffer and to perish as a result of the abuse of trust – that the trade of spying is not a necessary evil in a wicked world, but perfectly acceptable, an honourable calling, especially in the service of so noble and worthwhile a cause as Communism and the advancement of the Soviet empire.

Philby, seconded by Graham Greene, patted on the back by Graham Greene, was disparaging by implication and dismissing the principles to which my parents had devoted their lives, energies, resources, everything, and to which I could claim to have sacrificed my prospects and best years.

Furthermore, the politics he was so pleased with and proud of had carelessly and callously, and, history would agree, typically, killed my mother.

And I wanted to answer back.

NOVEMBER

L AST MONTH I managed at least to write about the past instead of the present. The weather was on my side: it kept me indoors. The mists and mellow fruitfulness of autumn were roughly hustled offstage by storms of wind and rain. Hope Cottage seemed to cringe and shudder. The drain blocked in Rickman's Lane and the waters rose in biblical style to within an inch or two of our front door. I was therefore pleased to spend the morning and a couple of hours after tea in this snug little upstairs writing room.

Gem brought me news of the great world: a writer's wife is like a general's scout. I lived in a social sense vicariously through her reports of wet walks with Cinders, libellous conversations with Octavia Pritchett in the Eastover Stores, enviable elevenses in the Tatler Tea Rooms, and errands of mercy run for Mrs Spedding, housebound, tied by the leg or legs, so to speak.

Halfway through the month the wind abated and the rain dried up, as if at a word of command from some saint. But I yielded to the temptation of summery conditions only to the extent of an hour's exercise in the late afternoons.

Together we retraced the steps Gem had been taking on her own, especially in the vicinity of Lewes Castle, with which she has quite fallen in love.

Our guidebook relates that the Castle was erected by William the Conqueror's compatriot and brother-in-arms William de Warenne in the eleventh century; lived in by various powerful persons until the fourteenth; had its flints offered for sale to the public at four pence a load in the sixteenth; and in the twentieth, in 1922 to be precise, was bought by Sir Thomas Stanford and given into the safer keeping of the Sussex Archaeological Society.

William de Warenne dearly loved his wife, notwithstanding her name, Gundrada, which grates on my ears. Gundrada was also loved in a different way, revered for her goodness, by the monks of the Priory that she and her husband founded.

Gem and I would climb School Hill and turn right in the High Street into Castlegate and gaze across the remains of the moat and up at the fine angular outline and bleached walls of the Keep. The road still goes through the arch of the Barbican, the original towered entrance to the fortified area: deep grooves in the huge stones were cut to hold the medieval portcullis in its lowered position. Beyond the Barbican is the ancient uneven Bowling Green, supposed to have been the scene of jousting four or five centuries ago.

Sometimes we circled round and back into the High Street via Pipe Passage, a twitten providing a different view of the Castle: its sheer impregnable exposed flank on steep man-made eminence. Pipe Passage is where clay pipes – in which to smoke tobacco? – used to be made, and boasts the house once bought and sold within the space of a few days by Virginia Woolf, a squat building, the bottom half of a truncated windmill, almost as odd as she was. Or we might explore the dwellings below, huddling in terraces and tiers on the northern side of the ridge. We would skirt The Paddock and Hangman's Acre, now combined into a sort of parklike playground, but looking shady and haunted, and proceed by way of The Avenue to gain a distant prospect of the Castle, pale and straight against the tawny curves of the Downs.

The sun shone and often set on our peregrinations. And we heard, or rather did not hear, the peculiar hush that descends at certain times of the days of each season, particularly in spring and autumn: my favourite atmospheric phenomenon, that sudden silence, that poised instant between now and then, pregnant with fateful choices and chances. In the scarlet and gold of the gloaming, russet leaves swayed down upon us. Flies sleepily buzzed and gnats and midges swarmed.

Occasionally night fell as we headed home by Keere Street, down the hilly cobbles of which the Prince Regent is said to have driven a horse-drawn vehicle for a bet, and through the groves and gardens of Southover.

Dogs less lucky than our one, whose owners had to shut them in during working hours, were out and about for their late constitutionals. Cindy, who carries canine impetuosity and intolerance to extremes, would decide to love or hate them from a distance of fifty yards. She flirts by springing four-leggedly in the air like a clockwork toy. Her vicious snarls and barks are not the foolhardy challenges to combat they can be mistaken for, but the equivalent of mayday appeals for help.

On three or four nights harvest moons, circular, orange and somehow magnified, balanced on the tight-rope of the horizon.

I retired early in order to be in the best possible shape for the battle with words on the morrow.

Setting aside my personal motives and the selfish satisfaction of writing a book and seeing it in print, I have reminded myself of the objective aim of mine: to draw attention to the unfairness and injustice of the politics that specifically promises to be fairest and justest. I would like to try to speak for those who did not or could not raise their voices against the oppressiveness of collectivist theory and practice, and suffered and still suffer more or less to prove Collectivism and its derivatives wrong.

But even at this late hour I feel I must take a little extra time off in which to plan my next move in the direction of authorship.

71

THE WHITAKERS kept pot-plants on the interior windowsills of the hall and sitting-room of Hope Cottage, and Gem has been cherishing them. The windows in question abut on the pavement and are at the eye-level of passers-by. Our privacy in the daytime is protected only by green leaves.

Determined strangers can and do peep in on us. But Gem is more afraid that strangers and neighbours are going to catch me peeping out at them through the greenery. She says children are scared to see the nose of a senior citizen pressing against the windowpane.

She exaggerates; yet I have to plead guilty to interest in and observation of the passing show. As a result, towards the end of last month, I saw Wendy Aylward leave her cottage at five-thirty in the afternoon in full facial warpaint and a long black evening dress. Was she on pleasure bent? Did balls begin so early in East Sussex? Idle speculation, in which Gem joined enthusiastically after all, had a field day: in fact it was the opposite of idle.

The very same thing happened on the next evening and the evening after that. Our explanations of Wendy's conduct grew more far-fetched. Was she dressing up for the edification of Graham Phipps-Hullett? Had injured wifehood unhinged her? But she looked no less sane as she drove off in her dented Mini.

Then Gem met her in the Eastover Stores: she had been, and for the rest of the week would be, ushering at Glyndebourne.

We had forgotten about the Touring Opera's performances. They were not much advertised; apparently they are so packed that they do not need to be. I wish we had remembered and gone. We are operatic novices, but music-lovers, curious, and, so far as we know, will not be here this time next year.

The voice of the people in the form of Bertha Prior's comments had something predictably cultural to say on the subject.

'I went to Glyndebourne once,' Bertha informed us. 'I was taken by a funny old duffer. He was made of money and couldn't spend enough of it on me. I wondered if he was pulling my leg when he told me the story of the opera. Well, he was pulling my leg, the other one – but that's different. What did I think of it, he asked at the end. Men never do know what they think till women tell them. An expensive way of having forty winks, I replied.'

'What opera did you see, Bertha?'

'Mozart, it was' – she pronounced the name Mostart for some reason – 'about two sisters who couldn't recognise their boyfriends when their boyfriends put on fancy dress. Now that's stupid, I promise you.'

'Didn't you like the singing?'

'I've heard better from the cats on my flat roof at night.'

'Or the show in general – didn't you like that?'

'Wait till you see ours on Bonfire Night!'

She was referring to the celebrations on the fifth of November, which are taken more seriously in Lewes than elsewhere.

Later, I asked my uncle in the newspaper shop how the foiling of Guy Fawkes' plot is celebrated.

He answered: 'Oh yes, sir – we have a march, and then the tar barrel is thrown in the river.'

'What's the point of the tar barrel?'

'It's set alight, Mr Loftus – a very historic custom.'

'Does the tar barrel represent Guy Fawkes?'

'Yes, sir. No, sir – we write on it in white paint "No Popery".'

I was startled: was my Pakistani friend a fanatical Protestant, or, despite his peaceful personality, a member of some rabidly anti-Catholic Islamic sect? But I did not like to trespass on these intimate preserves.

'Is there no conventional bonfire, Uncle?'

'Oh yes, many bonfires in Lewes, but not one for our Society – just the blazing barrel after we've finished marching. But that is already late at night.'

'I'm sorry – what do you mean by your Society? I don't quite understand.'

'There are several Bonfire Societies in Lewes, also in surrounding towns. My nephew Jahendra and I belong to the Eastover Bonfire Society. It is like a trade association for charity. We will collect money for our Victoria Hospital when we march with the other societies next week.'

'How long is this march, how far do you march?'

'At different times in the evening eight miles, I believe, and all in costume.'

'What kind of costume?'

'Oh – for example – the Borough Society has the costumes of Zulu Chiefs – they are traditional. And you will see the Chinese Mandarins and the Bali Belles, and novelties too, the Russian Bears and the Pram Parade.'

'Which costume will you be wearing, Uncle?'

'I shall be an Ancient Briton, sir.'

The Official Programme of the Eastover Bonfire Society sheds more light on the business: we bought one from boys who knocked on our door yesterday evening. Whatever happens here on the fifth of November has as much to do with seventeen Protestant martyrs who were burned alive in Lewes in 1550, as with Guy Fawkes who tried to blow up a Protestant Parliament in 1605. The religion behind the rite is rustically primitive and savage, although I feel sure my Uncle from Pakistan is typical in not bothering about the religious origins of what seems to have become a jolly evening out.

The savagery is prettily put in one of the Bonfire Prayers, which runs thus:-

'A farthing loaf to feed old Pope.

'A penn'orth o' cheese to choke him,

'A pint o' beer to rinse it down,

'And a faggot o' wood to burn him!

'Burn him in a tub of tar,

74

'Burn him like a blazing star,
'Burn his body from his head,
'Then we'll know old Pope is dead!
'Hip, hip, hoo–r–r–ray! (Three times)'

Gem is keen to see the fun: which makes me nervous. A community binge is a well known signal for burglars to break and enter. Battle-happy thugs and political agitators might take it into their heads to wreck this one. And Bertha warns us to block the letter-flap of our front door, so that boys will not be able to post fireworks through it. As I would rather not be mugged or assaulted, or have Hope Cottage burgled or burned down, and positively wish to protect my wife, the spoilsport in me suggests we should stay at home.

Besides, I am not convinced that the spectacle will be worth the risk of watching it. I remember similar time-honoured parades and commemorations in the West Country, which were as a rule tatty and anti-climactic.

But fate is against me.

I had just written the above when Gem produced a note she had received from Graham Phipps-Hullett, who, no doubt at Wendy's instigation, was inviting us to view the march from the vantage-point of his house in the High Street.

I bowed to the inevitable, and agreed we must not miss this opportunity as we had missed that of Glyndebourne.

I WAS completely wrong.

To begin at the beginning: the great day was grey and mild, damp but not rainy.

The centre of the town was sealed off to traffic early in the afternoon, and cars within the sealed area departed or in the last resort were removed. I wedged a bit of wood into our letter-flap: naughty boys were already about, fooling with squibs and thunder-flashes. Rockets were shooting into the sky from various gardens even before it got dark.

At sevenish we walked up to the High Street, intending to follow Bertha's advice, which was to watch the third of half a dozen processions, the so-called United Grand. We could then avail ourselves of Graham Phipps-Hullett's hospitality. We both wore layer after layer of clothing to keep out the potential cold of later in the evening.

We had to push through a large crowd milling round the War Memorial for unknown reasons, and squeeze along the inside edge of the High Street pavement, in order to establish ourselves on steps to the front door of a private house, where we seemed to be in an ideal position. We could see over the heads of the populace at once westwards, to the corner or kink beyond Keere Street, and to the east and back down the hill towards Cliffe and Eastover.

The blessed absence of cars; the smoke and smell of burning paraffin in the humid air, the cause of which puzzled us; the people lining the northern and southern pavements, and strolling in the thoroughfare and debouching from side-roads and twittens; also the parties of people seen in brightly lit upper rooms through open windows, eating, drinking, laughing, waiting – all changed the character of the street and intensified the exciting holiday atmosphere.

We were sorry not to have arrived earlier. I cannot recall if the street lamps were on or off. The picture in my mind's eye is of the indigo night above and the long smoky street flanked by golden glowing windows, perhaps a quarter of a mile of it. In the uncertain illuminations the venerable houses and shop-fronts, and the figures swathed in warm garments, might have belonged to a previous age. But a police van with a loudspeaker on the roof nosing through and cheered by the throng, and the garish chariot of a vendor of hot dogs, destroyed the illusion.

The general mood was extraordinarily good-humoured. Children abounded, including babies in arms and slung from parents' necks: children in pushchairs, riding on their fathers' shoulders, wearing neon necklaces and bracelets, wide-eyed, waving sparklers and chasing one another, shrieking and laughing. Members of family groups tried not to lose themselves. Lovers clung together. The best news was that the pubs had closed.

Nothing much happened for about half an hour – that is, nothing much compared with later happenings. The hot dog man and his customers entertained us without meaning to. His chariot, which he parked alongside our steps, had a built-in stove heated by bottled gas, and a hissing gas-fired storm-lantern hung from its canopy. He was the archetype of a street trader, in his thirties, jovial, rough and ruthless; and he would not have won the approval of the Clean Food Campaign. His culinary art was to toss eight-inch frozen frankfurters into a tray of heated fat, wipe his dirty hands on a dirtier rag, hack up an onion, reach into a cardboard box on the ground at his feet for two halves of a soft roll, lay some onion on one half of the roll and stick it there with a squirt of tomato sauce, add an anaemic-looking frankfurter, which had hardly had time to warm through, slap on the top half of the roll, and offer to the public for the price of a pound. Sales were brisk: his wares smelt better than they can possibly have tasted. We wondered how long it would be before the hungry smiles of purchasers turned into the grimaces of dyspepsia.

Other sights claimed our attention. A devil in black body-stocking and horned balaclava helmet, plus tail in the usual place, was collecting money in a bag attached to a twelve-foot bamboo pole from the people in the windows. Husky youths in the uniform of horizontally striped blue and white T-shirts were acting as stewards and factotums. A couple of them charged past dragging a large low sort of wheelbarrow with a partial metal roof. Then another such wheelbarrow clanked by, also being dragged at speed uphill towards St Anne's Crescent, where the marchers were to congregate.

We recognised faces. In the middle of the road the Reverend Crispin Peterson led a squad of assorted children, while Mrs Peterson galumphed along as rearguard. His thrusting chin and the steely gleam of his complexion were very militant here on earth.

As it were another mansion of Our Father's house was represented by Roman Catholic Father Byrne, Dadda Byrne of the Drewetts' cocktail party, on whose arm a buxon female of fifty or so leant heavily, much made-up and wearing a close-fitting cloche hat with a flirty floral appendage.

The odd thing was that the priest, patting the hand of his companion who bridled at the pastoral gesture, looked less celibate than the parson ignoring his legitimate consort and the fruit of their loins.

But I suppose it was odder that Father Byrne should be participating in a popular demonstration against the Pope of Rome.

When Gem spotted and pointed out Tracy Wilkins in the window above her grandfather Caleb Hocking's shop, I was reminded of an adjective applied to young femininity which I read in a book not long ago: she is a brimming girl – brimming describes her – brimming with her ardent yearnings to make the opposite sex happy and be made happy by it. Her hands were on the windowsill, she leant outwards and forwards on the long arms of youth, as if searching for someone. Her fair neat head on curved and rounded neck, and her countenance, seemed to be lit from within.

That police van somewhere out of sight was now broadcasting appeals to people to stand back on the pavements; and we could hear the thump and roll of drums in the distance.

THE PRECURSOR of the procession was a fiery radiance beyond the kink in the High Street.

The first marchers by the Fifteenth Century Bookshop

were carrying brands, torches, three-foot sticks tipped with tow and rags, and dipped in paraffin or tar, and alight: the cause of a previous procession's smoke and smell, which we had noticed earlier.

The yellow flames, leaping, bobbing, multiplied as more marchers rounded the corner. A whole forest of sticks, a forest fire, or perhaps more accurately a river of fire between the banks of buildings, flowed towards us.

A brass band played, or, again more accurately, bands in the plural. While we were surprised really by everything, the size – the endlessness – of the procession was most surprising. As well as the four main Bonfire Societies of Lewes, called Borough, Commercial Square, Cliffe and Waterloo, and the Eastover and a few more minor ones, Bonfire Societies from other towns and localities joined in, Newhaven, Haywards Heath. And each Society seemed to have its own band, either drawn from its membership or borrowed from the military – the band of a regiment connected with Sussex, or of the Salvation Army which had an interest in our moral values and cash collection. Somebody said there were eighteen bands involved. The home-grown variety included musical Brownies playing percussion instruments, and the Bali Belles – or are they Bells? – girls in Balinese costumes tapping triangles and hand-held xylophones.

Every single marcher was in costume, and usually the costumes were elaborate. We saw all those to which my Uncle had referred, and, if forced to choose between many near-equals, would have to award the palm to the Zulu Chiefs. They were about thirty in number, blacked up, covered in multi-coloured feathers and wearing nodding head-dresses of similarly colourful plumes four and five feet high. Apparently their fine feathers had once been a topical comment on the Zulu Wars of a hundred years ago; and other costumes have historical origins.

Incidentally we recognised Uncle in our Eastover contingent, although with difficulty. I had been amused by the idea of an Ancient Briton from Pakistan. But, for an immigrant wishing to become a complete Lewesian, who could not or would not be a Zulu Chief, the costume of a little sheepskin and a lot of blue woad was ideal. Uncle looked exactly like the other Ancient Britons, except for something neither ancient nor occidental about his horn-rims.

The bigger Societies were preceded by banners borne aloft. One such banner was of cloth of gold embroidered with coats of arms; twelve feet wide; stretched between poles like ships' masts; and supported by half a dozen men. We noted the Borough's motto, 'Death or Glory', which was a bit pretentious considering its members only had to march up and down Lewes High Street: or were we missing the ironical point of the joke?

Most Societies pulled along floats with set-pieces on board as unmistakably funny as they were pyrotechnically brilliant. For instance there was an eighteen-foot Guy Fawkes looking glum – and no wonder: at regular intervals fireworks exploded in his trousers, and showers of sparks gushed out of his mouth, nose and ears. The model of an astronaut sat astride a giant rocket with a slow-burning fuse; Britannia had Catherine Wheels revolving in place of her breasts. Another float seemed to have nothing on it but scaffolding and a cat's cradle of wires; then the fireworks attached to the wires ignited in sequence with deafening bangs until the message was fully legible – 'God bless our gracious Queen.'

Surely thousands of people marched past us. They must have processed for three quarters of an hour. The noise of bands, fireworks, cries of astonishment and appreciation, screams of fear and laughter, and clapping, applause from the onlookers, and the rattle of boxes and tins wherein to put our grateful contributions to charity, was augmented – if possible – by the continual rumble of the metal wheel-barrows that had puzzled us before. They were receptacles

80

for extinct brands. Stewards, who were as nippy as they were husky, scurried amongst the marchers, giving new brands for old, and consigning the latter to the nearest wheelbarrow, in each of which mobile bonfires of sticks raged alarmingly – flames streamed behind them.

Just as sounds assaulted the ears, sights captured – captivated – our eyes: game grannies on parade, infants in the guise of Red Indian Braves, and the ceaseless riverine flow of flares, the swirling billowing pall of smoke, and the dancing shadows on the fronts of houses.

Gem tugged at my arm again. She was pointing to a steward who stumbled along with a champagne glass in one hand and a bottle of champagne in the other. He had slicked-back hair and outsize eyes, and poured champagne into the glass and drained it, toasting the crowd with exhibitionistic gestures that seemed to say: 'Too bad you're not as lucky as me!' It was Reggie Drewett.

Then I saw Peter Cadwallader. He also was in steward's stripes, and neglecting his work to play. He was kissing Tracy Wilkins carnivorously in the darker doorway of her family's business premises across the street.

No doubt Peter's kisses were what Tracy had yearned for.

The wonderful procession disappeared below the brow of School Hill, heading for Cliffe and the River Ouse, into which to toss and incinerate an imaginary Pontiff in his barrel of tar; and almost everyone surged into the road to follow it, as if to be in at the kill.

We went in the opposite direction to Graham Phipps-Hullett's party.

WE APPROACHED the Phipps-Hullett residence from one side as the preposterous figure of Jeremiah Hooke approached from the other.

He looked weedier than ever, notwithstanding his erect cockscomb. But his leather gear and boots with steel toecaps again brought out the Blimp in me. I suspected him of every crime under the nihilistic sun of the younger generation, and assumed he had been jeering and sneering at the events of the evening.

I therefore spoke to him in the censorious accents which I had numbered amongst the worst attributes of elders and betters when I was his age, and compounded the mistake I had made at Downscene.

'Hullo, Jeremiah! I hope you've been enjoying yourself as much as we have.'

He seemed neither to know what I was talking about, nor to recognise me.

I jumped to the conclusion that his shy mumble meant he had not condescended to watch the procession.

'Oh but you should have – it's an exceptional spectacle!' And I added, speaking to Gem as she stepped forward to ring the doorbell: 'Mind out, darling, don't trip over Jeremiah's trappings!' – a satirical reference to his dangling straps and thongs.

'I was at the bonfire,' he said.

He startled me with his firm serious response to my ponderous jocularity.

'Oh – which bonfire was that – and where?'

'The Eastover one – I couldn't march this year because I was helping to make a bonfire in the playground of the kindergarten.'

'I see – well done – sorry!' I mumbled in my turn, deservedly snubbed, squashed indeed, and apologising for having misinterpreted his attitude both to this evening's secular rite and, probably, to the religious one the other morning.

The door opened.

Graham Phipps-Hullett bade us welcome: words such as bade, viands, anon – 'See you anon!' – loom large in his vocabulary.

Like beams from a lighthouse, goodwill towards men

shines out of his eyes, or rather through his thick specs. His great height and sloping shoulders might have insinuated the image of a lighthouse into my mind.

Graham belongs in the formerly respectable category of confirmed bachelor: that type which in our over-sexed days is held to be either half mad with frustration or a pervert. His goodwill is by no means reserved for the masculine gender. On the contrary, he is all over women, socially speaking, in his efforts to please or not to displease them. But Gem and I are agreed that, unhappily for Wendy Aylward or happily, she will never get the chance to laugh at Graham in his shirt-tails, let alone minus them. He used to work for some charity, and is now retired: he must be sixty.

'Come in – how do you do – come in and get warm,' he bade the three of us.

His sitting-room is panelled, was painted cream long ago, and has a very small reproduction of Vermeer's *View of Delft* hung high over the mantelpiece. A single bar of an antiquated electric fire glowed dully in the fireplace. The window looks into the High Street, where the revels had not completely ended; but the tattered curtains were drawn. A cold buffet and flagons of yellowish wine were laid out on the red leather top of Graham's desk, and a large saucepan of red wine stood on a tin tray on the floor.

The company was Wendy, skulking in the background so as not to look as if she thought she was the hostess; Cadwalladers, Foxy and Guy; three Hookes, Betsy and Brian as well as Jeremiah; Marian Travers, the femme fatale of Flood Street; Gregory Leplay and Charles Hart; and about six others from the parts of Lewes that were not Eastover, foreigners almost, with whom we had no truck.

Graham pressed his viands upon us.

'And what would you like to drink? I can offer you white wine or mulled wine – Chateau Phipps-Hullett – both run up in my cellar here – I buy the ingredients and the necessary equipment from Boots, and a bottle costs me a mere matter of pence – but I'm assured that the finished article is most acceptable. Do try a glass! I should be so grateful to have your opinion of this particular vintage.'

While I hummed and hawed, feeling a bit like a guest of the Borgias, the Cadwalladers advanced, presenting their empty glasses in military unison; and Guy Cadwallader, the whimsical squirearch, trotted out the famous old example of linguistic ambiguity, as if to encourage us: 'I can't recommend this vino too highly.'

A little later Gregory Leplay passed a witty remark on the subject of the wine: 'You can taste the grape.'

I opted for the mulled variety and took a reckless gulp and scalded my palate: it was hot, not warm – the saucepan was balanced on a concealed electric ring.

After Graham had done his hospitable duties, and Gem had been cornered by Wendy, I helped myself to a hunk of meat pie and a lettuce leaf and received the following advice in respect of the liquid refreshment from Foxy: 'Imagine it's Bovril!'

She was wearing a dress of threadbare brocade, which must have been curtains in its heyday. Floor-length as it was trying to be, it failed to hide her black plimsolls. Her lipstick had spread like a skin disease, and her fingernails were two-tone: chipped red and earthy brown.

But her confidence and friendliness are winning, and I am in receipt of an invitation to Cadwallader Place.

She said: 'The hotter the wine the slower people drink it – which is one way for mine host to waste not, I suppose.'

She explained: 'This stuff we're swilling isn't wine, or mulled, truth to tell; it's medicine from the chemist's, it's prescribed and dispensed. And mulling means sugar and spice and all things nice, which definitely aren't in it. But Graham's quite right, bless his heart, to boil it until it's too hot to taste.'

She was reminded by my plateful of solid pie and my

84

steaming beverage of the wartime snack known as tea and a wad.

We wondered which drink was most warming of the cockles of wintry hearts.

She claimed: 'Well – I'll be dishing it out to one and all on Christmas Eve, my punch, rum punch – it really stokes people up, and knocks them down too, because it's got the kick of a carthorse, although it's mostly tea. You'll have to try it – you will, won't you? Cads have a Christmas party every year with punch that packs a punch and then Black Bogy.'

I laughed at her pet name for the Cadwallader clan and accepted, notwithstanding the threat of whatever Black Bogy might be; and I told her how curious we had been about Cadwallader Place and keen to see inside.

She called it Cad's Pad and said: 'Oh – if you're interested, perhaps you could advise me. We're going to have to open to the public next summer. It's Peter's baby – you know our Peter, don't you? – not his flesh and blood baby, thanks be – his project, his money-spinner – but naturally poor old Ma has to do the dirty work, which she has no objection to, provided she gets paid for it. I'm tarting up a room or two. The question is, what would you like to see if you'd crossed Peter's palm with silver? What would you consider your money's worth? I've thought of a Prince Regent Room – the Prince-Regent-Slept-Here touch – the Prince Regent's popular because he was such a bad lad: how about that? If you tottered in, I'd show you round and you could give me your good ideas.'

I accepted this invitation too; and hope I did not put a spoke in the wheel of our friendship by enquiring naively: 'Did the Prince Regent actually sleep at Cadwallader Place?'

'Not that I know of – but there was nothing to stop him sleeping anywhere. Besides, I'll be doing the guided tours, so I can tell the public whatever I like, and they can believe it or not. Business is business after all, and Cads have to be kept in the style to which they're accustomed.'

And she winked and laughed slackly and bit back her teeth and held out her glass for more chemical wine.

GEM CONTINUED to talk or be talked to by Wendy, who, I learned later, was discussing not only her troublesome love-life but also her digestion and what was temporarily wrong with it. The matchmaker in Gem had been sorry to hear that Wendy had touched on the romantic subject of her intestines with Graham.

Meanwhile I had words with the Hookes.

Betsy's manner is discouraging. Her hostile glare and drooping voice made me feel that I was the worst thing that had happened to her for days.

Perhaps it was my fault: in a conversational sense I went over the top, gallantly singing the praises of the Bonfire Societies. She gunned me down with her snort of a retort that they were barbaric.

'Do you mean the Societies are barbaric because they're so against the Pope?'

'That's the least of it.'

I remembered her antagonism to the church attended by Jeremiah, St Luke's Eastover, an Anglican church, and, in case her attitude to religion was merely sectarian, ventured to enquire: 'Are you connected with Rome?'

'I've been there.'

She was deliberately misunderstanding me.

'Roman Catholicism, I mean?'

'Good grief, no! I haven't believed in fairies or fairy tales since I was a child.'

I tried again by insisting that we had much enjoyed the marching and music and everything.

She replied: 'I got Graham to draw his curtains so as not to have to see people making fools of themselves. But we

86

couldn't help hearing the beastly militaristic din and fire-works.'

The old soldier in me stirred – the arrogance of ugly women is another way of stirring men – and I accused her of being a proper wet blanket: at which, unexpectedly, she chuckled and beamed.

The next member of the Hooke family to twist my tail was Brian with his pedantic and insolent pseudo-courtesy.

'Good even, sir!' Brian's wary eyes behind his glasses remind me of boys who were bullied at school – and often deserved to be. 'I must apologise to you as a past officer and present gentleman and representative of the ruling class for our rustic junketings, which originated in disrespect for the old order.'

'Hullo!'

'Humble greetings!'

I said: 'But your wife objects to Bonfire Night much more than I do.'

'Bonfire Night is quaint,' he allowed, 'but intolerably intolerant by the standards of today.'

'Well, by my standards it's fun, and this century's the opposite of tolerant.'

'Ah,' he exclaimed, 'fun! What a delightful idea! How unspoilt of you! You'll have to come and give us your definition of fun and tell us how to have some.'

We were interrupted before he had time to argue the other point: part of the procession was returning, a band was playing louder, and Gem had persuaded Graham to pull back his curtains and open the window.

I un-hooked myself with relief, leant out, and Monica Drewett joined me.

Monica with her spotless skin and great brown pools of eyes is definitely attractive, even if the adjectives pneumatic, over-ripe, flabby, all apply to her.

She groused through her protruding teeth, a dental feature which has also been known to fan the flames of male desire:

87

'They're such rotters in there, they wouldn't let us see the big parade.'

But then she sounded and looked happier. Peter Cadwallader accompanied these marchers, and greeted her, smiled up at her from the pavement, and rang Graham's doorbell and dropped in, tall and dark and twitchy. Monica hurried to serve him with food and wine, like a biblical handmaiden.

The ideas occurred to me that she has a soft spot for Peter, and she was paying him homage and he was accepting it by arrangement.

If so, if their exchanges in public over stale pie and synthetic wine constituted an assignation, why had he kissed Tracy Wilkins an hour ago and half-eaten her alive?

Of course, Tracy would sharpen the edge of the appetite of most men. But I entertained suspicions that Peter's moral fibre might be as flexible as his facial muscles. And I recollected that one girl is the daughter of Mr and Mrs Bert Wilkins of Caleb Hocking Ltd, whereas the father of the other is George Drewett of Downscene, industrialist, financier, millionaire, poised to stand and deliver a valuable dowry.

How does Peter Cad earn his daily bread, and would he draw the line at letting a father-in-law earn it for him?

Reggie Drewett's arrival put speculation to flight.

Reggie was tipsy, his red face made redder in places by lipstick, his steward's T-shirt ripped; and his greasy hair fell forward and down and round his cheeks like horns. He hailed Foxy-Poxy and Betsy-Wetsy, pretended to hit his sister on the chin with his clenched fist, curtsied to Gregory Leplay and Charles Hart, and called for hard liquor with the following proviso: 'So long as it hasn't been brewed in your bath, Graham – I'm not drinking your bathwater, you mingy old darling!'

Gem came and leant on the windowsill beside me. The scene without was again remarkable. Hundreds, if not thousands, of torches flamed and flared, filling the High Street with the unsteady yellow illumination of bygone nights; and the bands still managed to play and the marchers plodded from the War Memorial to St Anne's Hill and on to bonfires which, someone informed us, would be lit in the vicinity of the wild upland of the former Lewes Racecourse.

We stayed put until the last straggler was out of sight, then said quiet goodbyes to Graham, hoping to slide out of his house without undue fuss.

But we were detained in the front doorway. I fear that fate has in store for us intercourse of the social sort with the Hookes. Betsy, who was also on the point of departure, proposed it in terms of shy pugnacity: 'I don't suppose you'd condescend to dine with us one evening?'

I was so taken aback by this attempt to be nice, or nicer, that I replied in the affirmative, much to my regret ever since. But perhaps she did not hear me say yes. She certainly seemed not to listen. In fact her response to my response was to mutter something angry about being kept waiting by Brian and his women.

We wandered down the hill to the homely peace of Eastover. Sticks which had once been torches, and had not been consigned to the movable furnace of a wheelbarrow, smouldered and glowed in the gutters. The smoke had cleared, and ahead of us the reliable outline of Cliffe Hill cut across the night sky, and the bright windows of the houses of Cuilfail perched on its western slope seemed to be keeping watch over the town.

I ASKED Bertha about Peter Cad's occupation.

She replied: 'Mr Peter lives on his wits.'

I thought at first she was criticising him, then realised she was applauding. And why not? We are all dependent on our wits, and if we can live on them are so much the wittier.

'Do you mean he's rich, Bertha?'

'He could be, couldn't he?' she returned darkly, and

89

demanded an account of our experiences on Bonfire Night.

But she confined our answer to three little words – 'We loved it!' – by butting in with reminiscences of everything she had done on every fifth of November in every one of her eighty-odd years, and most of the things done to her.

At length Gem managed to squeeze in her question about Father Byrne's female companion.

'Mrs Samson,' Bertha intoned with disapprobation: 'You saw her, did you?'

'Who is she?'

'Thomasina Samson calls herself a widow. Merry widow, we call her.'

'Is she a friend of Father Byrne?'

'Well, she's his housekeeper – and resident. Was she wearing that hat of hers?'

'Yes. Why?'

'She's as bald as an egg. I'd wear a wig if I was like her, and didn't have this lovely thick thatch of hair. But she sticks on that silly hat day and night too, for all we know. He must fancy her in it, although he shouldn't.'

We hurried to change the subject, before Bertha embarrassed us with her opinions of the Catholic priesthood, the flesh and the devil.

Another conversation, not with Bertha but with my sister and on the telephone, preys on my mind.

I braced myself and rang Rachel one morning to ask what her plans were for Christmas.

She said: 'We've got the Robinsons coming to stay. What's happening to you?'

She was alone. Jim was out of the house, which was a small mercy. On the other hand she had had breakfast in bed, proof that she was no longer her active self, and might be feeling weaker and worse.

We talked in the verbal shorthand of siblings. For instance I took the hint that she hoped to be spared tiring emotion by choosing to celebrate the festival with friendly outsiders, namely the Robinsons, who would never quarrel with Jim.

'Oh – we thought of not moving from Lewes,' I replied. 'But we could visit you earlier on in December, if that suited. Or would you visit us?'

'December's a bit difficult – always such a rush! Shall we put off until after Christmas?'

'Yes – if you like.'

'I do pine for a reunion.'

'Same here.'

'Just with Christmas coming it's difficult.'

'I know.'

'Can we meet somehow in January or very soon after?'

'Certainly, Rach.'

'What present am I going to give you, and what for Gem?'

'Nothing, please – please don't bother to give us any present – shopping's hell! What can we give you?'

'No – that's not right – your giving me a present and not letting me give you one. But I won't give you soap – tell Gem I refuse – no soap this year – it bores me, whatever it does to you two. No – I'll find you some souvenir maybe – I want to – and if you insist you can give me a rose for my garden.'

'Done! We'd love that – it's a deal.'

She chatted along horticultural lines for a minute, while I rejoiced in her faith in the future as represented by her request for a rose to grow.

Then I dared to ask: 'How's everything? How are you?'

'Not too bad – I have to take hundreds of pills, and I can't do much – but not too bad.'

'I'm glad. Has Jim been behaving himself?'

'More or less.'

'Are you looking forward to Christmas?'

'Well, you know I like any jollification – just so long as I can make the effort. How are you? How's Gem?'

'We're all right – thanks – and Gem sends much love.'

'I send mine to her. Will you ring again, Huge?'

'Yes, yes. And you'll ring us, won't you, if you need help – anything – even if you need nothing – won't you?'

'Yes.'

'Goodbye, Rach.'

DECEMBER

A FLOCK of postcards from the Whitakers flutters through the letter-box.

Our London is loved by Toby and Jane as we love their Lewes.

And they really seem to be feasting their aesthetic appetites up there. Even to read of the hours they have trudged round galleries and museums makes my feet swell; while their plans for the festive season exhaust me – a concert on Christmas Eve, Midnight Mass at Westminster Cathedral, then Matins at St Paul's, followed by a guided tour of the City and lunch laid on for their group of tourists in a Dickensian hostelry.

I spent most of my Christmases as boy, soldier and bachelor at Boltbridge; and Gem and I always kept Mama company. Not last Christmas, but the one before, was our first on our own. We did nothing: stayed at home in our flat, went to early church, took Cindy for her matutinal trot, watched the Queen on television, dozed, read our books and retired early. We mourned Mama, and prayed for Rachel, and missed the snowdrops sprouting thickly through the moss in the drive. It was nonetheless enjoyable, a delectable novelty, having neither to witness the deteriorating health of dear ones, nor to mend the inevitable blown fuses in the cellar, nor empty the buckets in the attic if it rained, nor worry over the cost of each mouthful of food and cracker pulled.

Unfortunately the relief afforded by the death of somebody cared for is temporary.

Moreover my experiences of Lewes combine with my memories of Boltbridge to remind me that I was born and bred a member of a small community, and to define my preference for a town rather than a city, for comprehensible scale, the individualistic dimension, for pace that strains not, and privacy and peace.

Gem says we like swimming in a little pool, even if we are not big fish.

The recent cold weather has not changed our minds. Our love of Lewes may not keep us warm, but remains true. We have had severe frosts for three nights, and the thermometer has not risen much during days of tricky sunshine and ice-blue skies. We toast ourselves in front of the gas-fire in the sitting-room, and use electricity as if we were never going to have to pay for it.

At times like these, Hope Cottage is less cosy than it looks. We sympathise with the immemorial ambition of genuine cottagers to move into a decent house as soon as they possibly can. Fierce currents of frigid air from untraceable sources assault the backs of our necks as we try to watch television. The utilitarian point of wing-chairs, high-backed settles, ingle-nooks and places to crouch within them, is finally and fully appreciated. Too little gas-fire means that we cannot sit in our sitting-room; too much makes our heads ache. The bricked floor in the kitchen has several chilblains on my toes to answer for.

Needless to say that Cindy reposes undisturbed in the snuggest corner under the stairs. But we are learning to do what must have been done by our predecessors in the dark ages of discomfort. We keep active in the daytime, then go to bed.

Yet we still count the blessings of this place, its charm inside and out, its topographical situation, and how well it works in most weathers.

The construction of such old Sussex cottages bears witness as a rule to the superior intelligence of their builders. Brick walls, which can harbour damp, are kept to a minimum. Upper storeys are made of vertical joists and horizontal slats for hanging tiles on. The flat local tiles are hung on oak pins: they do not rust and have enough give in them not to snap under pressure from sea breezes. On roofs, the tiles are spaced so as to exclude rain and snow, but admit light and especially rot-defying ventilation into attics, which were sealed spaces before the advent of gravitational plumbing and internal water-tanks.

Granted, a shower, a drizzle, a wet mist, seem instantly to permeate our home. Yet the effect of atmospheric conditions that dry, sun and wind, is equally instantaneous.

Amateur cottagers have to acclimatise themselves to living cheek by jowl with nature. They have to adapt to its meteorological moods. They have to take claustrophobia and rheumatics in their stride. On the other hand some degree of exposure to the changing seasons must be good for us, or at any rate better than the perverse changelessness of central over-heating and the chilly germ-laden swirl of air-conditioning.

Sussex folk-architecture is inclined to call the bluff of twentieth century technology. Smart people who insulate their attics by rendering them air-tight are asking for trouble. Proper modern plaster smooths indoor walls and creates nice sharp angles, but absorbs almost as much moisture as the crude cow-dung and horsehair kind and takes ten times longer to dry. Draught-proofing a tiny room can make a gas-fire sickeningly gaseous, and a wood or coal fire smoke. Central heating so shrinks and warps softwood timbers that whatever they are holding up falls down.

Although I would like to write something about another architectural phenomenon, the mathematical tile, possibly peculiar to Lewes and certainly a peculiarity, I need to complete at least my researches for my book before I chase any more red herrings.

Meanwhile we shiver a bit, and wonder if and how Mrs Spedding is keeping warm.

GEM HAS been looking in on Mrs Spedding daily, bearing thermos flasks of soup; and I accompanied her yesterday evening.

Mrs Spedding had her telly on as usual, but heard us open the front door and shouted out: 'If you're a burglar, don't you dare come in here and pinch my money!' – a novel form of security device.

'Oh, it's you, dear,' she said on seeing Gem. 'And you've brought your mister along. How nice! Come in, do, and make yourselves comfortable.'

Her instruction was not easy to follow. The room was lit only by a table lamp by Mrs Spedding's chair; very cold except in the immediate vicinity of the gas-fire; smelt strongly of old age and budgerigar; and there were a hard wooden chair and a stool for us to sit on. Moreover the telly was showing a western and we had to talk at the tops of our voices to make ourselves heard above the sound of gunfire. Timmy sat on the shoulder or rather the woolly bed-jacket of his mistress, which was the top layer of her onion-like vestments. The fixed stare of his round black eye and his intermittent screeches were not exactly hospitable.

'How are you coping with this weather?' I asked.

'It's the lav,' she replied.

'What?'

'The lav out there in the garden! I have to go, I was always dainty. And I can walk, though it's ever so difficult. But oh, the cold is wicked. I dread it.'

'Of course you do.'

She made me jump by yelling at the telly: 'Shut up, can't you?' But she did not attempt to adjust the set.

Gem produced more soup and Mrs Spedding said to me: 'I call it manna from heaven. Your wife's kept me going.

You're a lucky man, you are.'

She began to slang her Home-help, whom I knew by sight – a large black-haired female recognisable mainly by means of her plastic bags. Gem had warned me that we would probably hear such a hymn of hate.

'Help, she calls herself,' Mrs Spedding fumed. 'Helpless, more like! The only thing she's ever cleaned is her dinner plate. She says it's so dirty here it breaks her heart. What heart, I say! She hasn't got a heart, or a brain for that matter – I wouldn't like to think of what's inside her. I call her a murderess, I do! – because she'd bury me alive if she could, and she's told me she'd like to slit my Timmy's gizzard. Poor boy! He's the only boy that kisses me nowadays – aren't you, Tim? I'm not letting her get her hands on you, my dearie!' She turned back to us. 'I don't trust her with him. I don't leave him alone in case she sneaks in and catches him, the cat. I take him to the lav with me. We go together, you might say. He can't hardly stand the cold. He can't stand weather. But better be alive and cold than dead and colder, that's our motto!'

All this was delivered with humour and charm as well as ferocity.

I asked her if I might switch off the telly.

'Oh I wish you would,' she said with feeling.

I then asked why it was not possible to bring the lavatory – or a lavatory – indoors: had Albert thought about it?

'Oh, he's thought! He's a thinker, Albert is. But thinking isn't paying, is it? It's the paying for pipes and whatnot that's the awkward part.'

'But Mrs Spedding, there must be portable lavatories, the sort they have in caravans, and at show-grounds in the summer, which don't have to be connected to the water system or the plumbing. Have you ever considered something like that?'

'If you want the truth, dear, my legs caught me napping. They let me down without a word of warning – I could

97

have danced a jig this time last year. And I was in and out of the lav like a whippet – I never stopped to notice the weather. Now I'm so slow, it's different. I haven't got round to consideration, not yet. I haven't exactly considered nothing.'

'Would you let us?'

She addressed Gem: 'I shouldn't be discussing my lavatory with him at all – it's indecent, isn't it?'

Gem reassured her: 'We'll go and have a snoop round for you in the shops, Mrs Spedding. We promise not to put you under any obligation. Don't worry.'

'Well, it's kind of you. But I can't say I'm hopeful. I've this here nasty notion that Tim and me, we're going to meet our Maker out in the privy.'

The upshot of this conversation was today's visit to Brighton.

A couple of hours ago, at six o'clock, we were back in Mrs Spedding's sitting-room.

'What have you got there?' she asked. 'What have you been and done?'

Gem said: 'It's a present from both of us, just a little on the early side for Christmas.'

'Oh, you shouldn't have! What is it? I'd give sixpence to know.'

We thereupon unpacked the Liftalu, a new-fangled type of thunder-box, free-standing, a plastic apparatus looking like the conventional china job, with a re-fillable container for water for flushing at the top, and another container for chemical solvent and so on literally at the bottom.

Mrs Spedding gasped: 'It's beautiful!' – and then seemed to swoon or even expire.

Her eyes closed, her head flopped to one side, and Timmy squawked, made an enormous mess on her woolly jacket, and fluttered and waddled on turned-in toes into the refuge of his cage.

But immediately, while we wondered if we had killed

her with kindness, she revived, blinking, laughing and enquiring: 'Was I funny, dear? Did I have one my funnies, dear?'

Gem said yes, and was she better?

'I'm all the better for what you've brought me, though it did make me worse for a moment. Talk of being knocked down with a feather! How will I ever thank you?'

We demonstrated the workings of the Liftalu – it was a dry run, I hasten to add; and positioned it in the room, and promised to initiate her Home-help into the mysteries of its maintenance.

We sat and chatted for another ten minutes. But we guessed she was impatient to get her hands on her present, and perhaps not only her hands; and after she had expressed more gratitude in her gracious comic way – 'I've had a ton of presents from men, but this one beats all' – we rose to leave.

Her parting shot was a good example of what used to be called working-class solidarity.

She called out to us: 'You still employing Bertha Didcomb?'

We answered in the affirmative.

'Pity,' she said.

A COUPLE of temporal truisms apply to the middle of this month: time has flown, and been the happier for having no history.

No telephonic exchange with Rachel was more worrying than usual, and one or two were less so. We pleased Cindy by going for hikes on the Downs in the gloaming, and pleased ourselves by coming home to teas of hot crisp salty buttered crumpets in front of the fire.

The cold spell was blown to kingdom come by a gale. We made as much as possible of being beside the rough sea: watched waves hurling shingle across the coast road at

Seaford, got a bird's-eye view of choppy water by peering down between the planks on the pier at Eastbourne, and dodged the bigger breakers of high tide on the Undercliff Walk at Rottingdean. We drove to the hamlets in the lee of the hills – Folkington, Alciston – and to the picturesque villages – Lindfield, Fulking – which, because they are so sweetly typical, would break our hearts with nostalgia if we were ever exiled from our native land.

My friendship with my Pakistani Uncle deepens. While he sells me *The Clarion* and I buy it, we solve the problems of the universe.

One evening I addressed him as usual in the style of a respectful nephew, and thus surprised and was surprised by Betsy Hooke, who emerged from behind the greeting card display wearing pebble glasses and a curious expression.

She was heavy laden with shopping, and accepted my offer to carry it home for her. Short-sightedness may be part of the explanation of her habitually hostile attitude: she hits out to discourage unseen assailants from hitting her. She should wear her spectacles in company. Can she be vain? But her un-stylish hairstyle and shapeless clothes are surely meant to suggest she has risen above the capitalist frivolity of mere appearances.

She observed: 'I'm impressed that your family tree has a branch reaching all the way to Pakistan.'

Maybe a taste for her mordant humour, and voice of a dying duck, could be acquired.

She said: 'The nastiest days for me are having to shop for six hours and having to cook for the other six.'

'Are you going to have many to cook for at Christmas?' I asked.

'With luck and the wiles of a wife and mother, I may be able to repress the hospitable urges of my beloved husband and son. Christmas is the last straw of the year for this harassed housewife – don't mention it, please! Tonight's bad enough. It's Brian's birthday, and I've got ten of his

100

colleagues to feed, mostly female, of course. I call them the hungry hunters. Academic women have insatiable appetites of every sort – all that sitting down to study seems to work them up. I was trying to buy Brian a birthday card from your Uncle; but the messages on them are disgustingly banal. I can't and won't sink to paying good money for bad bourgeois trash.'

The Hookes in their terrace house in Flood Street have Marian Travers on one side and used to have Wendy Aylward on the other. Betsy wears her heart not on her sleeve, but in her ground floor window, which is blocked by posters advertising CND, Peace Studies, homosexuality, aid for the victims of war and disease, vasectomy, counselling for battered wives and abused children, Subud, Tai-chi and Yoga classes, increased funding for the arts, and meetings to protest against almost everything. I handed over her shopping at the top of her front steps.

'You are coming to dine here one evening, aren't you?' she reminded me.

'You'll have to cook and shop for us if we do.'

She was thus hoist with her own petard and laughed in a punctured sort of way.

I added: 'What you need is some sweating staff in your basement.'

She was less amused to have her egalitarian leg pulled, and, although she smiled and thanked me for my services, she shut the door with a definite bang of disagreement.

On another evening I met Gregory Leplay in the Patels' establishment: he was buying snuff. With his silver wings of hair and tall elegant figure he is a handsome man, seen from a distance. But at close quarters his protuberant snub-nose and wide mouth are somewhat porcine.

He was again civil and informative, and described the perennial Christmas Eve parties at Cadwallader Place: 'They're post-prandial – they start after dinner. Be sure to drink some milk to line your stomach, or take a tot of

101

indigestion mixture before you go, because Foxy's rum punch scours like Harpic. Black Bogy's a children's game for grown-ups, something between a sport and an orgy. But the house is rewarding – all ruined splendour – and luckily belongs to vandals who can't afford to do anything to it. It's worth seeing, too, because it may disappear tomorrow – I mean it may be sold to pay for wines and spirits, and provide Peter Cad with pocket money. I won't be at the party this year – I've got work to do, and I'll be staying with my mother – but Charles can hardly wait. Charles is more a social moth than a social butterfly – he flutters round any lit candle – I keep warning him not to get his little red wings singed.'

Every road in Eastover seems to lead to my Uncle's shop. The Reverend Peterson buys his copy of *The Clarion* at four-thirtyish in the afternoon, as I do.

Yesterday, at the newspaper counter, after we had exchanged our customary greetings, Mr Peterson unexpectedly seized and squeezed my upper arm, propelled me out of the door and into the street, and, eyeing me too closely for comfort and radiating faith and hope, demanded in a deeply sincere tone of voice: 'Tell me what you think of my ministry.'

I stammered some mealy-mouthed reply in my embarrassment.

I thought he might be going to try to shake the truth out of me, but he rushed on to his next question: 'Do you approve of my use of visual aids?'

In fact I disapprove. Mr Peterson in the pulpit is too like a conjuror: the burden of his sermons often seems to be that he can and soon will produce a rabbit from beneath his surplice. It was distracting, for instance, to be shown six varieties of apple in the course of his description of the Garden of Eden, and his children's toy space vehicles when he discussed the Ascension. Once we had a projector and slides, and on another occasion a film was shown. But the aged churchwarden erected the silver screen with the greatest difficulty, the Holy Land was mostly upside down, and in the light of day the filmed freedom fighters or terrorists in some wretched country, who had been able to buy arms with our alms, looked like hairy ghosts.

I said: 'Well – I'm not so keen myself.'

But I need not have minced matters to spare the man's feelings.

He warned me with complacency and a manic evangelical glint in his eye: 'We're planning a visual bonanza at Christmastide, which I'm convinced will win you round – I'm convinced of it – wait and see, sir!'

THE CLARION carried a front page story full of comfort and joy to see us through the holiday. The headline announced: 'Rival Santas battle in Brighton store,' and the opening sentence began: 'Blood flowed in the Grotto of Gifts . . .'

At about seven o'clock on Christmas Eve we were serenaded by Bertha and three unknown younger persons, two female and one male, ringing handbells. They played Good King Wenceslas and Silent Night, while we stood in our open doorway, and half a dozen passers-by stopped to look and listen with us.

It was dark but dry. Light issuing from the cottage gilded the intent faces of the bellringers, standing in a semicircle in their overcoats and scarves; and it fell on the road and formed sharp-edged patches, peculiar shapes of luminosity reminiscent of the perspectives of expressionist art.

We put money in a collecting-box bearing the legend in large letters daubed on it in red paint: For Children and Animals. Bertha had refused to collect for a religious charity: she is against the Christian religion, she objects to being told she is a miserable sinner, although she concedes that there may be nothing wrong with God.

Our offer of hospitality was refused: 'If we touched a drop

we'd make mistakes and get our necks wrung.'

Wishes for a merry Christmas were exchanged, and we thanked all the musicians for coming to play for us.

'I knew you'd love it,' Bertha said.

We congratulated her: 'How clever of you to ring bells – we'd no idea you also had that talent.'

'I can do anything I set my mind to, and always could,' she proclaimed modestly.

We ate our supper and went upstairs to change at nine o'clock – we were asked to Cadwallader Place at nine-thirty.

My dinner jacket was shamefully old, shiny and tight. I wished we were staying at home and was overcome with psychosomatic sleepiness. But Gem's glamour and glitter, her hair done that afternoon and best dress with sequins, changed my mind. As advised, I drank my milk like a child – she refused hers – and then escorted her to Wharf Road.

Peter Cadwallader opened the door under the portico: actually it was half of the double-door with original bevelled plate-glass panels. He wore a bottle-green velvet suit and velvet slippers with his initials worked in gold thread on the toecaps, and was smoking a big cigar. He smirked at us, showing small regular teeth and crinkling the skin at the corners of his eyes. He looked good with his winter suntan and band-leader's hair; and I attributed my doubts about his honour either to the softness of his voice or the hardness of my hearing.

We were in an outer hall, which was large, had steps and pillars to the right and to the left, a multi-coloured marble floor, a fine cast-iron fireplace facing the front door, and an oak refectory table some thirty feet in length, partly cleared for the coats of guests, otherwise sporting a neat array of luxurious gardening implements, pruning saws that folded like penknives, golden trowels, secateurs with additional functions, walking-stick dibbers.

Marian Travers arrived; and you could tell Peter Cad was a ladies' man by the way he kissed her – only on each cheek, but spinning things out with relish – just as you could tell she was a man's lady by the way she stood up to his kisses, unflinchingly, inclining neither to nor from him, and smiling at us over his shoulder.

For that matter Peter helped to remove my Gem's overcoat with rather more physical contact than courtesy required: Graham Phipps-Hullett would have done it differently.

I have to admit that Marian in a silver sheath of a dress was the personification of beauty going begging, and so on. She has such pretty curly blond hair, and luscious clearly outlined lips, and smooth elastic skin, and the physique of an athlete of a certain age. We chatted to her, while Peter was admitting Octavia Pritchett. Marian was hoping for a white Christmas; she enthused about winter sports; and claimed she looked forward to the Cads' party all through the year and was thrilled to bits by Black Bogy. Her conversation raises the suspicion that she is more jolly schoolgirl than sultry sex-symbol.

Octavia Pritchett was almost unrecognisable in gumboots, tweed coat with fur tippet, one shawl round her shoulders and another over her head, peasant-style.

Instead of how–do–you–do she said: 'Beastly weather!'

'Oh, Octavia, we were thinking it was too mild,' Marian remarked.

'You're so darned hot-blooded, Marian, that's the trouble. I always was a cold fish. What are you up to, Peter? Hands off, sir, if you please! Let's have less hanky-panky and more central heating.'

Octavia, as Marian guffawed inelegantly and Peter laughed without making a sound at her grim jocularity, was emerging from her sartorial cocoon, kicking gumboots half across the hall, extracting a pair of shoes from the pockets of her overcoat, divesting herself of outer garments, and releasing the long skirt of her blue brocade dress which had been hitched up in its waistband. But, at the end of it, her long nose and snarly smile were not quite my idea of a butterfly.

Peter cleared his throat and shouted hoarsely and as loudly as his vocal chords seemed to allow, imitating a butler: 'Ready, Miss?'

I could just hear him.

Amidst more merriment Octavia retorted: 'Lead on, Macduff, you cheeky blighter!'

Peter obeyed her, puffing his cigar, Octavia stumped behind him, irritably flapping her hand to disperse the smoke, Marian slunk along beside Gem, and I followed.

At the top of the steps on the right I tripped: the floor was missing some marble inlay. I now noticed that the mosaic of marbles of different kinds and colours was in a parlous state, that pieces of scagliola had dropped off pillars, that plaster billowed from walls, and a broken pane of glass in a tall sash window was stuffed with newspaper.

Nevertheless that outer hall, the architectural arts it displayed, its grandeur and elegance, and the patina of centuries of elbow grease on the great oak table, were lovely to look upon.

But the inner hall was better.

THE HOUSE was evidently much larger than its front suggested. The inner or staircase hall was domed, pillared again and with another marble floor, black and white in an intricate design. The stairs were made of some cream-coloured stone, and rose in a broad flight, which divided and doubled back on itself. Each secondary flight led to a landing, where colonnaded passages were visible. The space was lit by a vast electrified brass chandelier, suspended from the centre of the dome and positioned above the stairway. The painted surfaces were white and a sort of faded terracotta.

It was stunning. Yet a second glance even in the dim light,

the dimmer because so many of the candle-bulbs in the chandelier were not working, revealed more dilapidations: marble cracked and shattered, water stains everywhere, broken glass defacing the portrait of an ancestor. There were plastic bowls on the stairs, and logs for the fires were roughly heaped against a wall, which was plasterless and had bricks showing through. And the white paint was yellowish-grey with age.

Peter shepherded us through inlaid mahogany double-doors twelve feet high into an anteroom and then into the room beyond. It was a library, lined with bookcases in which dusty leather-bound tomes turned to powder behind brass grilles, and lit by the bulky crystalline basket of a chandelier with several detached strands of glass droplets drooping disconsolately.

We had heard sounds of revelry from the company here assembled, namely the senior Cads; the Drewett gang, which had dined at Cadwallader Place; Wendy Aylward lurking in the shadow of Graham Phipps-Hullett; Charles Hart red in tooth and claw, metaphorically speaking; and a gaggle, perhaps a score, of unknowns.

Guy Cad's smiles welcomed us in, but threatened his teeth with eviction. He wore a nice old brown velvet smoking suit, and exuded party spirit, having obviously consumed it in considerable quantities.

Guy's surrealist whimsicality is apt to startle, especially in view of his grey hairs and his standing.

He greeted us thus: 'Happy crispness! Happy nappies and happy nips!' – and took us across to Foxy, who squatted on a stool by the fire like a superannuated Cinderella, clothed in a one-piece rag and stirring a black cauldron with a long wooden spoon.

'If I move I'll burn the punch – sorry,' she said by way of an apology for staying put. Her face was purple in the heat and glow of the fire. 'But I'm telling you it's hell on earth down here.'

Foxy's legs were so wide apart that, as the saying goes, a coach and four could have been driven between them, and her black plimsolls were much in evidence.

Madge Drewett, who was in diamonds, encouraged her: 'You stick to it, dar!'

Somebody suggested: 'She's got to stick to it because it's sticky,' and everyone laughed.

'Hand over that tin of tea, Madge, old girl,' Foxy said. 'And I'll be ready in a couple of shakes of a duck's whatnot.'

She grabbed a handful of tealeaves from the caddy and tossed them into the cauldron. Perhaps she was more like one of the witches in Macbeth.

The Hookes had joined the party by now. Betsy blew a kiss in our direction: she was not wearing her specs – could she have seen us, who did she think we were?

Brian paid Gem a pedagogic compliment: 'I say, full marks!'

The comment he addressed to me erred on the side of lasciviousness: 'I trust your lady's kind as well as pretty.'

What type of female, or rather females in the plural according to Betsy, can be reduced to hunting Brian Hooke with his magnified eyes and hair like wire-wool, I wondered.

He enquired: 'Observe yonder bookcases – enough books there to make a bookworm squirm with envy – give me your opinion, pray, as to which volume is the most thumbed, read, marked and inwardly digested?' – a sarcastic reference to the literacy or lack of it of our hosts.

He proceeded by inventing the titles of books relevant to the Cads: for Guy, *The Dramatic Significance of the Fool*; for Foxy, *Fashion, Costume and Dress for Ladies Through the Centuries*; and for Peter, *The Virtue of Chastity, Handwritten and Illuminated by Monks*.

He was brought down to earth by Octavia Pritchett, who smote him on the shoulder and asked: 'How long would you have ignored me for?'

There is no one so bold as a bold old spinster: although,

in fact, Octavia is not only not as old as all that, but less bold than she pretends to be, for when Brian responded without fancy trimmings, 'Hullo, my dear,' and planted a brisk kiss on each of her skinny cheeks, she seemed to quail and wince.

Something metallic was being rapped over by the fireplace, and Reggie Drewett called: 'Oyez, oyez! Silence for Mumsie!'

Through general laughter at this witty sally Madge Drewett began to repeat: 'Foxy is ready, dars! Glasses are on the drinks tray dars! Fetch a glass and Foxy'll fill it with her punch!'

'Or try to. Steady the buffers!' Reggie interjected.

'Take no notice of my rude little boy, dars! Foxy is ready with her rum punch. It's a loving cup, dars. Fetch your glasses from the drinks tray!'

We duly queued up. Charles Hart was in front of us, decked out in weird evening dress, which he told us proudly he had designed. The shirt was copied from those worn by pre-revolutionary Russian peasants, but made of dove-grey satin: it had a collarless neckband and buttoned across the chest. His jacket was of powder-blue velvet with frogging in unlikely places, and his trousers were tartan.

He said he adored the Christmas Eve treat at Cadwallader Place: always a riot and with the sweetest people.

Guy Cadwallader, presiding over the drinks tray, was distributing paper napkins and calling them serviettes in a mock-refined accent: 'A serviette to stop you scalding your fingers, Moddom? Serviette for holding your glass, sir? Keep your fingers away from the hot bit, please, and hold by the bottom.'

Charles turned to say with his leer: 'Saucy!'

Foxy ladled her concoction into our glasses. It was not as hot as it was meant to be: which was lucky for me, since she poured half my ration over my hand.

George Drewett, portly and pop-eyed, announced: 'Wait

for the toast, ladies and gents, wait until everybody has something to drink it with!'

We bowed to his authority.

Then he said: 'Here's to the happiest of Christmases for our generous host and hostess, and health and happiness all round!'

We raised our glasses.

The punch tasted odd to me, and Gem murmured under her breath and seemed to be about to burst out laughing.

Foxy asked: 'What's it like?'

'Spicy,' a stranger volunteered.

'Spicy? That's not the object of the exercise,' Reggie said.

George Drewett intervened: 'Where's the rum, Fox? You've omitted the rum. This is lukewarm tea.'

And he smiled and his hamster's jowls quivered.

FOXY'S FORGETFULNESS caused much mirth; and the bottles of rum that Peter and Reggie rustled up and emptied into the cauldron, regardless of measurement, also helped to get the party going.

A window was opened, through which to throw our glassfuls of tea flavoured with stewed cloves and cinnamon. The new alcoholic mixture was insidiously delicious, and second helpings were soon applied for.

Gem remarked to Monica Drewett that Foxy's mistake was easy to make.

'Easier for Foxy than for most of us,' Monica replied. 'I mean, it's becoming a habit with her. Not long ago she gave us her recipe for jugged hare. It was awfully complicated – she wrote it in full – and we were tremendously grateful. But she left out the hare.'

I was struck by Monica's rosy cheeks and the brightness of her brown eyes, by her less ruminative expression, and the buck-teeth she had inherited from her father which gleamed more seductively moist than his.

Peter Cad was approaching. He carried the cauldron and I think I heard him offer us another dose of the mixture as before. Whatever he said, Monica laughed at it enthusiastically in her well-oiled intestinal way.

A tour of inspection of the rest of the house was announced.

Foxy summoned us: 'Come and see where the Prince Regent slept! We've just knocked the room into shape. We'll be showing it off to the public next summer' – and she led everyone out of the library and up the stone stairs.

She had clearly forgotten not only the rum in rum punch and the hare in jugged hare, but also what she had told me about the Prince Regent and his bedroom at Graham Phipps-Hullett's entertainment.

The bedroom in question had some surprising furniture in it. The bed was a four-poster, Jacobean-style, more wood than good, with a cast-iron royal coat of arms screwed uncomfortably to the bedhead. There was a hulking Normandy cupboard, eaten by worms or peppered by gunshot; the dressing-table was unmistakable twentieth century fumed oak; and the stool beside it must have been made by Peter in the carpentry class at his private school.

Reggie, who seems to specialise in calling a spade a bloody shovel, protested: 'Foxy-poxy, don't tell us the Prince Regent slept in that there bed – the mattress looks like Dunlopillo! And this room was empty six months back. You've been diddling, you diddler you!'

Foxy was found out, but unabashed.

On the contrary, she boasted: 'I got it from Henry's' – Henry being a disreputable auctioneer and valuer along in The Caves – 'I got it all from Henry's' – and then had to stop laughing to recapture her teeth.

'Well,' George Drewett cautioned her humorously, 'if you con the public into parting with money to see a bed slept in by the Prince Regent, which you actually bought last week, you'll be got under the Trade Descriptions Act.'

111

'But I'll only say he slept in this room.'

'Did he?' others chimed in to ask, as I had at Graham Phipps-Hullett's.

'Definitely! Guy's found papers to prove it. Haven't you, sweetie?'

The crowd turned to Guy, who, after the relevant queries had been put to him and repeated and re-phrased and explained, answered thus: 'Could be – I shouldn't wonder – what?'

Amusement deteriorated via hilarity into rowdiness. A couple of the younger unknowns of opposite sexes jumped on the bed in which royalty never slept, and were applauded for doing a suggestive dance. Foxy and Guy were neither able nor willing to control their guests: they stood idly by, giggling, and Peter was nowhere to be seen.

But the Drewetts took over.

Reggie boomed: 'Order, order!' mimicking the Speaker of the House of Commons.

Madge Drewett drawled: 'Now, dars, Fox is going to show us where we can and we can't hide when we play Black Bogy. Isn't that right, Foxy dar? You show us, Guy!'

George urged in the voice that had launched a thousand board-meetings: 'Now's a chance to rehearse your guided tour – imagine we're paying customers and you'll find it comes easy!'

The Cads complied: at least Foxy had a shot at guiding, while Guy pretended to dun people for money and then pocket it.

And the house spoke for itself.

The grand staircase leads not to the first floor but to the second: rooms for the domestic servants of yesteryear are sandwiched between the living and the sleeping accommodation of the gentry. These staff rooms have been the exclusive preserve of spiders since 1945, Foxy admitted: and probably death-watch beetle too, someone muttered aside.

We were shown a secondary staircase, circular and windowless, once used by staff. There was another connection between these upper floors in the form of a linen-room on two levels, beautifully equipped with pine cupboards with sliding doors and slatted shelving. The slats were visible because the shelves were bare.

Gem whispered to me: 'Foxy ought to claim that Mother Hubbard, not the Prince Regent, was here.'

The Cadwallader who built his Place was a glamorous nabob from India, Foxy said: but George Drewett corrected her, saying he was a drainage expert, had worked briefly for the East India Company, then cleaned up in Lewes literally and idiomatically – he installed the drainage system.

However his gains were gotten, he must have been more like Peter than Guy. I mean that the top floor of Cads' Pad is constructed for the convenience of lovers – lovers bent on illicit love in particular. That second staircase is secretive, and every bedroom can be reached without recourse to the public passages. The bedroom cupboards are built-in and walk-in, and provide both storage space for clothes and access into the bedroom adjoining. Each suite conforms to the same plan: a bedroom where the lady reposed, a closet converted into a bathroom, a dressing-room for the gentleman she was married to, from which he could sneak via the cupboard into the bed of the next lady in line, and so on in what puritans would call a vicious circle.

Priapic house parties composed of energetic guests, quick to avail themselves of these amenities, are obviously a thing of the distant past. Cadwallader Place is like Boltbridge Manor in that none of the bedrooms is waterproof, and most are unfurnished – the furniture has fallen to pieces or been sold.

Yet the Master Suite, as estate agents would describe it, still has noteworthy features. There are splendid views of the river and the eastern hills from its two windows, between which, in an unusual position architecturally, is an open wood-burning fireplace. The bathroom has an electric

113

apparatus for body-massage, Foxy's toy – or, in Reggie's crude terminology, Foxy's fancy – which inspired Charles Hart to roll a knowing eye heavenwards. In Guy's dressing-room is a table on which aids to the toilet of generations of male Cads are laid out as neatly as the gardening tools in the outer hall. I noted nail-clippers, files, scissors and tweezers; shoehorns and buttonhooks; hooks for pulling riding-boots on and jacks for pulling them off; a pin-cushion speared by gold tiepins and stock-pins and jewelled pins for cravats; ivory-backed hairbrushes and clothes-brushes; much ivory, monogrammed and yellow with age, also shagreen, bleached by the sun from green to beige; and hair-oil, shampoo, tonic lotions, Eau de Cologne – in a variety of containers, metal flasks for travelling, glass bottles with screw-tops in the shape of crowns or coronets, more bottles of glass and plastic bearing the insignia of royal patronage and noble custom.

Most of us were again thirsty by this time, and all were eager either to begin playing Black Bogy or to get it over. We descended the main stairs, avoiding the bowls and buckets of stagnant rainwater, and negotiated a moulting Christmas tree down in the hall. We peeped into the dining-room, where the spoils of dinner had not been cleared away, and trailed through the drawing-room, which was shuttered and had nothing in it except an out of tune piano and a chandelier in a ragged holland bag.

Back in the library we were given more glasses of punch, reinforced by having boiled on the fire and reduced itself during our tour of the premises; then told the rules of the game.

A MALE and a female, a he and a she, would be catchers. They would allow the rest of us two minutes to hide, then hunt for, capture if they could, and try to stop us reaching the library, which was home. Foxy and Guy as umpires would switch lights off and on, summon everyone and sort out winners and losers and set the next game in train. The black in Black Bogy referred to the darkness in which we were to play; and bogy is defined by the dictionary as what causes fear.

I felt I was past fooling around in the dark, but was reluctant to opt out and be accused of spoiling sport, especially considering that George Drewett, who must be older than me, seemed anxious to join in: he had turned up the collar of his dinner jacket so that the whiteness of his shirt front would not betray his whereabouts.

Moreover Gem had entered into the spirit of the proceedings, and assured me in an undertone that she knew a perfect hiding-place.

The first volunteers for he and she were the Drewett mother and son.

Reggie described their strategy thus: 'I'm Mumsie's legs and Mumsie's my brain.' And Madge warned us of hers: 'I sit on the stairs and wait to catch you all coming home, dars, that's what I do – I just sit on a cushion on the stairs and wait to catch you, dars – I pounce on you, I'm a pouncer, that's what I am!'

The Cads switched off the lights. In the staircase hall, female squeals mingled with male curses, and unisex laughter reverberated. Gem led me by the hand up the stairs, along a passage and through a door, which she closed quietly behind us. We were in the linen-room: I recognised it by the odour of musty lavender bags. Gem insisted on our descending the step-ladder into the lower chamber, which was on the mezzanine or erstwhile servants' floor of the house.

I had just got to the bottom of these steps when the door above was opened and we heard tiptoeing footfalls.

A woman asked in a soft voice: 'Where are we? Where have you brought me?'

It was Marian Travers. She sounded confident and

amused: she was pretty enough to have had a lot of experience of what is apt to happen in the dark.

'Don't you fret,' a man replied smoothly. 'Nobody'll disturb us here. I've got a much more serious question for you. What are you going to give me for Christmas?'

Marian laughed.

He continued: 'Everyone should be generous on Christmas Eve.'

The wild surmise that she was being importuned by George Drewett was now confirmed by her moan of remonstrance: 'Oh George!'

Somebody slapped something, a face, a hand, and Marian said: 'Stop it! That's enough! Where's the door?'

George replied, breathing a bit heavily: 'No – tease not!'

Then the door opened again; high-heeled footsteps hurried down the stone staircase; and cries echoed and the exclamation, 'Got you, dar, whoever you are!' – as Marian finished in the arms not of the Drewett husband but the Drewett wife, Madge, doing her sort of pouncing.

The next intruder into the linen-room was Reggie, the other catcher, hoping to flush out anyone still hidden with the following monologue: 'Fee fi fo fum! Do I smell the tantalising aroma of an Englishwoman? Do I smell the stink of an Englishman? Or is it the cat? Puss, puss! I've got a nose like a bloodhound, I warn you cool cats. Are you holding your breath? Well, soon you'll have to let it out and I'll know where you are and what you had for dinner. Come to Reginald! Fee fi fo fum!'

He departed.

We wondered if the time had come to attempt to reach the library.

But a board creaked over our heads, and the door of the linen-room slowly clicked shut.

A girl protested: 'But you don't mean it!' The voice was low, excited, pleading, seemed to be asking for contradiction and reassurance, and belonged to Monica Drewett.

The inaudibility of a hissed whisper in reply brought Peter Cad to mind.

She asked: 'Are we alone?' And then with mounting passion, as real writers would put it: 'Why are you so nice to me, darling? Why are you suddenly so sweet?'

After a pause we heard more hissing, the shuffle and scuffle of shoes, the rustle of clothing, and the exclamatory gasp: 'No, please, not now, not that!'

She was arguing with him: 'But you don't! You won't!'

She listened, laughed, weakened, flirted weakly: 'You say it to all the other girls.'

A hubbub broke out somewhere below.

She said: 'Later, later – don't make it difficult for me!' – and escaped, and was pursued, through the door.

When we emerged from the linen-room the lights had been switched on and were already about to be switched off for a second game of Black Bogy. People were crushed in the ante-room between the staircase hall and the library; the word was that two of our unknown fellow-guests would be the new catchers; shoving and pushing seemed to be in order; and we were plunged in darkness before we could see any of the lovers we had heard upstairs.

We retraced our steps. But on the landing at the top of the first flight of stairs we collided with the lofty and bony, but surprisingly solid figure of Graham Phipps-Hullett, and had to waste time in responding to his elaborate apologies, and were lucky not to be caught.

In the linen-room again, shortly after we had stolen down the step-ladder and hidden under it as before, we were startled by a yelp of female pleasure or pain in fairly close proximity. It was followed by recognisable half-stifled inter-sexual cries and groans.

We were left in no doubt as to what two people were doing; realised they were doing it in an adjacent bedroom in the old servants' quarters, accessible by way of a door in this lower part of the linen-room; and guessed that Peter

117

and Monica were carrying on from where they had left off, or – in the even earthier vernacular – Monica was being done.

Discretion urged us to beat a hasty retreat.

But we were arrested by yet another tryst in progress on the upper level. We were inescapably the filling in a sandwich of different kinds of love.

'My dear, this is hardly playing the game,' a man complained so loudly that I knew he wanted to publicise his difficulties and be extricated from them.

A woman shushed him.

'Let me talk to you,' she begged him angrily. 'You know my Christmas is going to be unbearable.'

'Tut tut,' he retorted. 'Reactionary twaddle! Christmas is tomorrow, tomorrow's Saturday, there are fifty-two Saturdays in a year, what's so special about this one?'

'Will you come and see me?'

'How can I? Be reasonable!'

'Reasonable? – When my heart's broken?'

'That's flattery, my dear.'

He was Brian Hooke, and she, believe it or not, Octavia Pritchett.

We were amazed to understand that Octavia had been, and entertained ambitions in her flat bosom still to be, the object of masculine desire.

As for Brian, Octavia was a shred of evidence that he was not only a dingy don but a dingy Don Juan.

She now sniffed and cleared her throat – an unseductive sound – at which he swore coldly: 'Oh damn and blast it!'

And as if to remind them of their passionate past, and mock their respective present yearnings to be together and apart, the joys of love in action were again broadcast by the couple in the nether regions.

'Dearie me,' Brian quipped.

But he had his excuse to skedaddle. She protested, 'No! No!' – and chased after him. And we seized our opportunity at last to get out of the linen-room.

We hung on to each other in the darkness and headed for the stairs, and a comical row broke out between Reggie Drewett and Charles Hart.

Reggie shattered the black silence with the accusation: 'But this is a great hairy man's hand!'

'Thanks for nothing!' Charles screeched.

'What? Is that Charles? You filthy beast, Charles, you squeezed my tiny hand! Keep off! Down, boy, down! Who do you think I am?'

'We know who and what you are, Reggie dear. Anyway – I was only feeling my way to the library.'

'And I've never heard it called that before.'

Their dialogue was rudely interrupted by the strange voice of a catcher: 'And I've caught you both!'

We had taken advantage of this noisy diversion and reached the lower unified flight of stairs. But we were not alone in doing so – we were in a queue without realising it. Therefore, when Wendy Aylward put her foot in a plastic bowl half-full of rainwater and collapsed backwards, we all went down like so many ninepins. Thankfully no one was hurt, except maybe by the irony of things. For Wendy landed on the unaccustomed knees of Graham Phipps-Hullett: Graham toppled Gem, Gem toppled me; and I fell on Betsy Hooke, who was perhaps subconsciously guided by the gods of matrimony to flatten Octavia Pritchett.

The uproar was considerable, the bowl bounced down to the marble hall and rolled round, and Guy and Foxy switched on the lights and illuminated the scene of bodies sprawling in undignified attitudes on their stairs.

APPARENTLY OUR hosts and fellow-guests were agreed that we had provided a climax to the second and last game of Black Bogy as farcical as hoped for, which compared favourably with the follies of previous parties.

In the library, even stronger punch was served, or, in more precise metaphorical terms, poured down our throats, as midnight approached.

Wendy was drying her shoe and the hem of her skirt in front of the fire, unattended by Graham, who was drinking rather a lot seemingly to recover from the trauma of having had a woman on his lap.

Octavia grumbled that she had twisted her ankle on the Cads' stony stairs, probably to account for her pallor and swollen eyelids, the true cause of which was pain in another part of her anatomy. Brian, for once, did not stray from Betsy's side: he was giving practical expression to the adulterous theory that a spouse comes in handy when a mistress or lover is on the warpath.

Monica and Peter rejoined the party separately. At first I wondered if we had jumped to the wrong conclusion in the linen-room. But then I noticed the extraordinary rosiness of her cheeks, as if their sensitivity had been chafed by a bristly chin, and a spider's web on the knee of his green velvet suit.

At a few minutes to twelve Foxy turned on a vintage radio. A hush descended as we waited for the chimes of Big Ben, and in it we could hear the persuasive church bells of Lewes summoning worshippers to the midnight service.

The hour struck; we drank a toast or two; parked our glasses, crossed arms, joined hands and sang Auld Lang Syne, the younger people forcing everyone to bow and bend faster and faster; and amidst laughter detached ourselves.

Some people kissed, at least I saw George Drewett kissing Marian Travers, who averted her head but awarded him the consolation prize of a tiny private pout of a smile – and Peter planted a chaste kiss on the forehead of Monica, which greatly amused them; and we and several others began to say goodbye.

Guy reciprocated our good wishes in familiar style: 'Oh – happy-haps to you too, and happy pips and pups, if it comes to that!' – and, when he had regained control of his teeth, kindly bemoaned our departure; while Charles Hart demanded with a rhetorical wriggle, 'What's the point of leaving? Is the ship going down?'

Reggie tried to detain Gem by kneeling at her feet and singing: 'The night is young and you're so beautiful!'

Foxy's group in the anteroom was playing a new game. George Drewett placed a cork on a small occasional table. A player had to approach at top speed, walking as quickly as possible or running, egged on by the spectators, and without checking trap the cork in the V between his or her outspread second and third fingers. Most players missed, not only those who were punch-drunk.

Madge got double vision after trying: 'I keep seeing two dars whar thar was one dar before.'

'Goodbye, goodbye!'

Foxy said: 'Oh don't go! Happy Christmas! And please stay in Lewes, don't desert us!'

In the outer hall Octavia was putting on her layers of clothing, like the Dame in a pantomime in reverse. Guy, who had accompanied us, asked if he should call for our coachman and carriage. Wendy and Graham followed us out into Wharf Road, where Graham immediately, and with no more than a fugitive wave of his hand, turned left for School Hill and the High Street. Octavia remarked grumpily as she proceeded in her gumboots towards Beggar's Roost: 'What a ridiculous party!' Wendy, at her front door, expressed a personal point of view with characteristic chirpy gloom: 'My husband Derek wanted the one thing – now Graham wants anything but – love's a silly muddle, isn't it? But I do hope you two manage to be happy for as long as possible.'

In Hope Cottage, having swapped festive greetings with Cindy, we retired to bed and eventually to sleep about three o'clock.

We woke as early as usual, feeling rough. But I gave Gem my present of an eighteenth century print of Lewes Castle, and she gave me mine of a nineteenth century History of Lewes, and we managed to laugh at our mutual pre-occupation with this dear old town and its inhabitants. We postponed ringing up Rachel until the evening. And church, probably our prayers, but also events therein not strictly religious, had a restorative effect.

The surprise promised by Mr Peterson was concealed behind a curtain across the chancel at the altar rail. His sermon started to re-tell the tale of the birth of Jesus. At the mention of the stable in Bethlehem he pulled a string in the pulpit, drawing the curtain and revealing a tableau vivant of the Nativity. Straw was spread on the encaustic floor-tiles; our two churchwardens of opposite sexes posed as Mary and Joseph, notwithstanding the facts that she is in her fifties and he a frail bachelor of seventy or so; a live baby was strapped and propped in a makeshift manger; and a donkey was tethered to the wrought-iron railing.

But the donkey brayed. Its wheezy, mournful and deaf-ening eeyores made the baby cry. The baby's mother shot out of the vestry to comfort and reclaim it. She must have frightened the donkey, which now kicked back and caught Joseph a crunching blow on the shin. He subsided in a swoon; Mary asked if there was a doctor in the house; and several members of the congregation, six or seven, probably nurses as well as doctors, pounded up the aisle. The donkey tried to retreat before their advance, panicked, shied and bucked, tugging at the railing and threatening to uproot it.

At this point Mr Peterson again pulled his string. The curtain closed across the dramatic scene, although profane noises, shrieks, swearwords, baby's bawling, and the odd semi-strangulated bray, plus sounds made by shoes and hooves and bodies in collision, did not leave much to the imagination.

The incipient hysteria of the congregation, its alarm, ragged chorus of advice and reassurance, and tendency to giggle, were quelled by the firm announcement of the next

122

hymn. Mr Peterson had abandoned his sermon; but the look he gave us, militant and at the same time meek, taught the lesson that he at any rate was not kicking against the pricks. We stood and sang: 'Say not the struggle naught availeth.'

JANUARY

W<small>E DID</small> not see the New Year in.

I was reluctant to make good resolutions. I could not resolve yet again to write my book in the coming months, though I still intend to do so.

As for the hopes associated with the turn of the year, and the beginning born of the end, I hardly dared hope that Rachel would be healthier and happier: for fortune, which has rained blessings on my own head, might consider me greedy and punish me by taking it out on my sister.

Similarly, I am inhibited in my prayers for fear of hearing a still small voice saying: 'I want gets nothing.'

Further explanation of my negative attitude to New Year's Eve may reside in my conversations with Rachel over Christmas. She was in that state of neurasthenic anxiety which no doubt finds its fuller expression in her disease. Even the undiscriminating easy-going Robinsons under her roof had summoned her self-destructive perfectionism as hostess and housekeeper. She was frantically pursuing the unattainable ideals of pleasing everyone, and of fun being had by all the people all the time. I know her spirit is as youthfully keen on jollification as ever; but her flesh is no longer strong enough.

Another of the less merry aspects of Christmastide was brought home to us about a week ago. We were woken by rapid footsteps in the frosty night – the hour was almost witching. A girl was running along River Road and round the corner into Rickman's Lane chased by a man. Her lighter weight and higher heels sounded different from his longer crashing strides.

My heart sank: I was afraid of being called upon to rescue an innocent virgin from the clutches of a drunken rapist or homicidal maniac. I was even more alarmed when the girl stopped – was caught – just beneath the northern window of our bedroom in Hope Cottage.

Breathless panting – or was it sobbing? – broke the nocturnal peace.

Then she cried: 'Why? What have I done?'

And in answer to the man's murmuring she continued: 'No – I won't! I can't take the pressure. And I don't have to. Good night! Goodbye!'

Her young voice had traces of the local accent, and was vaguely familiar.

He must have persuaded her to calm down, listen to his side of the story and pardon his offences, as male deceivers will; for after a brief and unintelligible discussion they proceeded together, in step, in the direction of Cliffe.

I was relieved. Gem extended characteristic sympathy to the victims of love. And we soon went back to sleep.

A day or two afterwards I was buying socks in the shop of the late Caleb Hocking, whose daughter and heiress Naomi, consort of Bert Wilkins and mother of Tracy, still rules the till. We and these older Wilkinses are by now acquaintances as well as neighbours in Rickman's Lane. He resembles a bald brown rat, sleek and energetic; she is a bulky matron with eyes that glitter behind her glasses – I would suspect Tracy of being a changeling, owing nothing to their unthinkable union, if I did not know that beauties are rarely the issue of beautiful people.

Bert had been inclined to call me his friend when he met me walking Cinders: 'All right, my friend?' And Naomi betrayed her social pretensions by passing remarks to Gem on ladylike subjects such as flower gardens and stately homes open to the public.

But the purchase of my socks was unexpectedly fraught with emotion. I no longer seemed to be the friend of Bert, who served me with antagonistic formality; and Naomi reacted to my observation that it was not too bad a day with a speechless scowl, then impaled my invoice on a spike savagely, as if to give me an inkling of what she felt like doing to myself. I hurried out of the shop and, yet again in the position of eavesdropper, overheard husband and wife snapping at each other.

The point of the recollections above is that their voices reminded me of the girl in the night. The story that Gem and I have therefore pieced together is that the girl was Tracy, and the man pursuing and inaudibly persuading her was Peter, Peter Cad, or the cad Peter. The pressure she could not take was his playing her false with Monica Drewett, the infidelity he had confessed to, or, more likely, which she had somehow discovered. And their reconciliation in Rickman's Lane must have been temporary, and the preface to their parting for ever: whence the disappointment and plain bad temper of her parents, robbed of the opportunity to be grafted on to the family tree of the Cadwalladers, and nursing a grievance against any representative of that class which had led them up the garden path, and had now gone and dumped their precious daughter in the middle of nowhere.

Poor Tracy – and Naomi and Bert!

Poorer Rachel!

Yet I have to confess that in spite of ailing dear ones, and hearts fractured for a variety of reasons, and the millions upon millions of people in direst trouble in the whole wide world, we seem to be managing to do the necessary in an existential sense: we keep smiling in this vale of tears.

The shortest day of the year is over and done with, spring is on the way, I may even make a start on my book, and the editor of *The Clarion* contributes to the gaiety of the nation with yesterday's banner headline: 'Lewes twins perish in blaze.'

JUST OVER one week ago Mama's housekeeper and companion, Mrs Shipp, Shippy, died in her cottage in Boltbridge, and Rachel rang up to tell us and ask us to stay for the funeral.

It was typical of her to assume we would attend the funeral: she was judging by her standards, which are that friendship takes precedence over everything else and nothing is more important than loyalty.

I did not want to go back to Boltbridge. Selfishness was dead against the long drive, the revival of memories, the varieties of strain involved, and even the temporary severance of my links with Lewes. On the other hand I had longed to see my sister, although I also longed not to see she was iller than ever – but cowardice could not be allowed to keep us apart. She herself had proposed the visit – we would not be forcing an entry into her home. Additionally persuasive was the information that Jim Claughton would be absent for both the nights of our stay.

Amongst the unpleasant side-effects of serious illness must be acknowledgment of the nervousness, and consequent guilt, it inspires in the majority of those who love you.

I was nervous not only of what I would see, but that my involuntary and indiscreet reactions might be seen.

Incidentally, that shaming nervousness is a sort of fear of the unknown: illness is easier to live with, at least for thirty-six hours as we did, than to have to imagine.

Rachel was summoned by our headlights and opened her front door and stood there calling: 'Hugo? Hugo!'

She is so small and thin, though perhaps no smaller and thinner. We kissed. She and Gem hugged each other. Her high girlish voice, and the warmth of her affection, are the same. Her house is like her, brightly lit and welcoming. She had tea laid out for us in front of a log fire, a plate of the egg and cress and mayonnaise sandwiches she knows I have a weakness for, chocolate biscuits and Mrs Haddon's fruit cake.

It was no use telling her she had gone to too much trouble: her desire to please is ineradicable. What a lovely tea, we said, how sweet and kind she was – and hurriedly changed the subject, veering away from such slippery emotional slopes.

She showed that she too was frightened of breaking the bonds of good manners, losing control and howling like a dog. Except for her perilous repetitiveness on the doorstep – 'Oh this is so nice – I've missed you so – it's so nice to be together again – I've missed you so badly!' – she eschewed personal or intimate conversation. Once or twice she eyed me speculatively, and I wondered if she was deciding whether or not to confide in me, or waiting for me to brush aside her reserve and wring some confession out of her. But second thoughts suggest otherwise: that she was watching to make sure I would keep up appearances and not let her down.

Besides, at the earliest opportunity, she told us she had invited the Boothroyds to dinner, Edgar and Nicole, really Mama's friends or lifelong acquaintances, worthy dull polite octogenarians, comparable to shock absorbers or a buffer zone.

She took us upstairs to our bedroom, her best spare, pretty and neat in a conventional style. She pointed out pictures from our old home which she had inherited and hung in hers; and back in the sitting-room, having mixed her dry martini and lit yet another cigarette and perched on the club fender, she reminisced about Shippy, Mama, the Manor in its heyday, in Father's lifetime, when the sun shone throughout the summer and winter's snow was deep, crisp and even.

At this stage of the proceedings she seemed better and happier. She always was as resilient as a bird that sings immediately after escaping the cat. She embodies the truism that luckily women have no memory for pain. She chattered with blithe animation, exaggerating, laughing.

Then Gem helped her to finish cooking the dinner and the Boothroyds arrived.

More martinis were consumed, and two different wines with the food. Rach appeared to be none the worse for them. But, later, because I was concerned for her nonetheless, I accompanied her when she descended the cellar steps in search of crème de menthe and permitted myself the priggish remonstrance: 'I must say you do hit the bottle at Tillers Grange.'

She gazed straight at me in the light of the bare cellar bulb, wide-eyed, reproachfully, just for a second, wounded by my lack of understanding, and retorted in a sharp defiant voice: 'Of course!'

I wanted to apologise, but missed my chance. I was appalled by my obtuseness and clumsiness, but could not have gone into my motivating sorrows without going into hers, which she was trying to drown. The worst of it was her implicit query: 'If I drink too much, if I smoke too much, what does it matter?'

We pretended to be unaffected by the exchange, and rejoined the others. Eventually the Boothroyds, who are as fit as only eighty-odd years can make you, departed. Gem let Cinders into the garden, I tidied the dining-room, and Rach filled hot water bottles for all of us. We climbed the stairs together and kissed good night at the top; and Rach bent and stroked and patted Cindy and murmured tenderly: 'I do love you.'

Was her declaration really aimed at me? Was she forgiving me?

We laughed and separated.

I did not sleep well that night.

RACHEL HAD taken it upon herself to organise the wake after

the funeral of Shippy, who had no known relations. As a result she was busy the next morning, collecting contributions of the proverbial baked meats from Shippy's friends in the vicinity. I drove her, Gem helped to fetch and carry, and we kept on passing and re-passing the gates at the bottom of the drive of Boltbridge Manor.

Its new owner is a Mr Lee from Wells, estate agent, family man, respectable and reclusive. Tied to and leaning against the gateposts were boards advertising firms that scaffolded and roofed, and performed surgical operations on trees. Mr Lee is doing those things which we ought to have done and omitted to do, owing to shortage of cash.

At eleven-thirtyish I picked up Martha Wright from Home Farm, the farm connected with and almost connected to our former home. Martha is the widow of Joe Wright, who bought it from Mama, and the daughter-in-law of Gaffer Wright, dead and gone for a quarter of a century. I also fetched Elizabeth Wickes, OAP and spinster daughter of our late head-gardener and the diminutive Mrs Wickes, who once swung her chickens to sleep for the entertainment of my sister and myself.

Rachel in her car had Josie Todd, born a Barrett, daughter of our cowman Juggy Barrett, whose stink of dung we used to find excruciatingly funny, and of Mrs Barrett who regaled us with gargantuan teas; and Mrs Hebden, relict of Geoff of Pinnock Farm, and relic of humanity, a crippled great-great-grandmother, the stowage of whose Zimmer walking-frame caused difficulties and frayed tempers.

In Boltbridge Church we formed a congregation of a score or so of mourners.

The party afterwards at Tillers Grange was geriatric – Gem in her early fifties was like a child amongst grown-ups – and almost exclusively female: the only other male was a nameless dotard who looked as if he was made entirely of blue veins and adam's-apple. My family's place in the history of the village was recalled with affection and gratitude. Nostalgic tributes were paid to the memory of Mama by those who had benefited from her generosity, or robbed her, or both. Even a few facile tears were shed at the sight of me. But cream sherry and cherry brandy cast their magic spell. Rustic complexions grew redder. Rude witticisms were shouted in deaf ears. There was hilarious speculation as to whether or not Mrs Hebden on her Zimmer would reach the bathroom in time. Genteel affectation capitulated to greed: the last cakes were snatched and stuffed between false teeth. The mood of the meeting was not sorrow because good-natured faithful Shippy was dead, but the competitive joy of re-discovering one was still alive.

I hope I did not show my sudden resentment of the gross appetites, enormous hips and sheer durability of these survivors, who accentuated the frailty of Rachel in her relative youth.

I even resented Rachel herself, tired out by the guests she was serving tirelessly, because she lacked the preservative qualities of moderation and commonsense, and had worried everyone who loved her since attaining the age of discretion or indiscretion.

Then Mrs Gridge, retired district nurse, drew me aside to ask: 'Who's your sister's doctor?'

Dr Ward, I told her.

She clicked her tongue and shook her grey head and treated me to the sybilline utterance: 'She'll be needing the best attention.'

Disagreeable experiences come in threes, they say.

Counting Mrs Gridge's prophesying as the first, the second was the following conversation with Rachel.

Round about four o'clock, when the last guest had gone, she complained of exhaustion, and I contradicted the implication that she was exhausted because she was ill: 'You'd be a freak if you weren't! You've never stopped today, you've done everything – I did nothing, and I'm whacked.'

But she would not be reassured, or reassure me: 'My exhaustion isn't like that.'

'What is it like?'

'I don't know – chronic.'

'What does Dr Ward think?'

'That's the question – what he thinks, if he thinks.'

'Don't you have confidence in him any more?'

'Not much.'

'But he used to be such a good doctor.'

'He's good if you're well.'

'But you are well, Rach!'

Her depressed and depressing silence provoked me to continue: 'Should you see another specialist? Shouldn't we look for the best man here or abroad, who'd check you over thoroughly?'

'I can't go through that again. Thorough check-ups are enough to make you ill. Dr Ward never stops nagging me to see best men – he's got twenty best men queueing up to see me. But I won't – I loathe doctors.'

'Nonsense!' The comfort I offered her was cold: I just got cross with her. 'You can't go on loathing doctors in case you're ill. It's stupid, really it is, to be so craven in that one way when you're so brave in other ways. Somebody might be able to help you, give you a boost or a tonic or something, and help your friends, too, by putting paid to your worries.'

'I wonder.'

'What?'

'I'm not right, you know – I've no energy or stamina.'

'Nor have I – nobody has any stamina at our time of life – that's only natural.'

I could read her face – her eagerness to believe me – as she seemed to read mine and therefore not to be convinced by my specious reasoning.

She said, almost but not quite daring to ask the question which I would not have dared to answer honestly: 'I wonder what's wrong with me.'

In reply I blustered, and more ominously than I meant to: 'It's nothing, Rach – it's temporary – you can be sure of that.'

Gem came to our rescue.

'Listen,' she said, 'the old prescription for peculiar aches and pains was sea air, a holiday by the sea. Please, Rachel, come and stay with us in Lewes. It's four or five miles from the sea – it might be the very thing for you. And we'd love it. And we'd have such fun together.'

She recovered herself, her poise, her social personality, and returned, smiling gratefully and vaguely: 'Perhaps in the warmer weather,' and suggested a cup of tea.

The third nasty experience, and strong contender for the title of nastiest, occurred between the hours of nine and ten that same evening.

We had just finished eating cold ham and baked potatoes in front of the telly when Jim Claughton walked in: he had not been due until the evening of the next day.

He enters a room as if it were a rugger scrum: short arms bent, elbows out and shoulders hunched aggressively.

Rachel was evidently dismayed, asked if he was okay, was ignored and relapsed into sullen silence.

Gem advanced to propitiate him with a kiss.

'Get away,' he said, 'I'm not interested in kisses of that sort.'

He berated Rachel obliquely for not serving dinner in the dining-room, and had a dig at ourselves for neglecting her: 'Your sister's full of good works. She's the Little Mary Sunshine of this one-horse hole. But she's got a Meals-on-Wheels mentality. She thinks the answer to life's a Meal-on-Wheels or a telly-tray. She ought to remember where charity begins. And considering you and your fine lady come and see her so seldom, you'd expect her to cook and serve a decent meal, wouldn't you?'

I argued with him, but feebly, for fear of goading him to become less benevolent.

What was I drinking, he asked.

Nothing, I replied.

Well – what had I drunk with dinner – what had I been given to drink – what had Rachel given me?

Water, I said – what I had wanted – a glass of water.

'Good God! I'll get you something more manly.'

'No, thanks.'

'Come on! Don't be standoffish like your late lamented mother. All right, all right – keep your hair on – and stick to your tipple and rust your guts. But I won't be accused of failing to offer a man's dram to a chum.'

Gem mentioned Shippy's obsequies.

'I couldn't stand the old cow,' he commented, and for good measure continued: 'And I don't want to hear another word, not one more word, about Boltbridge Manor and its marvels and multitude of adorable serfs and flunkeys – I've had it day and night ever since I made the mistake of marrying into the holy family!'

He stamped out of the house to park his car, leaving the front door open; re-entered, cursed Cindy again for barking at him, and grumbled that the sitting-room was freezing; opened his letters, throwing bills at Rachel, who had to catch them or retrieve them from the floor; tossed back his whisky exhibitionistically, and finished with a flourish of ill-temper.

'Talk of Welcome Hall! I hurry home to meet the wife's relations, and what do I get? I get it in the neck. Thanks a bunch! I'm off, I'm not sitting here with you moaning minnies, I'd rather be in bed with my smutty magazines – so I'll wish you all a bad night!'

RACHEL CRIED, and Gem asked if she was any nearer a decision in respect of her marriage.

Contrarily as ever, Rachel then rushed to the defence of Jim: he was just jealous, he did not like her having too nice a time, he was inclined to take against any representative of her family, and so on.

I enquired: 'How can I help?' And when she hesitated, I was for once quick enough on the uptake to say: 'We'll clear out as soon as possible tomorrow morning.'

She cried some more and thanked me and explained: 'I don't want you to go – but I'm no good at rows – I'm sorry – why is it like this?'

We comforted her as best we could and eventually persuaded her it was high time we all retired to bed.

Jim's curse was effective so far as we were concerned: my night was white – in two long nights at Tillers Grange I slept no more than three or four hours – and Gem's was on the grey side.

At breakfast the next day Rachel surprised us pleasantly by looking better than we felt. And she seemed cheerful: Jim was already out and about, she had no idea where.

While Cindy was being settled in the car, I had a word indoors with Mrs Haddon, Rachel's dear friend and daily lady.

'Take care of my sister.'

'I do! I will!'

'Here's my telephone number in Lewes. Contact me in an emergency. And you could pass it on to Dr Ward.'

'I'll try.'

In the winter sunshine we said goodbye, laughing conscientiously and waving. The driving mirror showed me Rachel turning into the house with bowed head and Mrs Haddon's arm round her waist.

Yet our visit succeeded not merely in making matters worse. No sooner were we back in Hope Cottage than Rachel rang to say we had done her a power of good, not least because Jim by way of an apology for misbehaving had promised her a holiday at one of those seaside golfing resorts in Spain: and she was now keen to follow our advice and laze on a beach in the Spanish sun.

She added politely that she still hoped to stay with us later on in the year. But I am afraid that she and I are equally ambivalent about seeking each other's company. The home truths we tell each other, tacitly and in spite of ourselves, are so upsetting.

However, since our return, knowing Rachel was more cheerful, I have relaxed sufficiently to remember better days at Boltbridge.

I remember that Mama's deafness was regretted generally because it prevented her participation in verbal fun and games. She could no longer hear or see jokes, and sometimes she would accuse her nearest and dearest of having lost the power of speech.

'Don't mumble, darling – mumblers are the bane of social life – they should be drawn and quartered.'

Occasionally the idea that she could be at fault escaped her: she was the strangest mixture of high-handedness and humility.

The time came when she found it difficult to differentiate between the sexes, grammatically at any rate, although she retained complete clarity of mind otherwise until the day she died.

She would tell me: 'Rachel had tea here. He's bought himself a pretty new party frock, which has taken the edge off his troubles.' No one laughed more than Mama at the revelation and correction of such errors.

She was much amused by Shippy's habit of greeting her in the mornings thus: 'Oh Madam, you do look awful – you must be feeling bad!' And likewise by being warned by a doctor in her ninety-first year that smoking might be the death of her.

She was an inveterate smoker, and belonged to the age in which fashionable people would – if they could – smoke a cigarette with grace. Hers was the art that conceals art when she smoked: her gestures were natural and unembarrassing. She mocked her doctor not only for his overdue warning to a nonagenarian, but also because her belief, possibly more reasonable than his, was that a puff of what she fancied had beneficial, prophylactic and curative properties.

One afternoon I had asked Martin Hardwell to tea at Boltbridge Manor. He was almost a nervous wreck, he had given up smoking a few months previously and was afflicted with every kind of withdrawal symptom, and nasal and bronchial ailments into the bargain. Mama enquired after his health. He complained of his catarrh and the rest of it. She urged him: 'Have a cigarette! I recommend cigarettes. You'll never be well until you smoke them.'

The beauty of her youth and her ladylike qualities came in for comment at Shippy's funeral. My own memories of her in her prime, when I was a child, are blurred and faded. But she had beautiful bones, a bone structure distinguished and immutable, underpinning her countenance, as it were; and a reward of her virtue was that she retained her facial charm in old age. Gem, meeting her in her mid-seventies, was also struck by the freshness of her complexion – and perhaps by her expert application of powder and rouge.

She wanted to look nice in order to please. She was out of tune with feminism: she always wanted to please men. Her susceptibility to the appeal of the opposite sex rendered her, from one point of view, a sort of St Sebastian cruelly punctured by the darts of Cupid, and, from another, incorrigibly flirtatious, though Rachel and Gem and I are agreed that her flirting did not go far beyond a sympathetic giggle over the teacups and cucumber sandwiches.

The practice of charity is no beauty treatment: on the contrary – to care for others is apt to mean not caring for yourself. If I am right, then I have been wrong to call Mama charitable. Possibly it was responsiveness that she went in for, open-minded and open-handed. Her strength or her weakness was her inability not to respond constructively to sorrow, need, sickness, adversity.

138

As for being ladylike, what is a lady, and was she not more than like one?

Trying to define the two words, lady and gentleman, is the English equivalent of the rabbinical teasers of Jewry, for example: 'Can God make a stone so heavy that He cannot lift it?' The majority of English people spend the major part of their lives wondering if they are, aspiring to be, or regretting they are not, ladies and gentlemen. Even objectivity finds itself confronted by the impenetrable subtleties of the subject.

A lady is not necessarily old or young, titled, well-born or rich. She is neither noticeably clever nor foolish, nor proud nor falsely modest: she hopes, if in vain, to be nothing that sets her apart from, and strains her relations with, her fellow-men and fellow-women.

My own idea is that she is blessed or cursed by having minimal quantities of suspicion and cynicism in her make-up, and absolutely no desire for self-advancement. Such characteristics are charming: a lady who is charmless is surely a contradiction in terms.

Mama grew ever more trustful. Her confidence in the human species was remarkable after nearly a century of intelligent observation of the ways of the world. Once, towards the end of her life, I arrived home to discover her shuffling round the attics on the arm of a man who did not look gentlemanly. He was of Middle Eastern appearance and wore a floor-length blue overcoat with soiled velvet collar. Mama introduced him as Mr Mactavish, an antique dealer, who had dropped in and had sweetly offered her pots of money for the junk in these storerooms, and was now interested in seeing the good furniture remaining in the rooms on the first and ground floors. I had to tell Mr Mactavish that actually none of the junk in question was at present for sale, let alone for sale at the prices he had offered, and escort him off the premises. I then entreated Mama not to consort with sharks and crooks in future, and waited to hear the house had been burgled.

But nothing happened. In front of me she had confided in Mr Mactavish that she was deaf and blind, or partially, and invited him to re-visit her on any day of the week except Wednesday, Shippy's day out, when she was alone. He was either more honest than I assumed, or felt obliged to justify her far-fetched faith in him.

Mama received assistance on the road to ruin. Many hands, including those in the till, make light work after all. The fact remains that she was not robbed so often as she seemed to ask to be.

I retain no filial illusions. There is a sense in which my parents denied me my birthright, and Mama wrecked my prospects and exploited me. Yet I would not wish to qualify any of the compliments showered upon her when she was alive, or the praises still being heaped on her grave. And I do not doubt that she would have cut herself in half to spare me the slightest distress, if she had been aware of it.

What came between us, latterly and only, was circumstances. Members of the older generation should so arrange matters as to be as little trouble as possible, if they wish to continue to inspire love in the hearts of their children rather than worry and alarm. The impracticality of Boltbridge Manor, combined with Mama's longevity, exasperated. Too many things went wrong too frequently and too far away, and getting there and coping and paying and getting back again and striving to maintain business as usual – the sheer physical struggle preoccupied me exclusively.

Time heals, they say. My experience is that time has restored sensation to feelings numbed by repeated blows to the nervous system and bank-balance. The consequences are by no means altogether pleasant. I mourn the chances to reciprocate affection that were missed.

I hope my actions, reflex and mechanical as they tended to be, reluctant as they tended to become, spoke louder than brisk words and the restive thoughts behind them. The memory affording me some comfort is that at least I never let her be evicted from her home.

She was lucky to have been so nice, so loved, and maybe to have had so many years of living – and living at Boltbridge Manor. But the word luck is seldom if ever applicable to the process of dying. Courage and stoicism could not completely conceal the pain of disablement, setting aside her deepening sorrow in respect of her daughter. She lost faculties one after the other, hearing and sight, the use of fingers, the use of legs. Perhaps for a few years she was terminally ill.

And illness puts politics in perspective. The seriousness of it shows up the careless frivolity of the game of politics. Illness draws us towards God and away from men who would pose as the divinity and usurp divinity's powers. At the same time it converts to instant faith in the value, the necessity, of quiet government, freedom from deliberate oppression, the observation of roughly just laws, and statutory encouragement of good neighbourliness.

Threatening, terrifying, torturing ill people seems to me incredibly base and vile, and the more so when motivated by cold impersonal political dogma.

Whence the subject of my book.

MY MOTHER at just about her last gasp, having virtually given away all her worldly goods, and for that matter Rachel's and mine, received a poison-pen letter, although it called itself a Rates bill, stating in red ink under the sign of the hammer and sickle: 'Rich bitches should and will pay more.'

It killed her, I believe. She had reason to feel wronged. She must have been so disillusioned by the evidence that her lifelong friendliness had evoked enmity.

Her ill-wisher was a single and singular individual. She should have recalled the fond esteem in which she was held by many, and forgotten the misconception and malediction of one. But she was old and tired, weak and vulnerable – and not unworldly because she was ignorant. She would have realised that the lone scribe had written under the influence of, almost to the dictation of, his or her fire-eating bosses in the Creedwell County Council – who had been elected more or less democratically. She had a loving nature, she needed to love and be loved and approved of; and a majority of the voters of her own locality, supported in principle by approximately half the electorate of her native land, and the millions of people preaching if not practising the same ideology abroad, were united in disapproving of her, hating her, and, through the agency of her red letter day, had tried and condemned her in accordance with the unjust and irreversible law of their prejudices.

Her Rates were already punitive. One hundred and eighty per cent more than she had paid to the previous administration, three times what she had paid three years before, was being demanded with menaces by the politicians in charge at Creedwell County Hall. And the likelihood was that the semi-official futuristic threat would be carried out and she would be dunned for still more money.

She did not have it. She had nothing left to sell, except the roof over her head. She gave up – perhaps chose to give up – the ghost in her own time and surroundings.

Now these politicians who exercised the power of life and death over Mama, nudging her towards the next world by partisan economic pressure, sentencing her with a sentence, were the collectivist-socialist-Marxist sort.

I know and admit that there have been and probably are good Socialists, worthy reasonable moderate men and women with soft hearts – even if, in my opinion, soft heads too. And radical nagging has helped to ameliorate the lot of society's eternal underdogs.

Everybody likes to dream – and most of us did in our salad days – of that Utopia of perfect equality between human beings and peace on earth for ever and ever, which

Socialism has the nerve to promise to create.

But in this country Collectivism – Socialism – has had its opportunities. Many nations have had experience of socialistic economics at work, or, rather, not working. Pragmatism has agreed with common sense that the only hope economically is not interference by the unbusinesslike bureaucrats of centralised government, but relatively free market forces. As for the seductive notion of equality, nature ridicules it; and you would have to strangle talent at birth, and lock up better-looking people, and somehow get rid of aspiration and ambition, and root out inadequacy and laziness, and stop parents favouring their children and children asking their parents for favours, and so on and so forth. Moreover nature would certainly say that peace – not fighting or being prepared to fight to survive, not destroying other organisms for survival's sake – is about as viable a proposition as pigs flying.

Such proven objections to Socialism pushed to its logical or illogical conclusions clearly carried no weight with whoever scrawled on Mama's Rates bill. And the pop-political groups lording it in Creedwell and elsewhere took the line that what had gone wrong with Socialism was dishing out not too much but too little. They were interested in revolution, not reason. They would leap without looking, and drag the rest of us, into that deep end.

My grieving anger had a broader basis than the supposition that one or more rustic Robespierres had murdered Mama. My family, all of us, had been dispossessed as much by politics as by prodigality. Collectivist fiscal policy ever since the war, taxation and financial mismanagement and inflation, had increasingly confiscated earnings and savings. If the politicians in question had not flouted the first rule of every child's guide to economics – spend more than your income and you will find yourself in trouble – I might be in Boltbridge Manor for better or for worse today. Perhaps we deserved to lose our treasure, perhaps it was our turn to lose; but in the longer term in the relevant period every citizen gained corroboration of the truism that one man's do-gooding costs the next man a packet.

Materialistic considerations apart, Collectivism – Hitler's National Socialist Germany and Marxist Russia – Nazism and Communism, or Communism and Nazism in that order – had caused the Second World War; and had disturbed the international peace of the post-war era with its imperialism, sabre-rattling and propaganda, its constitutional aim to export revolution, its fifth column of mercenaries and wreckers worldwide, and record on so-called human rights.

That Rates Bill shocked and frightened not only Mama. After her death I wanted to get as far away from Creedwell as soon as possible. But it pleased me to think I was retreating strategically in order to fight another day. I waited and wondered how to strike my small blow on behalf of Mama and all the other past and present victims of revolutionary idealism – or of the destructive delusions of revolutionaries.

My knowledge of the subject was even sketchier then, two years ago, than it is now. But having lived through most of this century, I could hardly help knowing that crimes more heinous than writing a few words in red ink had been and were being committed ostensibly to bring about the greatest good of the greatest number. And I had an inkling of the paradox or pathetic fallacy of politics: which is that almost everyone, ninety-nine per cent of the population of everywhere, wishes and prays for a quiet life, and is sooner or later embroiled in revolution – upheaval, violence, war civil or foreign, tragedy for many citizens, and years and years of re-adjustment and re-alignment with pre-revolutionary values.

Modern history suggested that no nation was immune from the process – a pointless progress from good to bad, or bad to worse, and back again. Hypothetically, even in a country like ours with its enviable record of stability and harmless political rivalry, its safety-net of legislation and its accommodating social system, making it to my mind as happy and dear as Shakespeare's John of Gaunt believed it to be, revolting politicians could succeed by their criteria and wreak havoc by yours and mine. And the likelihood was that they would do so in the name, and by means of the demagogy, of Socialism.

Of course the epithet happy in the paragraph above is contextual, comparative, and the roughest of generalisations.

Of course, again, the picture of the future that Socialism paints has undeniable attractions, especially for those who refuse to believe that politics is the art of the possible: wealth abolished, no more poverty, a brand-new order of equality, employment a prerogative rather than a privilege, our innate urge to better ourselves replaced by an altruistic resolution to serve the community – a pacific heaven on earth, setting an example to competitive acquisitive workaholic warlike nations, which will surely never try to take advantage of the defencelessness of their neighbour and will rush to render assistance when that neighbour goes broke.

And of course, once more, so long as there are people who are poor, envious, ignorant, impatient, insincere – in short, always, according to the Bible and the whole history of humanity – there will be Socialists.

But I had had one taste too many of the poisonous brew Socialism is capable of distilling, which it had forced down Mama's throat with lethal results. The idea occurred to me that I could get my vengeful feelings out of my system and indulge my literary inclinations simultaneously. I would write a book exposing the socialistic confidence trick, and warn my compatriots of the tyranny lurking over the radical horizon.

The purge of my writer's block of decades' duration was meant to be the spy Philby's autobiography and Graham Greene's introduction.

GRAHAM GREENE calls this autobiography by an author who had spent at least thirty years lying, cheating and earning the wages of dishonesty: 'an honest one.'

Graham Greene's fiction shows a special interest in and sympathy for sinners by both religious and secular standards. He is therefore running true to type in a literary sense by pleading in extenuation of his friend's conduct: '"He betrayed his country" – yes, perhaps he did, but who among us has not committed treason to something or someone more important than a country?'

However, his question raises other questions. Is he not over-egging the pudding of sympathy – is he not pulling our legs – by implying that your business and mine is betrayal?

Graham Greene divides the main body of his work into Novels and Entertainments. I must confess that I have always thought novels were meant to be entertaining, and fictional entertainments were novels. Be that as it may, I suppose he would class his Introduction to Philby as an Entertainment and not to be taken too seriously.

Yet when he writes of Philby, secure in the British Secret Service throughout the war, having 'long Sunday lunches at St Albans' and 'a pint on fire-watching nights at the pub behind St James's', I cannot help remembering my father in his POW camp, and friends of mine, friends I made in the army, fighting for five years for low pay and often crippling wounds, whose lives, provided they were lucky enough not to lose them, and marriages and careers were dislocated.

Again, Graham Greene in controversially sentimental vein refers to Moscow as the home Philby had never seen until he fled there to escape arrest and prosecution. And he is forgiving even to a fault of Philby's achievements: 'After thirty years in the underground surely he has earned his right to a rest.'

That 'surely' nags at me. Surely it belongs in different contexts? Philby in his Preface is surely too good to be true.

He writes: 'The public naming of serving officers whose work is supposed to be secret cannot fail to cause personal embarrassment. I have no desire to cause such embarrassment to former colleagues in the British, American and sundry other services, for some of whom I feel both affection and respect.' Is he telling us, is he expecting us to believe, that in thirty years he never revealed the name of an agent in the field, a spy operating behind the lines on behalf of Britain or its allies, to those sensitive philanthropic comrades of his in the KGB?

Philby has no regrets: 'It is a sobering thought that, but for the power of the Soviet Union and the Communist idea, the Old World, if not the whole world, would now be ruled by Hitler and Hirohito. It is a matter of great pride to me that I was invited . . . to play my infinitesimal part in building up that power.'

Graham Greene puts the same thought thus: 'In Philby's own eyes he was working for a shape of things to come from which his country would benefit.'

Surely the defacer of Mama's Rates bill would agree with Philby: he or she would claim that a country benefited from polishing off gentle old ladies. His or her political bosses in Creedwell would also see things Philby's way: that the Somerset of yore would be a better place if run on Russian lines with a Marxist-Leninist-Stalinist programme of swingeing reorganisation and reform. Like-minded politicians elsewhere would re-create Russia in our green and pleasant land in hopes of rendering it greener and pleasanter.

Such an end, the equitable fairer society of every revolutionary's fancy for the last few thousand years, is the justification of Marxist means: which start with the class war.

All is fair in war, we were taught at school. Marxism has taken that lesson to heart.

Two quotes from my recent researches throw light on

147

the psychopath skulking in the bureaucratic shadows who attacked my mother.

The apologist of Marxism-Leninism Ilya Ehrenburg tries to excuse the persecution of the traditional victims of radical revolution thus: 'Not one of them was guilty of anything; but they belonged to a class that was guilty of everything.'

I am sorry not to be able to attribute the following, that I have no record of who said or wrote it, for it sums up what has been, is and always will be wrong with practical Marxism: 'Acceptance of the idea of the class struggle exempts from human feeling.'

A Marxist could retort: 'Naturally you object to belated revolutionary justice, considering you are by birth and breeding a landlord and capitalist and exploiter of the working class and parasite. Your mother got off lightly: she should have been shot for her acts of charity – which are against the true interests of the workers, and constitute a challenge to their proper representatives. You cite history: I wouldn't attract its attention if I were you. For history is going to crush you and your sort, and take what is yours and give it to us, give power to the people, who deserve it and have waited for it so patiently. Look at Russia!'

Yes – well – look at it – glance at it for as long as you can bear to!

THE RUSSIAN – Bolshevik – Marxist revolution occurred in October 1917. In December of the same year the tasks of the Cheka, the secret police force which became the OGPU, then the NKVD, and is now the KGB, were formulated by government. The first execution by the Cheka was carried out in February 1918. In September 1918 five hundred hostages were shot after the assassination of Uritsky; and, still in 1918, the attempt by the Social Revolutionary Dora Kaplan to kill Lenin signalled the start of the Red Terror.

Jewry, since the war, has rightly kept the attention of the

world focussed on the holocaust, in which six million Jews and others perished in dreadful circumstances at the hands of the German National Socialists – Nazis.

But how many perished at the hands of Marxists in Russia?

The tally was, is, and probably will remain imprecise: no one was keeping count, Krushchev admits. The extensive research of the historian Robert Conquest suggests that the famine in the Ukraine in 1932 and 1933, combined with terror tactics, killed fourteen and a half million: 14,500,000. For the period 1930–1950 Conquest qualifies an overall estimate of twenty million by adding that it should be increased by fifty per cent: 30,000,000. According to Professor of Statistics Kurganov, an emigré whose figures are quoted but not vouched for by Solzhenitsyn, sixty-six million persons prematurely met their end between 1917 and 1959: 66,000,000. And the Russian brand of Marxism has been at it for a further quarter of a century.

The numbers are so astronomical as to be meaningless to most of us. Therefore ten or twenty million seem to be beside the point of the argument. Evidently more Russians than Jews perished for the sake of a political bright idea: just supposing Professor Kurganov is right, exactly eleven times as many Russians.

Sticking to that hypothetical 66,000,000, a bit of multiplication and division may aid comprehension. Revolutionary justice in the USSR, assuming it was not operational on the Saturday and Sunday of each week, sentenced approximately six thousand citizens – 6,000 – to a death of one sort or another on every single working day of the forty-two years 1917–1959.

The legalistic process was speeded up in most cases by not having to waste time on trifles such as proof of crime, or the defence or even the presence of the accused. Solzhenitsyn states in the last sentence of *The Gulag Archipelago*, published in the early 1970s: 'There is no law.'

I was wrong to refer to revolutionary justice: it is a

contradiction in terms. Revolutions are revolutionary largely because they are illegal and unjust. But Marxism as applied by Lenin and Stalin carried injustice to extremes.

The spy Philby was proud to have served it. But for the communist idea, he opined smugly as he rested at home in Moscow, his native country might have been ruled by Hitler. Graham Greene explains that Philby thought Britain would derive more benefit from Marxism-Leninism-Stalinism than from Nazism.

What benefit?

Granted, in the homicidal sense, Hitler would not have been good to or for us in Britain. Yet Stalin would have been worse. Marxists are pleased to believe that history somehow supports them. It does not support Philby: who asserted that by working for Marxism and against Nazism he had done his countrymen and countrywomen a favour, although, it could be argued, for every one of us Hitler would have killed Stalin would have killed eleven.

I must check the size of the population of Russia in 1917. I suspect that Lenin and Stalin reduced it — culled it — by about one third. And their victims were not all landlords, capitalists, parasites, aristocrats, middle class, bourgeois, rich, or for that matter enemies of the state or counter-revolutionaries. The ruling class in any country, the anti-revolutionary establishment, is numerically a tiny fraction of the population. The Russians who mainly bore the brunt of Marxism's essential oppressiveness were the workers, the proletariat, the broad masses that had sanctioned the revolution which promised to serve them, and the innocent, people like Mama.

FEBRUARY

S T MATTHEW advises us to let the dead bury their dead.

If I were to do so, the book I was moved to write by the manner of the death of my mother would be buried too.

Meanwhile life continues to provide me with excuses not to get down to work. Rachel sounds different on the telephone – her voice stronger, her mood more optimistic – since her sojourn in Spain. She has no complaints about the conduct of her husband there, and says she slept like a log and ate like a horse: which must have been better for her than eating like a bird and smoking like a chimney and drinking like a fish at home. Could it be that she has turned the corner and is going to get well? I would rather contemplate that happy possibility than try to tell the sad story of Collectivism.

A counter-productive home truth appertaining to my literary project dawns on me: that sorrow and wrath are more prolific than joy – although I tremble to think it, let alone set it down, for fear of tempting providence to alter my present personal scenario.

But I have been distracted from my duties not so much by metaphysics and hypotheses as by a practical proposition.

It was put forward by Gem towards the end of January, six months after we arrived in Lewes and at the halfway stage of our planned tenancy of Hope Cottage. Winter by then was showing its hand: the weather was cold and hard. The sky turned green and scarlet in the afternoon, stars scintillated instantly in the dusk, and the frosts were fierce.

151

I believe the thermometer never rose above freezing-point in the daytime. It was bad for the garden birds, although we fed them: they moped around and hardly had the energy to take evasive action when Cindy was on the warpath – but perhaps they have discovered she is all bark and no bite.

One evening after tea we ventured out for a tour of the town. We were undeterred by the dark. The windless crystalline air was simply bracing. And we expected to have the streets almost to ourselves.

We walked along Wharf Road, beside the shimmering river, up School Hill and into the High Street. Moonlight, sky-light, slanted across on to the opposite pavement – I believe there was a full moon. In bygone times, on bright nights when the moon was full, the gas-lamps lining the streets were not lit. We turned into Castlegate by Bartholomew House – the glaze on its mathematical tiles glinting.

The mathematics of these peculiar tiles seem to be nominal. They imitate bricks. They were used for a couple of centuries, and until not long ago. They came in various patterns, black, glazed and unglazed, several shades of red; could be quickly pinned to and hung from wooden laths; and the regular gaps between them were filled with mortar. They provide some protection against the elements, as proved by the staying power of the houses sporting them; and the finished article is almost indistinguishable from a good solid superior brick wall. But I suspect that their chief charm was snobbish. They were a cheap way of looking expensive.

John Betjeman wondered what the holiday-makers lying on the beaches of Britain were thinking about, and suggested: class. Betjeman, notwithstanding his family's Dutch connection, knew us better than that literal-minded German Jewish refugee Karl Marx. Marx summoned the workers in this country – not in Russia, which he called barbaric and despised – to rise and overthrow Capitalism. He might have achieved his object if he had revised his vocabulary. No true-born Briton likes to be consigned to the working-class. A Britisher, at any rate the male of the species, is a country gent – potentially, in his dreams and wishes, and his own estimation.

Thank God for the inborn and incorrigible snobbery of our race, which has so far spared us the futile horrors of egalitarian revolution!

Any English fool could have told Karl Marx to peddle his panaceas to a nation of peasants and serfs.

Mathematical tiles, as I was saying, enabled householders to turn their timbered houses into grand bricked edifices in a matter of days, at low cost, and without inconvenience. Architectural refinements were also available, for instance massive pseudo-cornerstones of wood painted white.

The stones of the twin arches of the Barbican of Lewes Castle, on the other hand, and the arrow-slits and so-called machicolation at the top, the extended parapet from which boiling liquid could be dropped on unwelcome visitors, are authenticity itself.

We passed the old Bowling Green. The hazards of its uneven sward, haunted no doubt by the medieval champions who jousted on it, were white with frost in the moonlight. From the vantage-point beyond Castle Precincts we looked over the roofscape of the houses below, into the sombre declivity of Gallows Bank and Hangman's Acre, and up and across to those westward Downs where the Battle of Lewes was fought in 1264, the lucky outcome of which was the introduction of parliamentary and eventually democratic government in place of the dictatorship of the monarch.

Cindy was let off her lead in Castle Lane and Pipe Passage: no other dogs or dog-lovers or dog-haters were about. She ran along the pathway on three of her four legs, and, when she glanced back to make sure we were following her obediently, her eyes glistened behind their furry veil. She seemed to be saying: 'Have we ever had more fun? Hurry, please!

There's always something better round the corner, you know.' The Castle above was not floodlit as it is in summer – the moon rendered floodlight, like the gaslight of nights gone by, unnecessary.

In the High Street again we had to shepherd Cindy across to Keere Street, where we got a good view of the pale valley and the distant sparkle of Newhaven.

I remarked that the steep pavement was icy and treacherous, and suggested that for safety's sake we might take the long cut home by Rotten Row and Grange Road.

Gem's reply was circumlocutory: 'Well – I'm in no hurry – it's not that I don't want to go home – it's more that I never want to leave.'

In plainer English, that is the question: to live or not to live happily ever after here in Lewes.

THE RAINS came about three weeks ago; and for ten days it pelted and poured non-stop. References to Noah were the common coin of social intercourse. The most truly British of all diseases broke out in epidemic form: meteorological despair. Foxy Cadwallader swore she would shoot herself; Betsy Hooke put the blame on the United States, which must have tested one nuclear device too many; Octavia Pritchett refused to shake the hand of the Reverend Peterson, who had failed to make his prayers for better weather heard; and our Cinders pretended to oversleep in the mornings and not to know what was expected of her when we shooed her into the wet world of the backyard. Mrs Spedding, although she had no call to brave the elements nowadays thanks to the Liftalu, complained darkly of drowning sensations: 'I feel it up to here, dear.'

The quip of that drinking man, Reggie Drewett, was repeated in the emporia of Eastover, into which people crowded for shelter, company and light relief rather than for merchandise: Reggie said he had seen the evil of water, so would never let another drop pass his lips.

My Uncle wobbled his head with extravagant sympathy, while Jahendra reserved his smiles for desirable female customers.

Another consequence of the deluge was that the drain in the gutter outside Hope Cottage blocked. A swirling puddle became a pool, which inched onto the pavement and threatened our front door.

Gem did not miss her opportunity to mock me for having celebrated the advent of spring on the shortest day of last year, two months ago on the twenty-second of December: 'Winter was icumen in, not spring – twenty degrees of frost followed by twenty inches of rain are not what most people mean when they refer to the joys of spring – and being flooded out of house and home is definitely not joyful.'

Wendy Aylward was more worried by the roadside pool than we were or than she seemed to need to be. She rang the local authorities. Within the hour stout jovial men had arrived to pump out both our drain and that one at the other end of Rickman's Lane, which was also blocked.

Wendy then called in partly to tell us she might have saved our bacon, partly to talk of love. She had dined and wined Graham Phipps-Hullett, she related with dated coyness, but he had arrived late and left early: did we think he was normal? She had tried to find her way into his heart by feeding him with fried seaweed Chinese-style and pork with oysters as eaten in Portugal. But she herself admitted the dinner had been disgusting: she must have picked up the wrong seaweed on the beach at Rottingdean, and she was afraid a few oysters were off. Gem therefore diagnosed that the trouble with Graham was probably gastric rather than emotional: at which Wendy giggled and concluded happily enough, 'Oh well – thank goodness for Glyndebourne!'

I telephoned Toby Whitaker to say his property and possessions had not quite been swamped. Like Wendy, he took the trouble with the drainage system seriously, and asked questions about the river, tide-tables, equinoxes, which I could not answer. He explained that too much rainwater flowing towards the sea, and too much seawater forced inland by the tide, could meet at Eastover and flood it; and that the Lewesian tributary of the River Ouse, the Winterbourne Stream, if it happened to be in spate, would pour still more water into an already overflowing receptacle, so to speak.

Such a concatenation of circumstances had occurred some years ago and caused considerable damage, Toby said. He had heard hair-raising tales of boats plying for hire in East-over High Street and ducks nesting in the cellars of Wharf Road. And a few older smaller less well-built houses had actually subsided and been washed away in the direction of Africa via Newhaven. He wanted the same fate to overtake neither Hope Cottage, in which he had money invested, nor ourselves.

I congratulated him on having got his priorities right, and asked if there was anything he thought we could or should do in order not to finish in Davy Jones' locker.

His reply was negative; and his last message to the troops holding the fort on his behalf – Gem and yours truly – was that he was damn glad to be out of it.

Although I laughed at Toby's jokes, in the afternoon of the day following our conversation I sloshed through the downpour to stand on Rickman's Bridge. It was low tide, and the brown river appeared to be minding its own business between smooth wet banks of mud. Swans floated below me, impervious to the rain, unconcerned by the fact that the surface of the water looked as if it was being shot at, flexing and twisting their snakelike necks to preen the feathers over their shoulders; and other swans downriver stood one-legged on an islet of weeds.

Homeward bound, I ran into George Drewett. He was in Wharf Road, standing by the embankment opposite Downscene, eyeing the river suspiciously, as I had. He wore a blue overcoat and black hat, and must have returned from work early. I offered him shelter under my umbrella, and he passed some remark about the monsoon season.

I enquired: 'Are we all going to be carried out to sea?'

'That's what I was wondering,' he replied.

Then he grinned dauntlessly, shaking his jowls at me, and again I laughed at the absurdity of the idea.

Two or three days later, as Gem and I were getting ready for bed, we heard fire-engines in River Road. It was ten o'clock: I checked the time. We said we were sorry for the people whose house was on fire. But heavy rain was still falling, and nothing exposed to it could possibly burn. I recollected that firemen were also summoned to cope with general emergencies and flooding. And looking out of our bedroom window I was alarmed by the sight of water simultaneously rushing towards and into, and gushing up and out of, the drain below.

YET BY the time we had put our clothes back on, and gone downstairs, the drain had done and was doing its duty: no accumulation of water remained in the roadway.

I wanted to investigate nonetheless, and clambered into gumboots and so on, and tried to find a torch that worked: the streetlamps had thrown in the towel almost before they were hit. Gem decided to stay in Hope Cottage with Cindy: they would be in the warm and the dry and could retreat upstairs or uphill if the watery worst came to the worst. Our houselights flickered and failed as we spoke: but she was sure she would be all right. She asked me to try to contact and persuade Wendy to join her.

At length I sallied forth into the foul black night. Wendy was either fast asleep or not at home. And since Mrs Spedding's house was in darkness – no glimmer of torch or candle – I thought it best not to disturb her, and proceeded

157

along River Road towards the blue and orange flashes of light.

Fire-engines and police-cars were parked down by Wharf Road, which was awash with water. The river had risen so high, ten or fifteen feet since George and I had inspected it, that it was slopping water over the embankment wall. There was a strong smell of fish and salt: most of the extra water flooding our river and reversing the flow in our drains was sweeping in from the sea.

In other words we were in the parlous situation described by Toby Whitaker.

A trio of females stood by the official vehicles. Their laughter mingled reassuringly with the agitated crackle of voices on intercom radios. The rainwear of each of them was characteristic. Octavia Pritchett wore a see-through plastic bonnet, an antiquated belted hunting mack, and seemingly hip-high fishing waders. Betsy Hooke was in an ethnic headscarf, a grubby anorak, sopping bluejeans and trainers – apparel hardly suitable for a woman of her age, but classless. Madge Drewett had on a smart souwester and overcoat of yellow oiled cotton and green wellies, and carried a multi-coloured golfing umbrella.

Madge hailed me: 'We're waifs and strays, dar! We're evacuees! The Drewett gang have gone far too far, as usual – perfect panic, dar – my George and my Reginald have turfed me out of my home – and all because they don't trust water, dar!'

Betsy said that Flood Street was living up to its name, the two inches of water here were two feet of water there; and, she added sarcastically, her lord and master had wanted her out of harm's way for a change – Brian and Jeremiah were taking care of the house and everything.

Octavia declared with her malicious chortle: 'I've come to see the fun.'

'We're thinking of nice quiet nightcaps at Downscene, aren't we, girls?' Madge shone the beam of her powerful

158

torch straight in the faces of her companions. 'We might as well enjoy ourselves, while you boys play your wicked games.'

I enquired: 'Where are the police and firemen? Where are George and Maurice, if it comes to that?'

'Ask me another, dar!'

Betsy said with the typical Socialist's gratitude to the guardians of law and order: 'I bet the police are breaking down my best Regency doors for no good reason.'

Octavia chimed in: 'I call their big white chief King Canute – he's turning back the tide.'

Two policemen on motorbikes roared up, dismounted, walked to the water's edge and without hesitation splashed off into the murk. The various radios continued to emit rude noises.

I addressed the ladies: 'But is Downscene going to be nice and quiet and safe for your nightcaps?'

Octavia said: 'Don't be silly – water wouldn't dare look in if Madge told it not to.'

Betsy challenged me: 'Why don't you come and protect us?' – and all three succumbed to scornful feminist amusement.

I declined – undertook to find out what was happening in Flood Street – suggested that if necessary Monica could probably bring me an SOS.

'Oh no, dar, Monica's hitting the high spots in the West End. You love us and leave us – we shall overcome! In the last resort we can rise above ourselves and take refuge in Beggar's Roost.'

And Madge pointed her torch at the beggar in person, namely Octavia, who winced and averted her head in order not to be blinded, or perhaps because she was horrified by the prospect of having to dispense expensive refreshments.

We wished one another good luck and parted: they rounded the garden wall of Downscene to get to its tarmac sweep and front door, and I waded into the flood.

Wharf Road must dip in the middle although un-noticeably in normal conditions, for icy water soon poured into my gumboots. It smelt not only of fish and salt, but also of sewage. Moreover it was water on the move, like the sea on a tidal beach, and pushed and pulled me in different directions. Without street lamps, and after the flashing by official vehicles, not to mention Madge's usage of the some-what offensive weapon of her torch, the night seemed darker than ever. My own torch had a flat battery and shed a pitiful red glow, and the lights in the windows of the houses in South Street across the river did not illuminate much: but even in daylight I would not have seen through the dirty opacity of the water. With no idea of where I was stepping, I stumbled into potholes and tripped on the pavement. Every so often a surge of water threatened to knock me over: no doubt the effect of a larger wave, that seventh breaker which is meant to be the big one, rolling in cross-country from Newhaven. I had to reach out for railings and things, so as to remain upright. And although I realised that to fall would be more unpleasant than dangerous, at least at present, the rain and cold and gloom and my solitude were alarming. The weight and irresistible power of the water, the gurgling, sucking, trickling, sinister sounds it made, and not knowing whether it was getting shallower or deeper, made me wonder what on earth I thought I was doing, and if I was endangering life and limb in a worthwhile cause. Encouragement was not provided by the answers that I was sight-seeing, and nothing but the embankment wall stood between me and total immersion.

I passed Cadwallader Place, its windows unconcernedly curtained. No doubt it was designed to be flood-proof, standing as it does, back from the road and on a little eminence. Anyway, the obsequious waters trespassed only a few feet up its rutted driveway. The terraced houses beyond it in Wharf Road, built for servants, now occupied by masters, are also set back behind their sloping strips of garden. The sea had moved in so quickly that I had feared interested parties might not yet be aware of the flooding. Thankfully, now, I noted the flicker of emergency lighting in and around these houses, and heard the cries of householders: 'What's going on – what's it like down there – who is it?'

I chatted to anxious semi-visible strangers over garden gates. Luckily their campaign to win permission for residents' parking in the thoroughfare had failed: a lesson must have been learned from allowing vehicles to park in Keere Street and spoil its appearance. But, although their cars were not in the soup, another metaphor applied to their situation: they themselves were on the horns of a dilemma. Should they get out of their homes while the getting was fairly good, or stay put, remove their furniture to first floors, keep their fingers crossed and trust the elements? If they followed the first course, where would they go? If the second, would they and their families end up sitting frozen stiff on the ridge-tiles of their roofs?

I made for Flood Street. I had promised to look out for or look after George and Reggie and Brian and Jeremiah, who, as I had been given to understand, were answering the call of duty: their gallant protective activities therefore merited support. Besides, I was not my sister's brother for nothing: my cold feet in every sense notwithstanding, I was almost as excited by the drama as she would have been.

THE HOUSES in Flood Street are urban inasmuch as they have at least three tall storeys, plus basements and basement areas, and their railings abut on the pavement.

The water was actually less deep, perhaps a foot or so. It lapped innocently against the steps to front doors and the stone and concrete kerbs in which railings were fixed. But through gaps in the kerbs, for instance where a gate opened, a miniature waterfall cascaded into the area below.

An occasional streetlamp now flickered quirkily and came

on, and I could see as well as hear hands being wrung and teeth gnashed, figuratively speaking, because of the inundation of all this subterranean property. People were standing on balconies, others scampered up and down basement steps like yo-yos, some were baling out with buckets, one or two men fiddled with overdue flood-boards. The screams of women and boo-hooing of children were accompanied by the sound of rushing water. Boys in a group seized their chance to splash one another.

The scene was lively, yet not crowded: which rendered it rather odd that there was no Drewett in sight. I had believed I was following in the footsteps of George and Reggie. Madge had said they were checking that immediate neighbours in Wharf Road and Flood Street had not gone under for the third time. The explanation of their elusiveness must be that they were doing charitable deeds in some poor old person's basement flat.

An odder thing, perhaps, was that the Hooke house looked empty. As Betsy had been wrong about the level of floodwater, so she seemed to be wrong about her husband and son taking care of their family home. Unlike the other houses, no light showed through the posters in the windows. What was Brian up to? Was Jeremiah lying drugged to the eyeballs in his squalid garret?

Resentfully, considering it was their job, not mine, but for fear of being cut to ribbons by Betsy's sharp tongue, I descended the stone steps into her area. For reasons never known, the water falling into it was more a drip than a gush, and a mere two inches covered the floor. But while I was down there my torch and then the few streetlamps went out. The complete darkness caused consternation. Through the hubbub I heard a knocking on a door somewhere overhead and the plummy voice of George Drewett.

He was standing on the front steps of the house adjoining, which, I suddenly remembered, belonged to Marian Travers. Indeed Marian had opened the door to him, and I could see her hand holding a candlestick and a curl of her golden hair.

He said: 'I've come to collect my fee for services rendered,' in that same tone of teasing lasciviousness in which, in the linen-room at Cadwallader Place, he had asked what she was going to give him for Christmas.

He must have done her a practical favour, probably and discreetly in her basement, out of sight of prying eyes. I had given him too much of the benefit of the doubt: he had been helping no one poor or old: he was hoping to help himself.

'Now George!' she scolded, repressively long-suffering, but with a contradictory giggle.

'This is the day of reckoning, my dear – or the night.'

'Well – you get a star for trying.'

'Stars are cold – who wants stars? And speaking of cold, if you leave me out in it any longer you'll ruin our reputations.'

The door closed. But through it I could hear laughter, a squeal and what sounded uncommonly like a slap.

I headed for home. The flooding was no worse, was therefore likely to be better soon; and mopping-up operations could not begin until most of the water was gone.

Instead of re-negotiating the flood, I turned left into the twitten called Grey Friars after the monastery that had once stood thereabouts, and looped back via Eastover High Street and Ship Alley to Rickman's Lane.

Ship Alley, not flanked by houses with candles in the windows, and because of its narrowness and high walls and overhanging trees, seemed darker than dark, and the relentless rain multiplied the misery of the scene. Consequently I was the more surprised by the revels in Rickman's Lane – the end of it farthest from Hope Cottage – the end where Bertha lives. First I heard roars of laughter, then noticed a shadowy brightness, and coming round the corner I found ten or fifteen persons, mostly men, milling about, partially undressed, wet through and thoroughly cheerful, as if at a street party.

They were grouped roughly in a circle. I caught glimpses

of water between bare legs with trousers rolled up, and remembered the drain twinned with ours. On closer inspection, a pond with a diameter of a dozen feet covered this drain, which, at intervals of two or three minutes, belched out malodorous air and spouted extra water like a geyser.

These belchings and heavings of the pond constituted part of the joke that amused the crowd, amongst whom, again to my surprise and almost my incredulity, I recognised the mixed bag of Reggie Drewett, Brian Hooke and Jahendra. They were not only together, and here when each of them was surely meant to be elsewhere, but also behaving strangely. Reggie and Jahendra in their shirtsleeves were kneeling in the middle of the pond, while Brian minus his specs was stamping up and down between them, creating waves and laughing as happily as a baby in its bath.

I asked someone what they were doing. Plugging the drain with a blanket, I was told. The need for some such measure was increasingly obvious, for the pond was spreading ever closer to the houses on the drain-side of the road, one house in particular, the front door of which was opened recklessly wide to allow light to be shed on the problem: the room within was aglow with candles and oil-lamps. But while I watched, the reversed flow of water in the drain regurgitated the plug or bung, and fountained grossly upwards and outwards, drenching the three activists, making most onlookers still wetter, spreading an unholy stink and causing general amusement.

Why did grown men seem so happy and pleased to be playing truant and fooling about in filthy icy water on a winter's night?

A figure in the open doorway cast a long shadow, in which, paradoxically, and in another sense almost literally, all was revealed.

The shadow belonged to Tracy Wilkins. The house under threat was Rookery Dene, the home of the Wilkins family, Bertha's nextdoor neighbours: brassy coaching lanterns, unlit, flanked the pompous oaken door. I also noted in passing that in Bertha's house there was no sign of human or canine habitation: but I was reassured by the reflection that the mistress of Minnie and Winnie in her own estimation was bound to be having a better time, whatever it was, than the rest of us.

Tracy was in plastic – or mostly out of it. She appeared to have nothing on except a rain-hat, abbreviated gumboots and thigh-high mack, a matching set in shiny red plastic. Her legs were long, shapely and bare. Her eyes were luminously blue, her teeth dazzling white, and her complexion re-interpreted the idiom – in the pink. Her gilded halo of hair added a sacrilegious spice to the almost pornographic picture. She was carrying a tray of liquid refreshments, and smiling with bashful condescension on all and sundry – she seemed to have got over Peter Cadwallader with a vengeance.

And of course that fun in the pond was funny business. The opposite sex was showing off to Tracy, competing for her attention and gratitude, and aspiring at once to be of service to her and to serve her, as the old chauvinistic pun runs.

Brian, Reggie, Jahendra and company now swarmed like bees round their queen. Mrs Wilkins, Caleb Hocking's daughter Naomi, trotted out with plates of edibles, and Bert bore armfuls of bottles. They too seemed to have recovered from the injuries done to the family concern as it were by the withdrawal of Cadwallader custom. They were clearly happier about the plurality of Tracy's suitors than they were perturbed by their unsuitability – Brian and Jahendra married, for example, and Brian nearing pensionable age – or, for that matter, than they were about the possibility of sewage in their sitting-room.

But I dared to stand and stare no longer. It had struck me that Gem could be having comparable trouble with the drain outside our home.

Brian spotted me and called: 'Greetings!'

I called back: 'You know your house is empty!'

'Isn't Jeremiah there?'

'I don't think so.'

'Drat the lad! He was told to keep his finger in the dyke. Curses on paternity! Curses on property!'

He was holding a glass of what looked like the sweetest sherry. He raised it in a toast to Tracy, drained it flirtatiously, and turned towards Flood Street, fumbling with his horn-rimmed spectacles and fixing them on his nose.

I HURRIED in the opposite direction, sorry to have spoiled Brian's sport.

The flood in front of Hope Cottage alarmed me: it reached round the corner to Mrs Spedding's front door in Rickman's Lane and Wendy's in River Road.

But water had not quite got into Hope Cottage; and I discovered Gem in our kitchen, calmly drinking tea with a bedraggled youth I did not at first recognise, very wet and with hair so flat and fair as to be almost non-existent: Jeremiah in person, being fawned upon by Cinders.

Jeremiah without his spiky comb of hair of many colours, which he has cut and washed, resembled a half-drowned white mouse rather than a sick cockatoo. His ears were unpinned, and he wore jeans and a zipper jacket: perhaps he has also grown out of his trappings and strappings.

I said I had just met his father.

He wanted to know where.

'Here – in Rickman's Lane – at the far end.'

'With Tracy?' he demanded.

'Well, yes, actually – why?'

'Oh – nothing.'

Gem sang the praises of Jeremiah, who had been standing by to hoist Mrs Spedding to safety if need be, and altogether behaving like a brick.

I thanked him and asked what had brought him to our part of Eastover.

He mumbled something about not seeing why he should be the one member of the family stuck at home, then asked me: 'Is Dad still with Tracy?'

I replied in the negative; at which he smiled and said decisively that he must be leaving.

We agreed that the tide was on the turn, parted with expressions of mutual gratitude, and he marched – or did he flutter? – in the direction of Tracy's candles and so on, although River Road would have been his quickest way home.

I had been a trifle put out to find that my fond fears for Gem were superfluous, and by the company she was keeping. Nor had I liked the indiscriminate fuss Cinders was making of our visitor: Cindy's worst fault is that she would fall in love with any villain who had broken and entered. But at last, here and now, I renounce my bias against Jeremiah, who is nowhere near as bad as I have thought he was, and not noticeably a chip off the parental block.

After he had gone, Gem and I walked to Downscene. The rain had become a drizzle, and our very own flood was subsiding. But it could be a different story in Wharf Road.

Madge, Betsy and Octavia all came to the door in response to our ringing and knocking. Evidently, even by candlelight, the fluid posing a threat to these ladies was not water. Madge's good humour was on the raucous side, and the other two were snappily jocular.

I explained: 'We only wanted to tell you things are improving. Is George back?'

'No, dar. You found him, did you? Back from where, dar?' Madge enquired.

I hesitated. I had briefed Gem about the various extra-mural and extra-marital intrigues of the evening, which I had spied upon. Neither of us wanted to sneak on anyone.

167

Madge repeated her question, drawling with more force: 'Back from whar, dar?'

'Flood Street,' I replied.

Octavia exclaimed in a knowing tone of voice: 'Enough said, enough said!' – in spite of which Betsy broadcast the accusation: 'He was patronising Mrs Travers' establishment.'

'Wicked old gangster-boy,' Madge remarked none too indulgently, although with traces of pride in her gangster-boy's virility.

Gem intervened to tell Betsy how kind Jeremiah had been.

The compliment fell on stony ground.

'I'm glad he was kind to you,' Betsy commented, glaring. 'But why wasn't he being kind to me? I came here on condition that he stayed with Brian, and they'd guard the house. I thought I could rely on him at any rate. Madge, where's my anorak? I want a word with that young man before he goes completely to pieces.'

Madge displeased Betsy, possibly to punish her for drawing attention to George's soft spot for Marian, by saying she had popped the anorak into the boiler-room, where it would not drip dirt over everything.

'Thanks for the dirty bit,' Betsy retorted sourly.

Their candles wavered towards the back parts of the house. We called good night and got no answers.

Octavia in man-sized woollen stockings remained in the doorway.

'I don't know what's eating Betsy,' she grated. 'I thought she was against possessions. But she's fussed more than anybody about hers.' Octavia rummaged for footwear. 'I take it that Brian's on guard in the Hooke house even if Jeremiah isn't?'

'No,' I replied. 'Brian's also missing, believed to be frying other fish – or he was. Perhaps it's the possession of her husband that Betsy's fussing about.'

168

'I see – well – she should be used to that – we all should – good night!'

And she began to climb into her waders.

I remembered belatedly that Brian was and is the object of Octavia's affections, and their painful dialogue overheard at Christmas.

But I would have compounded the mistake of my tactlessness by apologising for it. Life in Lewes seemed to be as complicated and dangerous as it was everywhere else.

However, the fire-engines and police-cars had left Wharf Road in peace. The river was flowing fast out to sea: puddles in the gutters were the only souvenirs of the flood. Occasional streetlamps again flickered, like craven soldiers returning to the battlefield after the war had been won. And the three-quarter moon emerged from behind clouds, the clock on St Michael's chimed midnight, and, comfortingly, Hope Cottage awaited us with open arms.

Gem stopped and pointed out a ghostly form some fifty yards distant in the drive of Cadwallader Place, probably female, draped in white, gesticulating in spastic fashion: Foxy in her nightdress, flapping her arms not at us but at George Drewett, whose bulky figure materialised from behind a stuccoed gatepost – had he been hiding from her?

We proceeded homewards.

But George caught us up and said he was relieved to see that we were alive and kicking.

Did we happen to know, he enquired with possibly contrite diffidence, if all was well at Downscene.

Yes, we prevaricated, not liking to forecast the reception in store for him – the house was undamaged.

He offered us an account of his doings in Freudian terms: he had been lending a hand in Flood Street, where some people were having trouble with their basement areas.

Yes, we repeated non-committally.

169

He relaxed and chuckled. 'That was Foxy, that was,' he said, thumbing over his shoulder. 'She was asleep until five minutes ago, and Guy still is. They missed the whole show – it can't have been this week's night of passion.'

We laughed at his suggestion that passion ever kept the Cadwalladers awake.

'I tell you true,' he assured us. 'Foxy knows her rights. She hasn't forgotten what's what. She calls it her rent and collects it weekly. She's a blood–orange and no mistake, is our Foxy – she's got that massage machine in her bathroom if Guy goes on the blink. The old boy hasn't much idea of what he's doing at the best of times, or what's being done to him. Basically, vague's the name of the game they both play. That house is wasted on them.'

The moonshine was confidential and George was in a communicative mood: he must have been satisfied with the remuneration he had received from Marian.

'I was born in the Caves of Eastover. My father was a builder and decorator. I soon decided to be like him in no respect whatsoever. When my parents died, I had their cottage demolished – I wanted no reminders of how poor we used to be. Times change, thanks to the good God, who must be a capitalist.'

He spoke of Downscene as we approached it.

'The site of the house was a spare bit of Cadwallader kitchen garden and a cottage or two. I meant my home to be a modern edition of Cadwallader Place. The Cadwalladers were the royal family of Eastover in my young days. Cadwalladers were Eastover. But I've come up and they've come down. And you live and learn, or some of us do. I can see what's wrong with Downscene now. There's no substitute for the genuine article. Maybe it's a stepping-stone.'

At this moment the streetlamps clicked fully on. We were standing at the junction of Wharf and River Roads. George's beady expression softened into his habitual amiable hamster-like grin.

170

'A stepping-stone to where and what, George?'

He emitted his bonhomous chuckle, gazed pop-eyed as if into the future, shrugged his thick shoulders and said: 'The point is that I'm Eastover today.'

MARCH

Rachel has been having headaches. It worries me that her head should ache more or less continuously and in the same place, somewhere above her left temple. On the telephone she said it was nothing, and I carried agreement to extremes – I said the heads of most people ached without ceasing. But she would not have mentioned the matter if it had not worried her too.

I changed the subject, then slipped in a question about Dr Ward: what did he make of her headaches? She had not seen Dr Ward, she replied. She continued with mounting excitability: she might never see Dr Ward again, he would only suggest tests and second and third and fourth opinions – she was sick of doctors telling her lies and running up expenses and doing her no good and scaring her stiff!

A few evenings later I rang again. She was calmer – I did not refer to her health. But Jim was in the offing and barked at her. In the end – that is, sooner than we would have wished – we had to stop.

Gem is inclined to blame the snow for Rachel's headaches.

February's freezing and flooding were not the last of the cards up winter's sleeves. March dropped a load of snow on us at the beginning of the month, and more has fallen in shower form every day of this last week, and the south-east wind from the sea has done its damnedest by blowing the snow into drifts in inconvenient places. Conditions seem to be worse in Creedwell and could be having an adverse effect on my sister's constitution.

I know I always feel mysteriously indisposed before snow. Rachel may have developed a related version of that sort of allergy.

A slightly different, but also necessarily optimistic diagnosis could be, in a word, winter. Too much time must have elapsed since I lived in the country and was so exposed to the element. I had forgotten about the vital struggle with the long cold months of the year, that war of attrition which nature declares in autumn and wages until it grudgingly signs an armistice in late spring or early summer. In London, in retrospect, I spent my days indoors or underground. Lewes has reminded me of the answers given by the older folk of Boltbridge when I asked how they were in the deep midwinter: 'Better for a wink of sun − starved of warmth − dying for summer − perishing!' Here as there, people who suffer from rheumatism complain of the screws, and wish they did not have bones in their legs. Perhaps Rachel's headaches are equally seasonal.

I am less comforted by the recollection that winter reaps its harvest of souls.

And in the privacy of this journal I would echo one of my sister's sentiments and add a selfish footnote: Rachel is not alone in being sick of sickness.

I do not really mean it − I should not even think it − but not having to fret over anyone ill or in trouble, not to be apprehensive, not to care, must make you feel wonderfully well, and enable you to write your book.

COULD THERE be an unidentified bug going round, which assaults the cheerful parts of the human organism? It seems also to have struck down the editor of *The Clarion*. His headlines have become blacker and less humorous. Here are a couple of examples that spring to mind: 'Octogenarian accused of raping Physio,' and 'Lewes family's despair at loss of one sextuplet.'

Bertha is afflicted, notwithstanding her modest assertions that she is superior to and therefore immune from our lowly infections. She rails at the climate, and grouses about the age and infirmity of her dog Minnie. When we attempt to reassure her by referring to the long life ahead of the other one, she comments gloomily and perhaps with sinister intent that Minnie and Winnie were always close.

She vents her spleen on Lewes District Council, which does not sweep every flake of snow from the pavements: 'I keep my parts clean – why can't they?' And she snipes at British Rail for failing to transport her to her Old Tyme Dancing.

But she reserves salvoes from her biggest guns for the events of the night of the flood as seen through the net curtains of her bedroom window.

'I woke up thinking I was at the seaside when those men started paddling outside Rookery Dene. Silly fools, all trying to catch young Tracy's eye – and she showing more than she should to catch theirs! I can understand why she wanted to walk out with Mr Peter Cadwallader. But he loved her and left her, and no wonder with her people packing their bags to be ready to move into Cadwallader Place. As for Reggie Drewett, he's not much, even if he can afford to be half-seas over. The same goes for the black bloke from the paper shop, he's got a wife and children, and probably other wives breeding like mice back where he comes from. But Tracy was parading in front of them in next to nothing, and Naomi was pouring sherry down their throats and Bert was stuffing them full of cheese straws. Wilkins are gentlemen's outfitters, that's what's wrong with them. Tracy didn't waste any time crying over Mr Peter, not she – she was soon ready and willing to fit out the next man who fancied her.'

We dropped the name of Brian Hooke, who had done his share of paddling in the pool in question.

'I pity his boy, the punky one, Jeremy, I do! He's been sweet on Tracy for ever and a day, and first he had Mr Peter to reckon with, and then he finds his own father playing fast and loose. He sees the old goat in the gutter at her feet, while she seems to be saying the customer can have what he wants and is always right. Of course Jeremy was downhearted – that's when he moped along here to Hope Cottage with his tail between his legs – though he did return to Rookery Dene later on to queue for one of the good night kisses Tracy was doling out. I put the blame on Mrs Hooke, who's all for charity as long as she doesn't have to be charitable. If she can't keep her husband happy, and out of her son's hair, what does she think she can do for the sad people in the rest of the world? Tracy's not a bad girl, even if she is trade from top to toe. I'm not saying she hasn't got a heart to lose; but she looks like losing her head. I had men galore when I was young and not so young – they told me how beautiful I was and they were going to kill themselves if I didn't give in to them. Well, I kept most of them alive, and had my fun, without ever acting common.'

Depression not merely seasonal has been visited on my Uncle. Neither he nor Jahendra live above the shop in Eastover High Street. Uncle resides somewhere in the hinterland up by the old race-course, and is always the first to clock in for work at six in the morning. Two days ago he arrived to find a brick had been thrown through his plate-glass window.

I have told him that throwing bricks through shop windows has always been the favourite pastime of our compatriots with weak heads and a taste for strong liquor, and the damage done has absolutely no connection with race, colour or creed.

He does not believe me.

The other day he remarked, his brown eyes swimming unhappily behind his spectacles: 'There are many kind persons in Sussex, too many maybe, Mr Loftus – it is easy to forget the unkind ones.'

'Is forgetting a bad thing, Uncle?'

'No – but being reminded is a less pleasant surprise.'

He rebuked me for saying the window would not cost a fortune to replace: 'The discomfort is not felt in the region of the wallet, sir.'

He continued: 'We are British. We live now in our own country. But we are also a minority. Minorities are not popular.'

'Everyone's a minority when it comes to bricks through windows, Uncle. And considering the popular people, who wants popularity?'

'We can be bashed, sir – the minority cannot do the bashing or really bash back.'

'What about the ballot-box and the law?'

'Oh yes, oh yes!' he repeated, wagging his head from side to side with disturbingly powerful scepticism and scorn.

Jahendra's reaction was more constructive.

'The police have been helpful,' he allowed. 'They say there are bad boys who go round smashing and grabbing – vandals and thieves, not politicians. But I wonder, Mr Loftus: should we change the name of the shop? Should we change our names? Patel is not British – Patel is from Pakistan – everybody knows Patel is foreign, including boys wanting to break foreigners' windows and foreigners' necks. We could be asking for trouble by sticking to the wrong guns.'

'What would you change your name to?'

'Paytle – Pattle – I don't know.'

He spelt out these variations.

I told him that Pattle looked and sounded more British.

He laughed and asked me: 'Will you advise us, sir? Take your time – no rush.'

I agreed to.

Meanwhile the snow continues to fall intermittently, reviving melancholy memories of the havoc it used to wreak at Boltbridge Manor: I dreaded it in advance, and then spent nights almost as white as the landscape worrying about the bills for repairs it would run up.

Daytime in Lewes thaws the snow into mucky slush, and night re-freezes it into a mini-geology of hills and valleys, glaciers, crags and potholes. There is scarcely a pavement which has not fractured a bone. Cindy virtually hibernates in her basket, and I would quite like to follow suit. Gem works overtime to spread comfort and joy. But even she shrinks from the prospect of dinner with the Hookes. The date was fixed so long ago that at the time we could hardly plead a prior engagement, and now we feel it is too late to chuck.

INGRATITUDE NOTWITHSTANDING, I must say that the evening was a compendium of the errors of hospitality.

We arrived and were eventually admitted by Betsy in apron and oven gloves, who was not only hot and bothered, but irate into the bargain.

'Brian's supposed to be opening the front door,' she said accusingly. 'I'm cooking for my sins. God alone knows when dinner's likely to be ready. And if you offer to help me I'll have hysterics!'

The Hookes' sitting-room is on the first floor and well-proportioned. But no curtains, a thin rug on bare boards, a single overhead light in a globular paper shade, steel and leather chairs and some jumbo pouffes, sternly remind anyone hoping for physical ease that the rule of the house is mind over matter. Pictures are abstract, and books are piled in rough-hewn shelves in the rear part of the L-shaped room, where a battered upright piano stands by a table stacked with dusty bottles.

The other guests were Marian Travers and Octavia Pritchett, already present, and Gregory Leplay and Charles Hart, still to come.

Brian wore a T-shirt and jeans, yet managed to make me feel that I was the one improperly dressed in my collar and tie and grey flannel suit by saying as I shook his thick-skinned hand: 'Oh dear – aren't we formal?'

Octavia also annoyed me by sniggering sycophantically at his pleasantry at my expense.

The T-shirt was emblazoned with the legend *Delight A Don Today*. It was too big for him, and his jeans were slung too low. He looked the more like academic mutton trying to look like fashionable lamb.

The grubby glasses of cloying liquid he now fetched and forced upon us was sherry: he declared in authoritative accents that it was Albania's best and full of fruit.

Marian scoffed at his jargon with affectionate disdain: 'Really, Brian, you're so funny,' to which he returned: 'Merci, chérie mignonne!' – a sarcastic reference to her generous measurements.

This exchange with its intimate ring persuaded me that Brian must have loved or been loved by Marian as well as Octavia. He is the unlikeliest Don Juan, and perhaps therefore the more successful: he can take women by surprise. And then he seems to possess the one essential characteristic of the seducer: he is willing.

On the other hand his pallid and sere complexion, and crinkly colourless hair and short-sightedness and middle-age, almost convince me he is not going to get anywhere with Tracy Wilkins in her glorious teens.

He sought our opinions of the sherry. I had been prefacing every sip with silent apologies to my liver. But guests have to be hypocrites, and I joined in the chorus of approval.

Gregory and Charles now entered the room and were greeted by our host thus: 'Hail, Ruritania!'

Their costumes were the cause, and to some extent the justification, of his rude remark. Gregory's trousers were tartan and tight, and his black velvet jacket was all lapels, cuffs, diagonal pockets with shaped flaps, darts, tucks and mother-of-pearl buttons. Charles was dressed for yachting: white bags and blue blazer.

Charles flushed redder than ever at the Ruritanian jibe, and shrilled with a resentful squirm: 'Hark at him!'

179

Gregory fixed his fine eye on the terrible T-shirt and observed: 'I'd keep extremely quiet about clothes if I were you, Brian.'

Octavia intervened protectively: 'His story is that the shirt was a gift from a student.'

'Undergraduate, please,' he corrected her, snubbed her for presuming that he required protection, and rubbed punitive salt into the old wound of her jealousy: 'As a matter of fact the undergraduate who made me the shirt is an undergraduette – a pretty child, fresh as a daisy and keen as mustard. I expect her to obey her own imperative. And the same applies to the company here assembled this evening.'

Gregory asked: 'What about you delighting us for a change?'

Brian replied: 'But I'm always delightful!' – and both Octavia and Marian giggled and shook their heads as indulgently as ex-mistresses are inclined to.

The conversational spotlight turned on Marian, who has agreed to lodge an Austrian singer for the Glyndebourne Festival, Hans-Peter Vilans by name.

'Hand-Peter Villain, I call him,' someone said, and somebody else: 'As long as he's not called Roger!'

'Marian, my dear, this gentleman – and we fervently pray he is one – have you met him?' Brian enquired.

She explained that Herr Vilans would not arrive in England until mid-April.

'Do you mean to tell us it's a blind date?'

She clicked her tongue and rebuked him: 'You're miles behind the times, Brian! Women and men can be friends these days, and share accommodation platonically. We've moved on since you were a naughty schoolboy. Anyhow, my arrangement's with Glyndebourne – not even with Herr Vilans himself – and quite above board.'

Gregory said: 'You'll have to take special care of him if he's a tenor.'

Gregory's warning tickled Brian and Charles, but mystified the rest of us. There was general laughter as we pleaded in vain to be let in on the joke. The chill atmosphere was warming up in the sociable sense.

Then Betsy flung open the door and announced bitterly: 'Dinner's served,' as if she would have liked to tack on the rider: 'And I hope it chokes you.'

We filed downstairs to the kitchen in the basement in a chastened mood.

But I managed to extract an explanation from Gregory of his reference to tenors.

'They can't hit their high notes after making love.'

BETSY'S EXASPERATED attitude to cooking, guests and her former impulse to feed them, painted pictures in my mind's eye of the monstrous regiment of modern hostesses, struggling to follow the gastronomic fashion, poring over recipes for foreign food, trailing from one shop to another in search of esoteric substances – truffles and beancurd, cardomoms, custard apples – and then going through the thankless phases of preparing and cooking the stuff, sweating and cursing, and finally in all probability poisoning themselves, their families and friends.

Today's ambitious amateur cooks may well end up as badly as the professional ones at Boltbridge Manor seemed to. The psychological explanation of the occupational hazard for female cooks is that they come to regard their culinary creations as babies. They are sooner or later driven more or less mad by – as they see it – conceiving and bearing babies, putting them on platters with various garnishes, and having them carved, salted and peppered, chewed, swallowed and digested. That may be another reason why most chefs are male.

We dined in the underground kitchen of the Hookes' establishment, sitting on string-seated chairs at one of those pricey tables of poor quality pine, illuminated by a smart low light-fitting on a pulley. I was on Betsy's right and had

Octavia on my other side and Gregory opposite.

The menu was stuffed vine leaves, bouillabaisse, unleavened bread, goulash and avocado salad with pine kernels, toffee apples and almond milk.

The worst of it for me, apart from the fact that I ate too much and drank too many wines – sweet white, sour red, and an outlandish liqueur tasting like cough syrup – the worst also for Gem was the tension. The atmosphere down here was even less cosy than it had been upstairs. Betsy had chosen food that mostly required her attention at the last minute, and was cooking and dispensing it, and collecting empty plates and stacking them in the dishwasher, throughout the meal. She would not be helped, she snapped at anyone who offered assistance, although her ill-temper appeared to be connected with the inactivity of her husband – he never stirred from his chair – or possibly with his activity in other spheres and circumstances.

I was conversing with Octavia when the first little eruption occurred.

Betsy silenced everyone by asking Brian: 'What was that? What did you say?'

He answered blandly, raising his voice and intoning as if to somebody deaf or half-baked: 'My neighbours have been marvelling at your exquisite fodder.'

'But what did you say?' she repeated; and then demanded of Gem and Marian, who were murmuring their compliments more directly: 'What was he saying?'

'Hush hush, my child,' he crooned.

'You should hush, not me!'

In soothing irritating accents he ignored her advice and confessed: 'I merely remarked, dear, that I personally often aspire to the unattainable ideal of a bacon and egg.'

He was shouted down. How could he be so ungrateful? Had he no palate? Where was his heart and what was the way to it, for heaven's sake?

Betsy muttered under her breath: 'Heart? What makes

you think he's got one? But he has got hands and feet, and it's a pity he doesn't make better use of them.'

Brian either did not hear or took no notice of this hint – at least of that part of the hint appertaining to the chores of hospitality.

Octavia carried on from where she had left off: she had been regaling me with an account of her relationship with her charwoman. Although no doubt her fling with Brian finished ages ago, she might have felt obscurely responsible for his boorish behaviour and eager to divert my attention from it. Closer inspection of her spiky visage defied me to imagine her in the positions of passion in the recent past; and the violence of her vocabulary when she gets going is un-seductive. She told me she is always trying to beat some sense into her char's head, that she twists her arm to broaden her mind, that she lets her have home truths between the eyes, and would like to rap her over the knuckles, kick her backside, stick pins in her and wring her neck. And she complained that, in return or in revenge, she is held over a barrel by said char, blackmailed, soaked, fleeced and bled white.

Octavia and Marian are exact opposites not only to look at, and in consequence of their destinies to date, but to talk to. Octavia is impersonal, unimpressionable, toughly tempered by spinsterhood, and so self-contained that she seems to be unaware of the identity of her conversational partner; whereas Marian, to whom I chatted across the table during a spell of Betsy's absenteeism, is receptiveness personified, ever ready to be entertained and amused, and, if with somewhat schoolgirlish enthusiasm, to play the sex-game of lingering half-smiles and conspiratorial glances.

I am now entitled to greet Octavia and Marian with kisses, which tell a similar story. Kissing Octavia is about as intimate as bowing from the waist, but less dignified – she rushes the contact, snatches at it, and repulses even as she submits; while Marian is warmly relaxed, and her firm and fragrant cheek is always just where it should be.

Towards the end of dinner the subject of Wendy Aylward and her matrimonial disaster came up for discussion.

Brian pronounced as follows: 'Wendy was astonished when Derek jumped on his own streetcar named desire, and clanked away into the sunset with Glenys Calthrop in tow. Why oh why, Wendy wondered. What was in it for him, she asked everyone – what could a common chit of a girl possibly do for a solicitor of a certain age, a clever cultivated man, except bury him alive under a scrum of screaming brats? And how was she to lure him back into her parlour? Open your eyes, I advised her – you're too late to open anything else. Look at the leading light of the Eastover Thespians, then look in the mirror, and reflect, my girl! Wendy's a goose, she's all talk and no do, she just lies back listening to grand opera. Derek had reached the time of life when a man needs a little excitement and encouragement: Wendy should have made a detailed study of the blue videos he brought home, instead of boasting that they gave her a chance to get on with her knitting. She should have kept a more comfortable house, and cooked what he wanted to eat, and so on. If she had ever tried to satisfy his various appetites, her story might have had a different ending – although not a happy one, because she's a born grizzler. If she'd condescended to stretch a point, or winked at the right moment, they might even now be twiddling their thumbs nextdoor like Darby and Joan. But instead of a bit of rope, she gave him an ultimatum. She virtually shooed him into Glenys' boudoir and tucked the two of them in bed. How to entice him back into the matrimonial web? Be as attractive as you were twenty-five years ago, I told her, and twice as sexy.'

Betsy denounced this account of the Aylward divorce in equally virulent terms, furiously flashing her spectacles at her spouse: 'Total misrepresentation of the facts of the case! Derek Aylward had the worst male mid-life crisis I've come across – or almost the worst. He was obsessed by sex. He was pathetic. No solicitor ever did more soliciting. And why should a wife satisfy a husband's excessive and perverse appetites against her will? Why should she watch complete strangers doing disgusting things to one another, and interfering with goats and donkeys, in her own sitting-room? Wendy wasn't wrong to keep her eyes on her knitting. She had every right to say no to demands that never were in any marriage contract. She was the innocent party; but she'd forgotten that it's a man's world; she was taken aback to be punished for her husband's guilt and evicted from her home and ruined financially. Yes, I agree, she's made mistakes. She shouldn't have shed a single solitary tear for a husband she shouldn't have married. Her divorce was good riddance to bad rubbish. Glenys Calthrop was the star of *A Streetcar* – but it transported her into the arms of Derek who was playing *Peter Pan*. Well – dirty old men live to regret their lust, if they don't die of it. Young women always have the last laugh at senile would-be Casanovas. But let the husbands try again, I say! There's no need for wives to take it lying down, not any more, praise be! We're legally entitled to our pound of flesh nowadays. Wendy should have sued for hers through every law-court in the country.'

These diatribes, obviously subjective, although who or what was at the bottom of the argument had not yet emerged, concluded with Betsy threatening to bring us our coffee upstairs.

CHARLES HART waited with me in the front hall for Gregory Leplay and Brian, who were using the ground-floor lavatory. A constructivist picture hung on the wall; but it might have been knocked together by Jeremiah when he was a child. The piece of furniture below it was a waist-high shelf-unit crammed with posters advertising Betsy's causes, Save the Whales and the Seals and the Rain Forests and the

Coral Reefs and so on. The top shelf was littered with junk mail, bunches of keys, secateurs, and what looked like the piston of an internal combustion engine.

Gregory and Brian joined us, and Charles said to Brian, pointing at the metal object, which, he explained later, he took to be a vital component of the Hookes' car or lawnmower: 'I'm sorry to see you're having engine-trouble.'

Gregory rounded on and corrected him: 'It's a Klipwitz, you fool!'

Charles blushed and apologised to Brian, who seems to see the funny side of nothing except his own laboured jokes, and now informed us without a smile that the object in question was a cast of Klipwitz's sculpture entitled *Happiness Two*.

We mounted the stairs to the sitting-room, where Charles and Gregory began to giggle together at the farcical incident. Brian must have noticed and decided to put a stop to rot of that sort. At the time he was on the receiving end of another of Octavia's broadsides aimed at her charwoman, and was not hiding his boredom and restlessness. In order to silence and escape her, quell the unruliness of guests and provoke controversy, which could have been entertaining by his criteria, he said loud and clear: 'Don't worry, Octavia! Wait for Socialism to get a grip, possess your soul in patience! There won't be any servants to annoy you, or masters or mistresses to annoy the servants, as soon as Socialism makes this a land worth living in.'

My hackles rose. But I could not very well bite the hand that had fed me. Besides, from my point of view, the subject was too serious for discussion at a dinner party; and I was afraid of losing my temper.

Gregory had no such inhibitions. He must have been simmering ever since his attire was mocked. And he is a self-made man, he has become a capitalist by means of his talent and industry, and takes a natural pride in his bank-balance, which he is prepared to defend from envy, crime and do-gooders.

If people were stupid enough to allow Socialism to govern them, he said, what was quite certain was that there would soon be no more top-class mansions in Flood Street for a couple of theoretical egalitarians to spread themselves in. There would be no more five course dinners, or having things both ways, running with the capitalist hare and hunting with the socialist hounds. As for grip, Socialism internationally was not getting but losing it: for the first duty of politics was and is to serve success — the more the successful are enabled to succeed the more prosperity is spread around — whereas Socialism had failed and always would because it served failure.

Charles was meanwhile hissing in my ear: 'Socialists are drab — I hate them. Give me glitter any day.'

Octavia had produced an old-fashioned powder-compact and was powdering her beak of a nose with what looked like flour; and Marian was talking clothes to Gem in a corner.

Betsy weighed in: 'Sorry, Grégoire, I beg to differ — Socialism doesn't mean not inviting you to have dinner here — Socialism should mean caring, unselfishness, consideration of others. There's nothing wrong with Socialism, except some Socialists!' — and she as it were threw the last three words in the face of Brian.

But he batted them back at her: 'May I just add that Socialism's tolerant, and sharing as well as caring — or isn't it?'

At this point Jeremiah walked through the sitting-room door: the time was ten-thirtyish.

His short monochrome hair showed the nice shape of his head. He greeted Octavia and Marian with the routine kisses reserved for parents' friends, also kissed my Gem, and politely shook the hands of Gregory, Charles and myself.

He seems to be fond of Gem, which does not surprise me. She was never put off by his former appearance, and she

187

ministered to him on the night of the flood, when his feelings had been hurt by his father and best girl.

Now, she must have referred with gratitude to the pleasure of keeping an eye on our drain in his company, for he replied in the booming voice of youth: 'Don't mention it – I should thank you. Actually, I walked back here by way of Hope Cottage – Cinders heard me and barked.'

I deduced from the above that he had been in Rickman's Lane and probably consorting with Tracy Wilkins.

Betsy not only jumped to the same conclusion, she based the following allegation upon it: 'You've been slumming again.'

She was standing poised in front of the marbled mantelpiece, like the figure of Justice, but sighted, if not clear-sighted, and with coffee cups instead of scales in hand.

'I don't know what you mean,' Jeremiah returned, oafishly defensive and aggressive.

'Ask your Father!'

Brian, no longer bantering, in tones tremulous with indignation, warned: 'I think the time's come to remind the members of my family of the ground-rules of hospitality.'

There was a dramatic pause, while it occurred to me that the cause of dissension throughout the evening had been Brian's unfaithfulness in general and his flirtation with Tracy in particular.

Then Gregory, a cool customer and maybe a cruel one, disinclined to let bygones be bygones, addressed Jeremiah: 'I wonder whether you go along with the politics of your parents.'

Jeremiah said: 'What?'

'We were talking politics before you arrived. At least I was under the impression that we were talking politics – but I could be wrong. And your mother and father have disappointed me: they approve of Socialism and claim they're Socialists. Of course it's sweet of them to stoop to the level of the common man. But I'm hoping that you as a representative of the younger generation don't share their quaint views.'

Jeremiah laughed harshly and sulkily, flushed red and responded: 'No! Mum's just mixed up. And with Dad, everything's for show.'

Brian's reaction to these hostile comments was to stride towards and out of the door, white-faced and shouting: 'I know what you're getting at and I won't stand for it!'

Betsy called and pursued him: 'Brian! Come back! Will you come back, Brian!' – rather as if he had been a disobedient dog. Jeremiah groaned with disapprobation: 'Oh no!' – and followed in his parents' footsteps. On the landing and down the stairs, words, as the euphemistic slang of our lingo describes a quarrel, were exchanged.

Charles grimaced nervously at Gregory and blamed him: 'You've gone and done it now.'

Octavia grated: 'Poor Brian!' – directing a dirtier look at Gregory.

But he sat on both of them: 'Poor Brian nothing! He owns property in Brighton – he wheels and deals in property in secret – he's richer than he wants anyone to know – he's king of the humbugs, or married to the queen – why should they get away with trying to make the rest of us feel insensitive and greedy?'

Marian rose both above the drama and to her feet, and murmured with a calm curly smile: 'It must be late – time always flies with Betsy and Brian – I'll have to be going.'

Somewhere a door slammed viciously.

The senior Hookes rejoined our group, he declaiming with hands pressed palm to palm under his chin in an attitude of penitent prayer, 'Deepest regrets! Permit me to grovel,' while she reiterated in a heartfelt aside, 'How I hate men!'

In due course, after innumerable lies had been told, for instance that no one had taken exception to their family row, that it had amused us and provided an interesting and exciting climax to a charming evening, we departed.

In the street, without more ado, Gem and I headed for Hope Cottage. The cold night and the snow discouraged procrastination. Marian only had to descend one flight of exterior steps and ascend another in order to be at home; and Gregory and Charles undertook to escort Octavia to Beggar's Roost.

Needless to say, Gem had not missed the point that the cause of all the trouble was the plebeian maiden with whom neither well-brought-up sons, nor well-behaved husbands on any account, should so demean themselves as to associate, according to a class-conscious Socialist.

We arrived with relief at that slum of Rickman's Lane where we as well as the Wilkinses reside; and agreed that the best bit of nine out of ten dinner parties was discussing how much we had not enjoyed them.

NOT THE communist conspiracy to rule the world at all costs, but the social life of Lewes continues to preoccupy me.

I pray with apologies to St Augustine: let me be literary, but not yet.

And I console myself with a couple of reflections: that recent doings of the smart set of Eastover cry out to be chronicled; and that books not written voluntarily are never worth the paper they are printed on.

A few days after the Hookes' party the thaw set in, and the postman brought us our invitation to the wedding of Monica Drewett and Peter Cadwallader. A romantic optimist might connect the two events: the warmth of true love and the beginning of the end of winter. We cynics merely reminded each other of the passage of arms between Monica and Peter in the annexe to the linen-room on Christmas Eve, and did our sums and drew corroborative conclusions from the unmistakeable evidence of haste. For the wedding was announced before the engagement; and the marriage, thanks to some special licence or requisite dispensation obtained from the authorities, was to be celebrated at St Luke's in a fortnight.

Perhaps the high spot hit by Monica in the West End on the night of the flood was Peter's proposal to make an honest woman of her.

The reception would be at the bridegroom's home — a departure from convention and custom, Gem informed me. But I approved the common sense of holding it in rooms and a garden bigger and more beautiful than those at Downscene.

Eastover throbbed with excitement — I mean gossip and mainly bad feelings. Invitation cards, large, thick, embossed, and gilt-edged in every sense, were in short supply.

Bertha waited for hers in vain.

But snobbery and conceit helped to sweeten the sourness of her grapes.

'I wouldn't go, I'm sure, not if they begged me now on bended knee,' she told us. 'It's Drewetts, not Cadwalladers, I blame. Who are they, when all's said? They're only money, not class. George Drewett's father was a working man, and where that Madge came from I wouldn't like to guess. Mr Guy Cadwallader, he always did remember that my mother was employed by his father at Cadwallader Place. But he's a different person these days, he's got so absent-minded — I expect he's been knocked sideways by Mr Peter having to marry a girl like Monica. No — it'd make me too sad to see a lovely young boy sell himself so cheap — and buy trouble into the bargain. Besides, they've picked a day when I'm at Old Tyme Dancing, which wouldn't be the same without me. I'm sorry but I'm busy, if Drewetts should think better of it.'

Mrs Spedding took an interest in various aspects of the nuptials: 'Got the gun out, did they? He must have run for his life, but they stuck to him — Drewetts do have sticky fingers. Still, he's scattered his wild oats and no mistake — and not far from here neither. The Wilkins lot, they'll be climbing up the wall and biting the carpet. They thought they had him in the bag, but he was too slippery for the likes of them. A fortune's worth more than a pretty face. And who'd sneeze at Cadwallader Place? Bertha had her invitation yet?

We said no to this last question.

'Poor old soul!' Mrs Spedding commented with merciless humour. 'It would have been a nice change for her to go to a wedding that wasn't her own.'

Gem broached the subject of Bertha's breeding, saying that if by chance she was half a Cadwallader she was not being asked to the wedding of her natural step-nephew.

Mrs Spedding's cackle of laughter caused Timmy to squawk resentfully and deposit a dropping on her shoulder.

'Tell me another, dear,' she scoffed.

At the end of the month the weather was as lamb-like as it had been leonine at the beginning. Wedding bells that seemed to peal victoriously summoned us to Eastover Church at midday, and sunshine streamed through the south windows as the bride and her portly father processed up the aisle.

The best man was the bride's brother, Reggie Drewett. Peter and Reggie both wore pale grey morning-suits, stick-up collars and satin cravats fixed with jewelled pins, and pink carnations peeping out of maidenhair fern in their buttonholes. Peter was smirking and twitching in an unreliable manner, and Reggie's eyes in his red face are definitely too big and blue to be true.

Everyone was there, as they say: I mean half a dozen of our Lewes friends and acquaintances, and perhaps two hundred strangers. Wendy Aylward had managed to seat herself next to Graham Phipps-Hulett. Was he praying for deliverance from the evil of having to marry her? Our view was partially blocked by the broad back of Marian Travers, whose hat with a positive herbaceous border round its brim posed similar problems for Gregory and Charles in the pew behind us, and provoked unchristian complaints. Bald-headed and bottle-nosed Dadda Byrne whispered and grinned with broken teeth into the veiled ear of Octavia Pritchett.

Monica's dress was virginal white, and sufficiently loose and flowing to cover a multitude of sins. Her sole attendant was a bridesmaid not known to us: there would hardly have been time to make more than one frilly frock. Madge Drewett, resplendent in purple silk and stiffly corsetted, bent down with difficulty to rearrange the train of her daughter, who swayed and grimaced at her in a way suggestive of faintness and nausea.

But in spite of the bride's morning sickness, as Charles called it, and the inaudibility of the bridegroom's vows, and the embarrassment of the address from the pulpit, Monica managed to get Peter's ring on her finger.

The peroration of the Reverend Crispin Peterson's sermon was as follows: 'In this age of permissiveness and promiscuity, how refreshing to find two persons wishing to plight their troth publicly and receive the sacrament of marriage before uniting their love and their lives in the fullest sense.'

The unspoken queries of the congregation ballooned into the mote-filled ecclesiastical air as if in a strip-cartoon: when did Mr Peterson last have his eyes tested? Why did he think he had had to be where he was at such short notice?

Charles Hart joked at the reception after referring to Mr Peterson's plurality of offspring: 'His trouble is that he's never looked under the gooseberry bush before leaping.'

MONICA HAD recovered by the time we had queued for an hour or so in order to add our congratulations and kisses to the hundreds she had already received in the staircase hall at Cadwallader Place. She smiled with teeth protruding proudly and thanked us for the electric kettle: in fact our gift had been a set of fruit plates.

Peter smirked at us, pulled faces in the manner of someone who has got himself into or perhaps out of a scrape, winked, raised his eyes skywards, embraced Gem and shook my right hand with his left, and mouthed sweet nothings – nothings so far as I was concerned since I could not hear them.

We exchanged further greetings with Foxy and Guy and George and Madge.

The latter's eyeballs remind me of the axles of cartwheels: her eyelashes, separated and stiffened by mascara, are like the spokes of the wheel.

She was much amused by Foxy's dress: 'Her glad-rags are dusters, dar!' – and indeed it did bear a certain resemblance to checked dusters of various colours sewn together. The Cads joined in the laughter, juggling with their teeth, and Foxy contributed her mite to the merriment by confessing: 'I got it from Help the Aged.'

We followed along to the dining-room at the rear of the house, and into the garden, which is larger than expected and, like its owners, delightfully uncultivated – just lawn, Irish yews and old fruit trees with silvery lichened bark, and high ivy-clad flint walls surrounding it.

Drinks were served, and, through the arched entrance to a marquee, tables clothed in white and decorated with flowers and laid for lunch were visible.

We were standing in the precociously hot sun at the top of a flight of uneven overgrown stone steps, when Reggie Drewett approached, waved his champagne glass at the luxurious scene, and observed: 'My Daddy's more religious than any of us suspected – he's cast his bread upon the waters, as the good book asks us to.'

Betsy Hooke emerged from the house. At first I noticed nothing wrong. She said: 'Where's Jeremiah? I wasn't at the wedding. But I gather the fools were well and truly spliced.'

'You're speaking of the fool of a sister I love,' Reggie reproached her, teasing and rolling his huge eyes. 'But tell me, Betsy-wetsy, which particular hedge have you been pulled through backwards?'

She was wearing an everyday skirt and sloppy-joe pullover, no hat, and her mouse-brown hair was uncommonly straight and greasy.

She replied: 'Brian's run off with that slut Tracy Wilkins you men are so mad on!'

And notwithstanding her fighting talk, her lower lip trembled and turned inside out and tears gushed from under her specs and dangled on her chin.

'Oh poor Betsy,' Gem exclaimed, extending the hand of friendship in her direction.

Betsy brushed it aside, shrugged, gulped, stumbled down the steps and was lost in the crowd.

Reggie was heartlessly hard-boiled: 'I can't help feeling sorry for Brian – he must have had so much difficulty in choosing between Betsy and Tracy.' He was then summoned to help to shepherd guests into the marquee.

Gem, although sympathetic still and as ever, pointed out that Betsy was hoist with another of her petards: at the dinner party she had advised wives to let husbands go and pretty well challenged her own to do what he had done.

I spoke my piece about the hypocrisy of Socialists: Betsy playing at classlessness, but quick to try to put Tracy in her place by calling her a slut in a slum.

Gem then said: 'I suppose Tracy's rebounding from Peter getting married. Perhaps we should feel sorry for her, too. And what about Jeremiah?'

Lunch, at least, was predictable: rich food, voices hoarse from shouting, a waggish speech from the best man, and the bridegroom tongue-tied and whispering in response.

I sat between Wendy, who exuded fellow-feeling for Betsy, and Marian Travers, who was forgiving of sins of the flesh and not especially interested in other people committing them. Gem's neighbours were Graham Phipps-Hullett, unsettled by Betsy's plight or the passions of Brian or both, and Father Byrne, who, in the context of the beginning of one marriage and the probable end of another, made the broad-minded statement that sex was a Catholic priest's bread and butter.

Eventually, when Peter and Monica had driven away in a shower of confetti, rice, old boots and shaving foam at four o'clock, we were able to offer up thanks to our Cadwallader and Drewett hosts and hostesses.

George Drewett took my arm and piloted me towards the front door.

'Do you happen to recall a conversation we had after the flood?' he enquired, chuckling and with his hamster's jowls quivering happily. 'Prophetic, wasn't it?'

I had to ask him to explain.

He did so: 'Foxy and Guy are moving out of here and we're moving in.'

'You mean you've bought Cadwallader Place?'

'No! Why spend money if you can save it and make it? Foxy and Guy are going to rent a cottage of ours in Grey Friars Twitten, and hand over to Peter and Monica. But this is a big expensive house to run. The plan is to create a flat for the young people on the top floor. And in the meanwhile I've arranged to take care of the rest.'

I volunteered some platitude to the effect that dreams can come true.

His face assumed a slyer expression and he sighed with mock-resignation: 'What it is to have a desirable daughter!'

I had scribbled the above – I was finishing my account of the Cadwallader wedding – when the telephone rang.

Gem was out with Cindy.

It rang and rang, and five minutes ago I answered.

Dr Ward from Boltbridge was on the line. He told me Rachel's disease has spread into the bone of her skull.

APRIL

Whoever scrawled the message on Mama's Rates bill was probably a nobody. The Creedwell Council Treasurer in his letter of apology made out that the culprit was a part-time ex-office-boy.

I too see the red pen in the hand of youth. For youth in general has no mercy: it has no experience and believes it will never be old.

I see a young man or possibly a young woman, someone deeply ignorant or at any rate limited, yet a little cleverer than his or her associates; someone capable of taking an interest in our social system and deducing that politics could change, improve or destroy it; someone vain enough to want to be different, and lazy enough to prefer knocking down to building up; and someone in a state of psychological confusion as to who is an enemy and who a victim.

His or her relevant contribution to that glorious revolution, soon to fulfil the hopes of the downtrodden masses, at least in theory, was mortally to wound one philanthropic old woman.

They are the fantasists, the lunatic fringe, the vandals of politics, such types. And they are living proof of the irresponsibility of intellectuals, who set the trends that they follow.

The intelligentsia should be forced by law to spend some years in remote parts of the country, where they would be exposed to the fall-out from their brainwaves.

The chemical genius who invented tranquillisers, for

instance, or the apostles of permissiveness, may have been applauded in scientific and aesthetic circles. The consequences in Boltbridge in Creedwell were, and so far as I know still are, disastrous. The ploughman on his tractor, the shepherd in his cote, the cowgirl calling the cattle home, all are now on tablets prescribed in lavish quantities by overworked doctors, who have seized the opportunity to keep their patients quiet. The yokel of yore, the honest son of the soil, is either heavily sedated or mad for sex.

I exaggerate.

But life in villages and hamlets, and on the land, is not like that lived in centres of sophistication. Work with crops and livestock, subject to the weather and fraught with disappointment, seems to develop some parts of the personality, in particular the faculties of patience and acquiescence, at the expense of other parts, in particular the ability to discriminate, and the courage to disagree with and stand up against the current opinions of the national community. Besides, there are not so many alternatives, choices of interests and pastimes and so on, in the back of beyond.

At Boltbridge as I knew it, fashions were swallowed whole, if belatedly; and their effects were inescapable. A farmer's boy with dyed hair and safety-pins in his nose and ears, wearing a home-made version of designer tatters, stuffed with recreational drugs, brainwashed by uncensored pornography and convinced that sex with any stray female was his prerogative, attracted more attention and created more chaos than an equally up-to-date guttersnipe in a city with two thousand times the population. And if radical politics ever intruded into that rustic idyll, the result was simply goodbye to neighbourliness, to the essential spirit of co-operation, and peace and pleasure.

Untutored country folk are apt to take too literally the wayward advice of highbrows, and often ruin their own and others' lives thereby.

Yet credulity is not a crime: I would call it a fault on the right side, preferable to wariness and caution. And naturally the young idea is not to be left too far behind by the bandwagon.

Moreover, oddly enough, I am not against progress in principle, and realise that in order to get anywhere it often has to begin by being, or seeming to be, extreme.

But extremism is always risky, and politically, at least as rule rather than exception, always wrong.

I refer to Marxism and the violent revolutionary upheaval it calls for, to Marxism which brooks no opposition, and to its begetters, disciples, informed adherents, publicists and apologists, who are surely culpable.

They had the mental equipment to learn and teach, they had access to education, research, history, they were born to lead, or they could or did achieve positions in society which enabled them to exert influence, and they believed and proclaimed that they knew better: they should have known better still – I am thinking again of Philby, to whom it was 'a matter of great pride' that he played a part in building up the power of the Soviet Union and Communism, and of all the superior self-congratulatory so-called fellow-travellers of his era.

I lay at their feet the roll of honour of the sixty-six million Russian people, who are alleged to have died of Soviet Communism between 1917 and 1959.

To my knowledge nobody has yet tried to tot up the grand total of those uncounted millions plus the millions who died in the holocaust of National Socialism or Fascism, which was the backlash against, and owed much to, the Soviet system; plus the millions of casualties of the 1939–1945 war, a major cause of which was Communism's seizure of power in Russia and its relentless threats against other countries; plus the millions who have perished prematurely in Russia and its empire between 1959 and the present day; plus the millions upon millions of victims of Marxism and Soviet-style tyrants elsewhere in the world.

AGAIN AND again in the Second World War, homosexuality proved it was loyal and brave beyond the call of duty. A considerable percentage of the deeds of heroism and fortitude were done by homosexuals.

Yet homosexuality also provided the USSR with several of its famous spies of the Philby vintage, although seemingly not Philby himself. At least Burgess, Maclean and Blunt suffered more or less from what is called the British Disease in France. Negative motives can perhaps explain, though not excuse, their treachery. Throughout their most actively sexual years they could only make love to other men by breaking the law: which was changed so as to allow homosexual acts between consenting adults much later on. Puberty therefore launched them on a career of crime – none seem to have had the disposition of monks. Doubtless it also engendered resentment of the political establishment, the legal authorities and the police; and urged further lawbreaking in support of the theory that one might as well be hanged for a sheep as for a lamb.

In the twenties and thirties of this century Russia must have looked like the spiritual home of the homosexuals destined to spy for it, even if André Gide is supposed to have renounced Communism after discovering that it permitted mixed bathing. For Russia had abolished the old rules and regulations, conventions, classes and classifications, and claimed to offer freedom from the shackles of the past and a really new and altogether better deal. And to encourage and assist it in its formative phase, and switch loyalties, was to kill two birds with a single stone: express disapproval of and dissociate oneself from the puritanical hell of one's native land, and serve humanity in general and probably minority interests in particular by advancing the cause of the Soviet heaven over the horizon.

Intellectuals, too, have been known to nurse a grievance against their fellow-citizens, and especially against the establishment. The occupational hazard for persons with brains bigger than mine and possibly yours is the unhappy conviction that they are not receiving their dues of recognition and reward.

For the potential intellectual variety of spy, the lure of the USSR in its earlier stages would have been twofold: Communism promised to be strictly meritocratic, and it looked cleverer than Capitalism on paper.

Even across the gulf of half a century I catch a whiff of the unholy incense they must have inhaled with satisfaction, these intellectual spies like Philby, or spies combining intellectualism and homosexuality like Burgess and Blunt, because they were righting the wrong of the attitudes of their compatriots and actively proving they had the courage of their convictions, because of their open-mindedness and far-sightedness and differences from common or garden fools, and because of their enrolment in the crack regiment of the forces of enlightenment.

Soon they had yet more arrows in the quiver of their self-justification: the revival of German nationalism, the advent of Hitler, and the moral rectitude of rallying to support the politics and power of the USSR, which alone could and would save civilisation from barbarous Nazism.

Obviously, beyond the shadow of doubt, as Philby argues in his autobiography, they were not ordinary traitors, betraying their friends, relations, colleagues and countrymen and countrywomen for gain or for psychopathic reasons – nothing like Judas Iscariot.

No – they were bravely re-ordering their priorities and allegiances in the best interests of the masses – they were moved to do it by an idealism probably beyond the comprehension of those they were doing it for: they were steeped in the higher humanitarian philosophy and in advance of slow-witted or half-witted public opinion, and they recognised the infinitely greater scope and deeper compassion of Marxist Russia.

The Bolsheviks got to the top of the greasy pole in 1917, and the Nazis in 1933.

By the time spies had started spying for Russia in order to defend everyone from Germany, Lenin and Stalin between them had already shed more innocent blood than Hitler ever managed to.

If Philby and Co. really were as clever as all that, why were they not in possession of available facts appertaining to existence in the USSR? If they were as idealistic, humane and honourable as has been claimed, they could hardly have known what was going on and still dedicated themselves to the service of Russian Communism.

The clerk who was pleased to bully my poor old mother into her grave I have called ignorant. Setting aside considerations of homicidal mania, I think the same applies to the spies in question, converted to Communism in the thirties, although they were highly educated and sufficiently well-off or well paid or both to acquire culture. They belonged to the middle class, and surely privileged pilgrims on the road to Moscow, such as they were, embraced egalitarianism in the belief that they were more equal than others in an intellectual sense, and would remain so materially: arrogance is almost synonymous with ignorance.

Why had those know-alls not condescended to read the writing on the wall? Why did they not do their homework? Philby in print boasts that he is brainier, craftier and better informed than everyone who trusted him, and Graham Greene would have us believe he was not a villain through and through. Had Philby never looked into the ominous history of ancient and modern Russia? Had he never heard of the opinions of Russian wiseacres which had been in circulation for many years?

Dostoevski (1821–1881) was dead against radical revolution: 'Starting from unlimited freedom it will arrive at unlimited despotism.'

Leontiev (1831–1891) warned: 'Socialism is the feudalism of the future.'

A Socialist asked Tolstoy (1828–1910) if there was not a difference between the killing done by a revolutionary and the killing done by a policeman. Tolstoy replied: 'There is as much difference as between cat-shit and dog-shit. But I don't like the smell of either.'

Tolstoy criticised Marxists thus: for their materialistic philosophy, and misunderstanding of the real needs of the people; because their conception of revolution was change by violence; and because their leaders would be content to seize power, which they would then retain by force, reverting to the very oppression of the masses that they had set out to destroy.

Tolstoy also said that economic ideals were not ideals.

The disillusioned censure by Rosa Luxemburg (1870–1919), a lifelong German Communist, who was arrested after a riot in Berlin and assaulted by army officers, dying of her injuries, was based upon direct experience: 'The remedy invented by Lenin and Trotsky is worse than the evil it was supposed to cure.'

But Philby seems to have believed Soviet propaganda, which Lenin himself called 'Com-boasts' and 'Com-lies.'

Since he worked for two masters and therefore cannot be accused of idleness, of not bothering to investigate, charity perhaps suggests he was not so much ignorant as criminally silly.

PSEPHOLOGISTS, who study opinion polls, tell us that democratic elections are never won by the opposition party, they are lost by the government in power.

Philby and Co. turned against the country that bred them, and wanted, possibly amongst other things, to wreak revenge on what or who had somehow offended or injured them, for instance by not honouring their intellects or not tolerating their homosexuality, or maybe, more objectively, for socio-political reasons. They would have said, they have said, that they could not abide the inequality and the injustice of Capitalism.

But who were the Russian champions of liberty and fair play, and what were the effects of Communism in action, that were worth fighting for, or, rather, that made it worth fighting against our democratic politicians and politics?

I quoted Tolstoy, who was in favour of social change in Russia, but not by means of violent revolution. He was thus taking issue with Lenin, who retorted by calling Tolstoy 'a worn-out historical sniveller.'

There was no nonsense about Lenin, who, incidentally, loathed intellectuals. Here is his comment on the famine of 1891: 'This talk of feeding the starving is nothing but an expression of the saccharine-sweet sentimentality so characteristic of our intelligentsia.'

As soon as he could he set up the secret police, then called the Cheka. The historian Prokovsky explained Lenin's views in Pravda: 'The secret police sprang from the very essence of the proletarian revolution, of which terror was the inevitable consequence.'

Lenin backed the Chekists when they asked for more power to fight counter-revolutionaries and for permission to torture, and attacked the 'narrow-minded intelligentsia who sob and fuss.' He added: 'When we are reproached with cruelty, we wonder how people can forget the most elementary Marxism.'

The initial consequences of this element of elementary Marxism as he interpreted it were as follows. Two months after the revolution, the Cheka was given its orders. Four months after the revolution, the Cheka executed somebody. By April 1918 the Cheka had set up its own three-man courts, the notorious Troikas. Then in September 1918 the Cheka was instructed to sentence and execute without reference to the public tribunals; and it not only shot five

204

hundred hostages after the assassination of Uritsky, it also brought into being the concentration camps.

The good times, for which the collectivists and egalitarians of this world, and the disaffected, the destroyers and the ignoramuses had yearned and striven, had arrived.

The masses celebrated by getting drunk. The Tsar and Tsarina and their children were thrown into prison and shot, and soldiers of the most famous regiments of the Tsar's erstwhile army, appointed in succession to do guard duty at the Winter Palace, got drunk on his wine. These soldiers were dismissed, and others from different military sources were posted to do the job: they too got drunk. The leaders of the revolutionary movement in the army took over: they got drunk. The fire brigade was called in to flood the cellars: they got drunk. Eventually some sailors succeeded in guarding the place, having bound themselves not to drink on pain of death.

Democracy was another early casualty of Lenin's rule. In 1918 the elected Constituent Assembly gave a large majority to the other revolutionary parties: Lenin's Communists immediately dissolved it. He proclaimed that the 'workers' would not submit to government by 'peasants.'

Voltaire might have invented especially for Marxists his telling witticism to the effect that speech was given to man to enable him to hide his thoughts. Lenin was perhaps the ablest of the Marxist practitioners of argument and explanation by means of high-class gobbledygook. In 1919 he stated: 'We recognise neither freedom, nor equality, nor labour democracy, if they are opposed to the interests of the emancipation of labour from the oppression of capital.'

The Communists may have been persuaded that by taking and not letting go of power they were acting on behalf of people in general and the working-class in particular. But Trotsky had prophesied years before: if the Party substituted itself for the working-class, the Party organisation would substitute itself for the Party as a whole; then the Central

Committee would substitute itself for the Party organisation; and finally a single dictator would substitute himself for the Central Committee.

Again, the communist revolution claimed that its aims and objectives permitted it to 'transcend bourgeois morality.' As Robert Conquest writes in his Preface to *The Great Terror*: 'Every sacrifice of humanist principles was made in the name of the true interests of humanism.'

Three and a half years after October 1917, in March 1921, the sailors of the Soviet Navy at Kronstadt, who constituted a sort of revolutionary Old Guard, rebelled against the revolution. They complained that it had 'brought the workers, instead of freedom, an ever present fear of being dragged into the torture chambers of the Cheka, which exceeds by many times in its horrors the Gendarmerie administration of the Tsarist regime'; and they submitted demands for a bit more democracy. They were shot.

From 1921 onwards the Party represented no one and nothing except itself, and, really, waged war against the masses.

At the 10th Party Congress in 1921 Lenin himself admitted it: 'We have failed to convince the broad masses.' But he was never one to give up gracefully. His recipe for success was to 'override the trade unions and dismiss their recalcitrant leaders, in order to break popular resistance, and prevent the free formation of opinion.' He added that opinion had to be formed by the Party.

And in 1922 he confessed: 'We are living in a sea of illegality.'

Thus, although in his Testament written in 1923, the year before his death, he objected with untypical sensitivity to Stalin's 'rudeness', he ushered in government by the brute force of either fanaticism or self-interest, and set the scene for Stalinism.

IN THE revolutionary free-for-all the peasants seized land

from the landowners and from one another, and traded their produce for cash in accordance with capitalist rules. They did what came naturally, looked after themselves and their families as best they could, and so fell foul of the communist theorists of central government, who resented their ability to blackmail the nation by supplying or by not supplying food, and their independence. The Ukraine, called the bread basket of Russia, was especially offensive in the eyes of officialdom. The Ukraine grew more grain than was good for it, and was a state within a state, having its own language and seething with nationalist and even separatist feelings.

Although, after ten revolutionary years of civil war, disorganisation and impoverishment, there were no farmers or agricultural workers who were well-off by European criteria, the single dictator of the USSR, Stalin, decided finally to solve the problems of kulaks who were 'rich', peasants who were 'individualists', and the Ukrainians. He would teach them all a lesson, and, as a result, 'encourage' other groups of workers and ethnic minorities to strike out on their own.

The de-kulakisation and the collectivisation of the country was accomplished between the years 1929–1932. It was done in a terrible hurry and by savage compulsion. Between January and March 1930, in those three months alone, ten million peasant holdings were joined up into collective farms.

Those about to lose their land, homes and livelihoods, fought back. They slaughtered and sold their animals, which would otherwise be stolen by the state. They would not work on the collective farms. And they lost their lives. A further statistic is a measure of the compensatory success of Stalin's agricultural policy: in 1953 the USSR was producing less food than in 1916.

But was Stalin downhearted? He forged ahead. He knew nothing about agriculture or the countryside, but a thing or two about the politics of tyranny. The failure of his

207

collectivisation programme had the immediate effect of creating a shortage of food and, more ominously, of seed-corn from which to grow the daily bread of the future. However, grain could be requisitioned and – in a reassuringly socialistic word – re-distributed. The recollection that requisitioning it in 1918 had caused a three year famine also came in handy. Stalin's grand design was, at a stroke, to feed his people and quell the opposition, or at least some of it. He extorted grain from the Ukrainians, he stripped the Ukraine of everything edible, and closed the Russian-Ukrainian frontier.

The Ukraine is roughly five times the size of England. Between 1930 and 1937, 14,500,000 people, give or take a few millions, perished as a result of Stalin's terror-famine. According to the census of 1939, the Ukrainian population was then 28,000,000.

The relevant arithmetic is again approximate, because, as Krushchev wrote in his memoirs, 'All we knew was that people were dying in enormous numbers.'

How could Stalin do it, not only morally, but practically?

The Russian political tradition was autocratic. In 1881 Tsarism enacted the Law of Extraordinary and Temporary Measures, which was contradictorily permanent. It suspended legal procedures and civil rights, sanctioned summary courts martial, censored newspapers, closed institutions and outlawed meetings. There is no question that the revolution in 1917 was popular. But within months it, and Lenin, had broken their promises in respect of freedom and democracy. By the time Stalin took over, the Russian people seem to have resigned themselves to more of the same, that is to say to more autocratic and despotic rule.

Lenin's reference to Stalin's rudeness is the euphemism to crown all euphemisms. Stalin was so rude that he killed his friends as well as his enemies. And terror is effective in the short term – I mean for fifty or a hundred years: witness the USSR itself and its colonies, or the countries conquered and incorporated into the Thousand Year Reich, or, on a smaller scale, Nazi–occupied Lyons in France, where Klaus Barbie and kindred spirits in the Gestapo flayed a few suspects alive and broke up the organisation of resistance in a matter of months. Although the heirs of democracy living in stable un-invaded lands may find it hard to imagine or believe, they should try to in the interests of their own security, and vote accordingly: human nature and the life of a nation can be dominated if enough people are killed, hurt and frightened.

Stalin was backed by a force possibly even more persuasive than his secret police: neo-religious enthusiasm for Communism. Older party members, able to compare the communist present with the Tsarist past, who had observed the betrayal of the revolution, might be privately disillusioned; yet no doubt many could not bear to renounce their faith, recant, and admit even to themselves that their lifelong hopes, and the crimes committed in the attempt to realise them, had been a dreadful mistake.

And the revolution was still sufficiently young to satisfy youth's craving for change. The younger generation, children of 1917, who were now coming of age, had been indoctrinated in communist schools and by communist propaganda. They seem to have believed implicitly that Communism was good for you, Communism was best, and would with historic inevitability usher in the worldwide millennium. The size of the country combined with the control of information in order not to upset the ideological apple-cart: a Communist here had no knowledge of what had been done to a Communist there, and news was uniformly positive. Moreover the official line about the richness and insolence of kulaks, whose offence was rather to be poor but proudly self-reliant, was effective.

Therefore Stalin could boast in *Pravda* in 1929: 'We have gone over from a policy of limiting the exploiting tendencies of the kulak to a policy of liquidating the kulak as a class' – without worrying that so sinister a statement would cause public alarm and despondency.

The reasoning of idealists in the subsequent period is nicely put by Koestler's fictional interrogator in *Darkness at Noon*: 'It is the Stalinist willingness to face the necessary filth and horror of historical progress that gives a superiority over sentimental humanism.'

The non-idealistic point of view was expressed by a high official who had helped to carry out Stalin's orders in 1929–1932: 'We have won the war.'

Some of the negative consequences of de-kulakisation, collectivisation and the man-made famine in the Ukraine were as follows.

Lenin's widow pleaded with Stalin not to prosecute the class struggle by means of famine: in vain, of course.

Two students from a Technical School managed to inform Stalin's wife, Nadezhda Alliluyeva, of the cannibalism of starving Ukrainians. She told Stalin, who had the students arrested and packed off to concentration camps, and instituted a purge of all young Communists in schools and colleges who had been doing their bit of his dirty work in the Ukraine. Nadezhda Alliluyeva's quarrels with her husband over the famine are supposed to have led to her suicide in 1932.

Moscow, that is the government of the country, had no more pity than Stalin. As an activist remarked, perhaps apologetically: 'Moscow does not believe in tears.'

Stalin, again, boasted of the success of imposing his 'revolution from above' – another contradiction in terms – which crushed Russian peasantry and the Ukrainian nation; but Pasternak in *Dr Zhivago* states that 'collectivisation was an erroneous and unsuccessful measure, and it was impossible to admit the error.'

Whence, because of the impossibility of admitting the error, because of the need to hush up the enormity of the crime, the silencing of accomplices; whence the purges of students involved, and in time of the army and the secret police; whence the murder of 1108 of the 1966 delegates to the XV Party Congress in 1934 – they knew too much; whence, at the XIV Ukrainian Party Congress in 1938, the fact that only 3 delegates remained of the 86 of the previous year; whence, in short, the homicidal paranoia of Stalin, his mania to cover his tracks, which resulted in the Great Terror and contributed generously to the possible total of sixty-six million deaths from Communism by 1959.

Bukharin, who had been considered Lenin's natural successor once upon a time, and, ironically, had been an ardent supporter of the secret police and their methods, spoke out against the events of 1930–1933, contending that they had de-humanised the people working in the Soviet apparatus: he was tried and executed.

Evgenia Ginsburg, who made the mistake of working for a man accused of Trotskyism, and therefore incurred the suspicion and displeasure of the authorities and spent eighteen years in prisons and concentration camps, writes in her account of her experiences *Into The Whirlwind*: 'Step by step, as they [the secret police] followed one routine directive after another, they climbed down the ladder of the human condition.'

Stalin would have denied it. Stalin denied everything, that there was any famine, that he was in any way responsible. He had ignored repeated warnings that too much food was being requisitioned; he refused to modify his excessive demands for food; he posted guards at the frontier to stop food getting into the Ukraine and Ukrainians getting out; he used genocide by starvation as an instrument of policy.

And his government, his ministers and minions, who must have known what was happening, since it could not have happened without the assistance of their departments, personnel, resources, supported him, or, at least at the time and when it mattered most, raised no valid objections to the deliberate creation of the famine and the elimination of witnesses to it.

Indeed a leading member of the government, the same Bukharin whose conscience was soon to smite him, confirmed that 'the Soviet apparatus' – which I understand to mean the governmental establishment of the USSR – was involved in the crimes of 1930–1933.

It was in 1933 that Philby 'threw off his last doubts' and left Cambridge 'with the conviction that my life must be devoted to Communism.'

MONSTERS ARE not monsters in their own estimation.

Philby seems to have been able to convince himself that there was nothing wrong with his treachery, and the damage it did to his native land, and the nasty deaths it reserved for his colleagues who were on active service in the USSR and wherever Russia ruled. Perhaps he has to be judged by that law of psephologists: it was not so much that Communism won his loyalty – if he was loyal to anything – as that Capitalism lost it.

But can he have tricked so many of his associates for so many years, yet failed to master the ABC of contemporary international politics? He must have realised that in the capitalist democracies, far from perfect as they may be, it was not – and is not – the done thing for Prime Ministers and Presidents to starve vast proportions of the indigenous population to death, or commission any crime comparable with the Leninist-Stalinist terror.

Perhaps his conversion to Communism was personal, an act of homage to some influential man or woman, a gesture of revenge against one or more of his compatriots, the outer and eventually visible sign of an inner crisis, or the expression of a warped personality.

Nevertheless, in his autobiography, he argues that his politics were objective and rational. He trots out the anti-Fascist argument, that favourite excusatory hobby-horse of the class of capitalistic Communists of the early thirties.

But Hitler only came to power in 1933, by which time Lenin and Stalin had already killed millions. Fascism taught Communism nothing about the inhumanity of man; it was the other way round – Communism taught Fascism how to terrorise, and that genocide was a practical proposition.

Granted, later on, Hitler competed for the prize for beastliness, and became belligerent. He conquered most of Europe, and, having lulled the USSR into a sense of false security by means of a treaty of non-aggression and mutual friendship, he invaded it. The warmongering of Hitler's school of Collectivism was at last the vindication of those who had sided with the rival school of Marx, Lenin and Stalin.

They had never been able to object too loudly to Hitler's dictatorship of Germany – it would have been a case of the pot calling the kettle black; moreover he had gained power more democratically than the Russian dictators. They were scarcely in a position to whine about his policies of internal repression, which were child's play in comparison with those in Russia. What could they say when he annexed smaller countries, considering that Russia was doing the self-same thing, for instance in Lithuania, Latvia, Estonia?

The truth was that Communism's detestation of Nazism, and vice versa, was more like professional jealousy than the antipathy of opposites. They were both socialist parties. They employed similar methods. But Communism had always lent respectability to prejudice by claiming that Hitler was about to scar the face of the earth with rapine and pillage. And now, as his tanks trespassed even on the Russian steppes, he had proved them right.

I would not and could not defend Hitler. Yet his National Socialists ruled a capitalist country: he therefore had some reason to believe that if he did not do it to the USSR, the USSR would do it to him – witness the following statement which emerged from the Lenin School of Political Warfare in 1931: 'War to the hilt between Communism and Capitalism is inevitable. Today, of course, we are not strong enough to attack. To win we will need the element of surprise. The bourgeoisie will have to be put to sleep. So we shall begin by launching the most spectacular peace movement on record. There will be electrifying overtures and unheard-of concessions. The capitalist countries, stupid and decadent, will rejoice to co-operate in their own destruction. They will leap at another chance to be friends. As soon as their guard is down, we shall smash them with our clenched fist.'

No – Communism in power was no better than Nazism; and those who would put an honourable gloss on their shameful bed-fellowships in the 1930s were like Beatrice and Sidney Webb, if they were not villainous – the Webbs, eminent British Socialists, were conducted on an official tour of the Ukraine during the famine and reported back that the Ukrainians were all fat and happy.

Stale buns, somebody protests: Communism cannot be arraigned retrospectively for what it did and failed to do in its infancy any more than Capitalism can, for instance in America, where it killed off the Red Indian people. Times change, things have changed in the last thirty or forty years, Russia and its colonies are no longer Stalinist, a modern Communist could say.

By way of answer I would parade some of the major battle honours of Communism since 1945: crushing popular rebellion against Soviet influence in East Germany, and building the Berlin Wall to stop mass emigration to the capitalist west; crushing rebellions against Soviet interference in Poland, Hungary, Czechoslovakia; taking over Cuba, where the communist government tries to make ends meet by hiring out the conscripted Cuban army to fight for Russia; conquering Tibet; invading Afghanistan; and being up to its neck in the bloody shambles of South-east Asia, in the continuous conflict in South America, and in Africa, where Africans belonging to the wrong tribe keep on dying of starvation and thirst in unthinkable numbers in spite of being ruled by avowedly Stalinist leaders.

But perhaps the last and best argument in defence of Communism is economic and moralistic.

Economic life without competition, without the profit motive, ordered and arranged with scrupulous fairness by disinterested experts, is a dream as sweet for some as it is boring for others; and likewise the morality of no one having more than anyone else, and of everybody being equal and having equal opportunities and helping to do the national chores and so on. Inexperienced youth in the thirties might have been drawn to the utopian and messianic sides of Communism, which could still plead that it had not yet had time to keep its promises.

But every adult with a modicum of sense and sensibility would have known it was dangerous rubbish. Marxist theory, minus force, will not overcome nature, which blesses or curses some human beings with talent, and all with ambition of one sort or another. Men and women have wants as well as needs; and they are going to tread on toes, euphemistically speaking, to get what they want. Talent clambers un-stoppably towards the top of the social pile. And power, social, financial, religious, political, is acquired with difficulty and seldom willingly relinquished. Power does not of its own volition wither away, as Marx with all the optimism of a malign Micawber prophesied that it would.

History has now set its seal on the always obvious deduction that Marxist government, in order to withstand the inevitable unpopularity of not letting people do what comes naturally, has to break the law, intimidate, terrorise and kill. As for the economics of Marxism, they have ruined many a nation. The proof of Marx's economic pudding is that it is no longer on the menu in the USSR, nor, in effect, in China. After all, most leaders have to try to feed their people, and come back to believing it can best be done by the release of the energy of enlightened capitalist self-interest.

Philby got everything wrong: German Nazism was never more repressive and cruel than Russian Communism; if Nazism had won the war it could hardly have been greedier or more imperialistic than Communism; and the dictatorship of the proletariat of the USSR has not withered away in seventy-odd years; the world revolution that Marx forecast, and Marxists have worked and waited for, has not occurred; nowadays Marxism is unfashionable and in retreat, except among primitive peoples; and the economics of Communist-Socialist-Collectivism is a dead letter.

But Philby was a professional liar. He may have believed nothing he wrote in his autobiography.

The questions remain: how could he make the extra-ordinary statement that owing to the evil of the era of Baldwin and Chamberlain, Prime Ministers of our gentle homeland, whose politics never killed a single soul on purpose, he had decided to devote his life to Russian Communism, which, at the time, was already well on its way to killing sixty-six million? Why does Graham Greene, influentially famous and wealthy, lend support to such topsy-turvy values? Was Philby mad? How has it ever been possible for any grown-up of reasonably sound mind to believe in the fairy-tale of Marxism? What does a clerk in Creedwell imagine he or she is going to gain by cocking a snook, however lethal, at a class enemy?

Marx belonged to a race which in Christian countries was, and to some extent still is, accursed; also, in Germany, and then in England when he sought and found sanctuary here, to an ethnic minority. Having therefore experienced preju-dice and discrimination, he aligned himself with the oppo-sition to a social order that restricted and threatened his existence. He was against those presiding over that order, the ruling class, the rich, the successful, the exploiters in his terminology, and for the lower classes, who could and would make the revolution for him and wreak revenge.

Marxism in theory may lighten the darkness of poor innocent folk, hopeless and hungry, who feel they have been disinherited and forgotten. It assures them in their weakness that they are potentially the strongest force in the whole world. It exhorts them to combine, mobilise, rebel; it encourages them with the prophecy that they are anyway destined to come out on top by virtue of some mysterious historical process; and describes the promised land, where they are going to live happily ever after, the masters now of an equitable society, the armed champions of pacifism, setting an example universally admired and followed.

Karl Marx was another Jew of genius to cash in on the formula for success which would render the pleasures of privilege more widely available. He anticipated in his own area of political philosophy the achievements of Jews in Hollywood USA, who put theatrical entertainment on film and sold it cheap to cinema audiences; or, for another instance, Marks and Spencer in this country, doing the same thing with high quality goods previously reserved for the carriage trade.

Marxism is the secularisation, popularisation and vulgarisation of Christianity. The central and vital article of faith in Christianity is resurrection and life after death. As Voltaire explained: 'To found a religion is easy – all you have to do is die and three days later rise from the dead.' For the rich to wait until death elevates them into heaven, that is to say higher still, is not difficult; for the poor the delay can be intolerable. The worm's eye view of Christianity confirms that there is one law for the rich, already in a sort of heaven, and another for the poor, already in a sort of hell: more especially as Christianity does not guarantee belated justice in the form of preferential treatment up above for those who have endured the purgatory of poverty here below.

217

Karl Marx fished in the muddy waters of such odious comparisons. He abominated exploitation: he exploited the Christian message – the faults we are quickest to detect in others are invariably our own. His glad tidings were paradise now, instantly, or at any rate after a simple surefire little revolution, and not an uncertain posthumous incorporeal unimaginable paradise, but a paradise of life rather than death, for the living instead of the dead, vouched for by history, familiar not frightening, familiar yet better by far, and better largely because the former bosses and upper classes would be locked out of it.

Marx called religion the opium of the people. But the Christian religion's prediction of an after-life in heaven just might turn out to be true; whereas his promise to the impatient, his promise of heaven soon on earth, was bound to be broken.

Marxism's other heresies include setting up a golden calf and graven images for worship. By a golden calf, I mean the Marxist implication that as a result of the revolution the old poor will become the new rich. And images of Marx and the dictators he has spawned, and sometimes the mummified remains of the latter, are displayed and bowed down before in communist countries.

But the most heretical part of Marx's theorising, also further evidence of history's tendency to repeat itself – I refer to the rejection of Christ by Judaism, and indeed to the Crucifixion – is the reversal of what constituted the beginning and end of Christ's teaching in all its beautiful brevity: love thy neighbour. For those three words Marx substituted a trio terribly ugly, brutal and sad: the class struggle.

Another brilliant Jew, Sam Goldwyn, is said to have said: 'Nobody ever lost money by under-estimating the public's taste and intelligence.' Marx preceded him in a political rather than a commercial sense by appealing mainly to baser instincts, envy, avarice, vengefulness, spite and so on. The theme was common enough: radical politicians on the outside have had recourse to it ever since the year dot in order to get in. But Marx's cry of 'Down with the rich and up the workers!' was different in that it sanctioned total war, totalitarian war, utterly ruthless and relentless, against the class enemy – in practice whoever did, could or would oppose the dictatorship abusing power in the name of the people.

Admittedly it was not his fault that his near-contemporary Sigmund Freud made the discovery that none of us is wholly responsible for what we have done and do: our unconscious mind is the culprit. Sin is not sin, and crime is not crime, Freud was telling everyone blithely while Marx bayed for the shedding of blood; and we are never to blame.

Yet thus, by the unholy alliance of political and scientific opinions, nostrums discredited by experience, the efforts of the Christian churches over two thousand years, and of charity, virtue and civilisation itself, have been frustrated in some countries and altogether nullified in others.

Marxism has been backed throughout by the blank moral cheque of psychology.

The psycho-analytical craze instigated by Freud is another dinosaur: at least today's favoured treatment of mental disorder is chemical.

But bad political and medical fashions are superseded too slowly in the view of their victims – the first of which, the first and last of the myriad victims of the Marxist revolutionary movement, was, in a single word, kindness.

It was the standard bearer of authentic humanitarianism, almost everyone's champion, protector and friend, the guardian of youth, the moderator of passion, the comfort of age and illness, scion of trial and error, infinitely lovely and precious.

But General Marx and Colonel Freud instructed and commanded the rabble of their forces not to bother about the reactionary irrelevance of kindness: let it lie where it had fallen and be trampled into the dust by the hobnailed boots

219

of revolution marching forward into this cruellest century.

THAT WAS to have been the subject of my book.

Since the death of my mother I have meant to write about the Marxist class struggle and its attractions for people like Philby and furtive clerks in Council Offices venting their spleen on imaginary foes in the form of old ladies at their last gasp who are assumed to be better off.

Perhaps, if I had been poorer still, I would have had more sympathy for the Marxist experiment and its failure. No doubt the rich never were or are kind enough to the poor. On the other hand two wrongs do not make a right. And the answer to the riddle of existence cannot be to kill everybody luckier than you think you are.

Besides, no one has ever been able to indicate exactly where richness begins, or the precise sociological points at which the middle class becomes upper and lower.

But everyone who is anyone has always known that – to paraphrase Jesus – the poor we have always with us; that they present an insoluble religious, political and social problem; and the relationship between them and their financial superiors has been, is and will be tense.

Consequently good people throughout history have devoted more or less of their lives and their resources to easing that tension, and to alleviating and trying to improve the lot of the poor.

Marx may have had the same idea in the first place. But wherever he started from he finished by insisting that the various social classes must struggle even to the death against one another, and that the eventual and inevitable victory of the lower class over the upper classes would abolish poverty.

Soon after the victorious October Revolution in 1917, Lenin reminded the Russian people that cruelty was elementary Marxism; and Stalin's struggle against the Ukrainians was as cruel as any Marxist could wish for.

The repetitive drama of the abolition of poverty in the Ukraine begins with the arrival of political activists and secret police in a village. They summon the inhabitants and call on the poor to denounce the rich. But the interdependence of these country cousins has bridged the gap between the haves and have-nots — anyway nobody has much — and religion has taught that setting man against man is wicked; so they close ranks, as usual in a small community in a crisis, and refuse to co-operate. The intruders therefore have to act not on the votes of the majority or on any democratic principle, but on the advice of the worst, laziest and even criminal element, motivated by jealousy and malice, and sometimes on the word of a single individual or the village idiot.

The scenario above is fact, not fiction.

And the cruelty does not stop when those at whom the finger has been pointed have been shot, and their stores of grain and livestock have been confiscated. For how are the starving survivors with starving children to feed — how are they to continue to be kind and neighbourly?

Ukrainians were reported to have eaten their neighbours.

The idea that such things could not happen here is an illusion. Things as horrible, deriving directly or indirectly from Marxism, have happened almost everywhere in my lifetime.

I can imagine without difficulty the de-kulakisation of Boltbridge: the village or the county cordoned off from the outside world, the arrival of a squad of fanatics commanded by that clerk from the Creedwell Council Offices, and Bob Perry delighted to do the denouncing.

Bob was ostensibly a scrap-metal dealer, and actually a thief, poacher, rustler of farm animals, trouble-maker and drunk, and the father of a brood of hooligans and prostitutes, peddling dope and sex. The Perry family would have jumped at the chance to have a go at those who took exception to it, and a giggle at the expense of more solid citizens.

Not only the lady of the Manor, my bountiful Mama, caught in the act of privately re-distributing her wealth, would be arraigned as a bloated plutocrat and condemned to death. The proportion of the Russian population killed by Communism in its heyday was roughly one third: shooting the richer men and women of Boltbridge, the beneficiaries of the land, farmers and farm-workers, smallholders, tillers of allotments and kitchen gardens, also the owners of houses and cottages, would produce the same sort of result. Then the crops grown, especially the seeds for next year's sowing, and the cattle, sheep, pigs, goats and poultry, would be requisitioned and removed in a convoy of lorries. In due course unscrupulous fighting for food breaks out, and the young and the old die, and the remaining males and finally the females.

I cannot agree with Graham Greene that Philby, who dedicated his life to the service to Marxism-Leninism-Stalinism even as it committed genocide by terror-famine, who was personally responsible for the liquidation of any number of friendly class enemies with his double-dealing, thereby 'earned his right to a rest' in Moscow.

Everybody makes mistakes.

Philby and Co. chose to be traitors in order to serve with apparent loyalty the cause of Communism in the USSR, where nobody believes in it any more, and privilege is rife, and the land is being de-collectivised and the profit motive has been re-introduced and Capitalism called by other names is encouraged. Marx, probably, to allow the old fool the benefit of the doubt, failed to foresee that his theories and his concept of the class struggle would be as destructive as they have been. Freud was wrong to give criminals and liberals the chance to blur the dividing line between good and evil; and inadvertently and in a roundabout way he and Marx together, by helping to create the USSR and absolving it of guilt, by helping to set the homicidal-genocidal example of the USSR which was followed by Nazi Germany, did their fellow-Jews a grave disservice. Lenin, at least, knew he was doing wrong; and Stalin cannot have intended to become the most monstrous of all the monsters of human history. And the poor, the masses, who wished and voted and fought for Communism, and still do so in backward parts of the world, were and are wrong not to appreciate, neither to have drawn the obvious conclusion nor learned, that their fate is to suffer more than any other class from the extremism of radical politics and the trouble it stirs up at home and abroad, and to provide almost all its casualties.

But some mistakes are worse than others. How is Marx to be forgiven for perverting the course of kindness?

My plan was to write the story of the repercussions of his scholarly malevolence.

I cannot. At present I cannot bring myself to think, let alone write, of the agonies of men and women and animals. I feel that I ought not to add by one jot with my jottings to all the cruelty, pain and unhappiness.

MAY

Bᴜᴛ I feel I must record the following.

I was numbed for some days after Dr Ward's telephone call, although, thanks to Gem's strengthening influence, I hope and believe I managed not to sound different when I rang and spoke to Rachel.

Then one night I woke at three o'clock – in the silence of the sleeping town I heard the clocks of the churches of Lewes strike three – and, in a strange manner of speaking, death dawned on me in the dark.

Talking to Dr Ward I had realised my sister could not survive, barring miracles. I had observed Mama dying over the years. I had often seen dead soldiers, if only as a result of accidents. At my age I should have grown accustomed to death. And I have dreaded Rachel's for so long – she has certainly had her revenge on me for frightening her when we were children: why was I not expecting and braced for it?

In the night I woke up fully not just to the final disappointment in store for Rach, but to the facts of death – I mean parting, ending, annihilation, nothingness. And fraternal regrets were soon combined with subjective considerations. What if my own wife were to be sentenced suddenly, unjustly and painfully to die? What if I were to find myself on the brink of the abyss?

And the word that mattered and shattered was not 'if' but 'when'.

How was life to be lived in the shadow of death?

The fact that my thoughts were hackneyed made them no more tolerable. The fear of death: I had read about it over and over again, have known and know people obsessed by it, and thought I comprehended it. But I must be obtuse, or the latest of late developers. Sharing it – suffering from it – was another matter. I could not, and surely would never, get over the discovery that life was a literal dead end.

I had existed in some sort of limbo between present and future: waiting to inherit from my father, then from my mother, marking time in the army, planning to write my book, promising myself that round the next corner or over the horizon I would get the chance to come into my own. What a waste, I said with one breath, meaning I had not given the here and now its due or enjoyed it sufficiently. But with the next breath I asked: how is one to live, if not in hope of starting or finishing some project, passing some test, learning, developing, being better, getting better, recovering, recuperating? And the answer came back that every hope is in imminent danger of being dashed, that one is bound to be interrupted sooner or later, and therefore plans are hardly worth making, intentions are hardly worth having, and what is round that corner and over the horizon is actually and unavoidably a sheer drop into blackness, obliteration and the void.

The preoccupations of the present were futile, I realised, and that very last chance which I had been looking forward to was no chance at all, but death.

The physical effect of such realisations was that I seemed alternately to roast and freeze, and could not rest or lie still, went to the lavatory, tiptoed round the cottage, returned to our bedroom, where Gem still slept peacefully, and left it again. I had to switch on the electric fire in the study, then lean out of the window to cool off in the crisp matutinal air of spring, scented by blossom and ringing with birdsong.

Mama had entertained the idea of death more hospitably than me. She had never noticeably shrunk from it. And my friends, my contemporaries, and the populations of Boltbridge, London, Lewes, of Creedwell and Sussex, provincials, city-slickers, and all those shoppers in High Streets, and strangers and foreigners, everybody clinging to the surface of the spinning earth, apparently they were unafraid. Were they living in blissful ignorance, as I had lived, or were they simply braver? How could they forget? How could they laugh so often and so loud? I envied and admired them.

As for the dead, my dead, and every person who had ever died, who had stepped over the edge, they were heroic.

What was Rachel thinking and feeling?

I had agreed with Dr Ward that she should not be told, if it was possible not to tell her, why her head ached. Dr Ward, again in an attempt to spare her useless alarm, had not given a full account of the relevant test to Jim Claughton.

But Rachel compensates with intuition for what she lacks intellectually. Although she was unlikely to ask for answers she did not want to hear, I suspected that she either had guessed and would soon guess at the truth – no doubt kindly old nature would drop a disagreeable hint or two. And I shuddered, sweating and shivering, on her behalf, at that prospect, because of what I imagined she was going or about to go through, and because she has always been such a sensitive hypochondriacal type.

Moreover she is an activist, not introspective or philosophical, not attuned to death. How was she to bear it? How was I to bear not only it, but her inability to do so?

I had been grateful to Dr Ward, not for the first time, for he had looked after Mama; but in those small hours I inwardly accused him of siding with death, advancing its cause, and coming between me and my sister. Thanks to him, I now had a darker secret to keep from her. Thanks to him, I could no longer pretend not to see that our ways were parting or had already parted, if temporarily.

And a side-effect of his treatment of myself was to induce a sort of schizophrenia. Simultaneously I was for rushing down and consoling Rachel, and for rushing in the opposite direction to escape the ordeal of lying and crying.

The purely practical problems also distressed. When I spoke to Rachel after Dr Ward had spoken to me, I suggested a visit to Boltbridge. She hedged. She procrastinated. She seemed to be more averse than usual to our meeting. How was I to force an entry into her home without putting ideas into her poor head and even scaring her to death? How, from a distance of two hundred miles, was I to make sure she was being properly cared for?

Pacing the floor of my study roused Cindy, who sleeps in a basket on the landing at the top of the stairs. She stalked in, yawned, stretched and wagged her tail, surprise in her black eyes behind the springy arcs of fur that I should be up and about in the early morning. She looked at me and licked my bare foot with sympathy – although only dog-lovers would believe that the gesture was sympathetic.

The canine cure-all was somehow curative in my case. I stroked her rough coat, while she gazed deeply into my eyes as if with encouragement. She reminded me that God's creatures are wonderful, so much so that it would be a pity and a shame to confine their existence to a single short span.

I stroked and patted Cindy, and prayed for life after death, and that Rach would be happier in heaven than she had been on earth, and that we were all due to be reunited with our dear ones and our dogs in eternity.

I REMEMBER, when I was young and recently commissioned in the army, going to offer condolences to the next of kin, the sister, of a Hussar killed in an accident in a tank on a training exercise. I forget her name; but she was an impressively dignified married woman of thirty or so, who said she would never get over it, and politely dismissed my jejune references to time that heals and to the bright side, and showed me out of her house. I thought she was exaggerating, and reported back to my C.O. that she would come to terms with her loss. Youth cannot comprehend the blow or setback from which there is no recovery.

Last month, notwithstanding Gem's and Cindy's help, it was my turn to feel I would never get over saying goodbye to Rach if I had to – or get over death introducing itself so pushily to me. My fancy was to change the name of the cottage from Hope to Hopeless. I had neither the heart nor the stomach to record our life in Lewes, to meet our friends or summon any interest in their doings, or stroll along to collect the evening paper and have a chat with Jahendra and his and my Uncle. At last I saw eye to jaundiced eye with the editor of *The Clarion*.

I just cringed in my study, trying to organise notes for my book by transferring them into this journal, and then coming to the conclusion that I would not want, let alone be able, to write it.

April is my favourite month; and this last April was marred by nothing except my mood. Earlier every morning the sun rose over Mount Caburn in a water-coloured sky, and swung round to set in a blaze of glory, and later every evening, behind Ditchling Beacon. The nights were positively vulgar with their stars like too many diamonds. And gardens bloomed, and trees blossomed, and birds sang and mated and nested, and I kept on thinking of Rachel and what she would soon be missing, and of how many joys there were for all of us to miss sooner or later. I sighed contrarily for meteorological conditions filthy enough to enable me to find consolation in the phrase: might as well be dead.

But Gem steadfastly refused to accept that her sister-in-law's cause was lost, and the other member of my household, Cindy, was and is interested in death only inasmuch as she aspires to mete it out to cats and rabbits. They would not sink to the level of my low spirits, and took me on their walks along the South Downs Way, the immemorial path high and dry on the ridge of the chalk hills round here.

We love the names of the hamlets that seek shelter in the lee of the Downs, Firle, Littledene, Tilton, Alciston. The dwelling called Bo-Peep by the cart-track which once connected Brighton and Eastbourne must have been inhabited by a shepherdess. The South Downs Way closely follows the coastline in places, at Seaford Head and Beachy Head for instance, then meanders inland. The scenery it has to show is various, but always magnificent: the white cliffs dear to popular songwriters and native sons and daughters coming home to this old country, our silver sea and the ships that sail it, the range of receding hilltops, and, stretching into the blue northern distance, the great flat low-lying weald of south-east England, the 'wald' or forest fraught with peril which our forefathers avoided if they could – where their descendants pay exorbitant prices to live.

Sheep graze fairly safely in upland pastures they have to share with walkers like ourselves, ramblers and tourists, and dogs like Cindy and others larger and even less obedient. Blasé cattle chew the cud. Occasional fields are ploughed and are now sprouting green, and the landscape below is bright with the flowering of the hawthorn trees in hedgerows and spinneys.

Were pilgrims able to reach Canterbury via the South Downs Way? I identified with faithful pilgrims to the extent of relying on the intervention, or if the worst came to the worst putting my trust in the promises, of the divinity.

We often took something to eat with us and walked for hours measured not by the chiming of clocks but the songs of larks. The salty air from the sea, provided it was not trying to blow us over, and the bounce in the cropped turf seemed to render us inexhaustible. At last, more because we were hungry than tired, we would find a secluded vantage point and devour sandwiches and apples. And then again, perhaps at seven in the evening, having driven home and briefly put our feet up, we would sally forth to wander round the town.

One such perambulation took us through the Caves of Eastover to Southover. We passed another Hope Cottage, as picturesque as ours but smaller, and inspected the municipalised Grange Garden with its official lines of flowers. And we proceeded by Grange Road and the steep twitten in Rotten Row to St Anne's Church and its churchyard.

Notwithstanding the eyesore of the nearby Council Offices, erected on the wrong site, to the wrong scale and in the wrong style a decade or so ago, and having to look out across a carpark to Newhaven, we were not disappointed by the view of the long blue valley and the tombs and monuments, lichened, set amongst spring flowers, and providing platforms and perches from which blackbirds warbled and trilled their sunset challenges.

On a miniature gravestone by the lych-gate I read the mysterious inscription: 'Here lieth the body of Little Benjamin The Ruler died 1717' – and was moved almost to shed a tear for Benjamin whoever he was and whatever he ruled before he was laid to rest in his child's grave, and for my little sister.

But at the farther end of the churchyard I came across the burial ground of the Medhursts. I had heard or read about the misfortunes in the last century of the Medhurst family. Samuel Medhurst was a millwright with premises close to St Anne's in Western Road, he made water-wheels which provided the power to mill grain, and he married a certain Philadelphia. The rest of the story is told by means of the individualistic funerary furnishings he chose, which resemble low cast-iron goalposts, two or three feet high, with the wording embossed on the rusty crossbars. Samuel and Philadelphia's eldest child, another Samuel, died when he was nine months old; their second, another Philadelphia, at four months; their third, Margaret, at ten months; their fourth, Benjamin, at six months; their fifth, Naomi, lived for three years; but Reuben and Frank survived for only eight and eighteen months respectively. The last three of their ten children, Ruth, Boaz and Mark, reached the ages of twenty-two, thirty-six and thirty-eight. Philadelphia died aged seventy-five in 1884, and Samuel aged eighty-eight in 1887.

What was my justification, my excuse, for crying as it were before I was hurt, because I might lose Rachel one day and Gem on another, if they had not already lost me, and because I myself would have to do as Mama and Father and every other man, woman and organism had done since God created Adam — what right had I to cry and complain, considering the mortal blows the Medhursts had to bear even in extreme old age, the ten children they buried and mourned, and the sixty-six million Russians who were not permitted by Marxism to die of natural causes or with dignity?

My BIRTHDAY falls on the twenty-fifth of this month of May; and Gem advanced the idea that we ought to throw an evening party to celebrate my survival for three score years, to show appreciation of the hospitality and entertainment we have enjoyed in Lewes, and say farewell or au revoir to the natives. No doubt she was also hoping to cheer me up. The party would have to be postponed until June, when she would have had time to plan and prepare the festive board: but did that matter?

No, I said. I trust I was grateful enough. But I wondered whether Rachel would be dead or alive by the date in June that Gem had in mind.

One afternoon in the encouraging weather I returned to the paper shop.

After warm mutual greetings, and while Jahendra served sweetmeats to schoolchildren, I chatted with my Uncle in a sort of bower of pornographic magazines.

How was Madam, he asked. Well, I thanked him and

232

Providence – and how was his wife – or should I call her Aunt? Very fine, he sniggered in reply.

'Have you been away, Mr Loftus, have you been on holiday?'

'No, Uncle – busy – and my sister's ill.'

He jiggled his head in a gesture indicative of sympathy, and enquired: 'How many sisters, sir, do you have?'

'One only.'

'And brothers, allow me to ask?'

'None.'

'I am so sorry for you.'

'My sister may get better,' I added in defiance of his undertaker's tone of voice. 'And she isn't all that bad.'

He said: 'I am glad,' but still seemed to regard me pityingly through his horn-rims.

He then voiced his afterthought and, probably, explained the over-population of Asia: 'But it is not nice to have no more sisters or brothers.'

I changed the subject.

'You know we're leaving Lewes at the end of July, Uncle?'

His reaction reminded me of Victorian tragedies on the stage: 'Ah – so soon?'

'My wife wants to give a party before we go. But I don't know if I can face any social occasion with my sister in poor health.'

'We have to live, sir.'

'That's true.'

'We always must do what needs doing. Mrs Loftus is very polite and kind.'

'Uncle, would you and your wife come to our party, and Jahendra and his wife?'

'Oh, thank you, sir. Thank you and Mrs Loftus, please, sir. We will talk it over. We will think it over, if you permit. But we are most grateful, believe me.'

He detained me as I made a move to depart: 'Mr Loftus, we have something to tell you, and we have something to ask, if you can spare a half-minute. We have waited, and could wait till another day, if you are hurried.'

I was not, and said so.

'We have received information from the police that the boy who broke our plate-glass window has been caught,' he announced.

After expressing gratification I enquired: 'Who is the boy, or what is he? You suspected he was a racialist and political bully. And you were afraid the arm of the law would prove to be short.'

'I was not right, sir. The police have been impartial and efficient, and the boy is nine years old – he is already on probation for stealing. I was too hasty in my judgment. It is a mistake to fear the worst.'

Although the last aphoristic admission may not have been aimed at me, it applied to my situation, and beneficially.

He continued: 'We must still take precautions – vote correctly, as you advised us – and we shall change our name. We wonder – have you thought of which name we should change it to?'

My answer was apologetically negative. The truth, which I did not tell, was that I had quite forgotten about the nominal naturalisation of the Patels.

Uncle squirmed with embarrassment verbally as well as physically: 'We would not offend you, sir, we would do nothing to offend Mrs Loftus, and we cannot know if we are acting properly or impertinently, it is unknown except by trial and error, but we would assure you that our question is the sign of our respect – we are respecting you by asking very humbly if you would allow us to take your name.'

I was startled. I said without exaggerating that I was honoured, and thus at least changed Uncle's anxious expression into white smiles of relief. But I added that I needed a little time in which to think over his suggestion and talk it over, just as he did in connection with our party.

My reluctance mainly related to complications that might

arise from the proliferation of Loftuses in Lewes if we should ever come and live here.

Uncle seemed to have confidence that neither colour nor creed were behind my hesitation. He extended his small brown hand and gave mine the tiniest politest squeeze of gratitude, meanwhile chattering to Jahendra in their own language.

Jahendra said how sorry he was to hear my sister was ill and that I was brotherless, and added with a broad consolatory smile: 'But we could carry on your family name for you.'

More compliments and professions of goodwill were tossed to and fro, as in some battle of flowers, until at last I managed to beat a retreat.

Gem was amused that anyone should think it necessary to ask our permission to become a Loftus, to which name we owned nothing like a copyright, and even more so by my exercise of some assumed prerogative to grant or not to grant such a permit.

A day or two later we received an answer to our letter to the Whitakers.

We had written to Toby and Jane to propose a permanent swap of our flat in Harrington for Hope Cottage: qualified valuers could ensure it was a fair exchange.

They are against it. They are right: if we thought otherwise we would not have made the proposal.

Fortunately for us in these past nine months, unfortunately in the longer term, Eastover is an extremely popular place to live in. Houses are expensive, and at present there seems to be nothing for sale we would like to buy and could afford.

Gem is not attracted to any other area of Lewes. We both quail before the prospect of a complete residential upheaval including a move into strange surroundings. Hope Cottage, which we have got to know and love, would have been different. In our cosy corner formed by River Road and Rickman's Lane we have always felt at home.

It therefore looks as if our sojourn in Sussex really is coming to an end.

I told the Patels that we had no objection to their changing their names to ours by deed-poll.

Gem wanted to know if I was going to issue them with a pseudo-monarchical warrant to supply our newspapers; and she reminded me that we would have to start asking other guests to our party.

BERTHA, HAVING ascertained that Mrs Spedding feels she is not fit for parties and will not be coming to ours, has volunteered to help us. Bertha's compassionate attitude to an old acquaintance, invalid and neighbour is expressed in pithy terms: 'I'm not skivvying for that common woman.'

Yesterday the list of ready and willing guests, who have accepted our invitations, was as follows: the senior Cads, Foxy and Guy; the junior Cads, Peter and Monica; George and Madge Drewett and Reggie; Graham Phipps-Hullett; and the Reverends, Crispin Peterson plus Mrs Peterson, and Father Byrne – surely the first of the theological lessons dinned into the clergy is never to reject manna from heaven.

This morning we decided to drop a few more invitation cards, and ring the odd doorbell if we dared. The weather tempted me from my study: a milk and water mist was evaporating in the spring sunshine.

Wendy Aylward accepted after checking dates in her diary: she will be ushering at Glyndebourne for three nights a week throughout the Festival. She pretended to be frightened to death by the possibility of having to miss our fun, thanked effusively and then begged us: please do not go back to London and please do come to the opera. But the latter request is as utopian as the former, since, as she admitted, there is not a single ticket to be had at any price.

We penetrated deep into the Caves of Eastover, where Gregory Leplay and Charles Hart live in a warehouse they have converted into a desirable residence. In their pretty front garden we met Charles wheeling his basketwork trolley towards the shops. Gregory, who wore a pale pink shirt and white slacks, was training clematis to grow round pillars of wire he had personally designed. They were welcoming, swore we were not intruding on their privacy and that they simply pined for our party, and insisted on showing us round their home, as they had intended to for ages. A fat black tomcat basked in the sun on the garden path. They called it Oscar: because it was wild, they claimed.

Gregory conducted our tour of the interior. On the surface his relationship with Charles is somewhat retrogressively reminiscent of that between the stern pedagogue and the naughty pupil who is bottom of the class. They squabbled over the dates of almost every piece of furniture in the house, and appealed to us to settle their petty disputes. We took refuge in our ignorance: we were anyway blinded by the science of their references to late fourteenth, mid-seventeenth, belle époque, fin de siècle.

Their good taste verges on the ghastly. Gregory lectured us about mineral colours mixed with scumble glaze on walls, and vegetable dyes subtly tinting curtains and covers, and the pickling of wood. Charles interrupted and interjected irrelevant observations, and giggled and grimaced at us when he was reprimanded. Eventually he bustled off to prepare elevenses: his appearance is more fiery than his housewifely temperament, thank goodness.

Gregory's decorative handiwork merits praise and received it from us, notwithstanding touches of vulgarity, for instance orange cut velvet on a lavatory seat. And how could he have named the place Wares House?

Coffee was served under an Italianate loggia in the cramped back garden. The chairs we sat on, the mugs we drank out of, and the modish artefacts indoors had all been designed either by Gregory, Charles swanked vicariously, or by a BF – best friend – of theirs, Martin, who was soon coming to stay in order to do work at Glyndebourne.

Gregory hoped we were getting to Glyndebourne before we rode away into the metropolitan sunset.

We replied regretfully in the negative and referred to our conversation with Wendy.

'Oh but Martin should be good for a couple of seats,' Charles said.

Gem denied that we wanted to be a nuisance; I modified her fib by suggesting that for being a nuisance we were prepared to bankrupt ourselves; Gregory, who is successful and well-to-do, declared that money was beside the point; Charles chipped in that anyone who had not been to Glyndebourne had not lived; and in a flurry of thanks and handshakes we took our leave and moved on, walking round the corner to the Edwardian bungalow inhabited by Octavia Pritchett.

The beggar was not roosting – Octavia was out.

But Marian Travers down in Flood Street was in with her lodger surely in every sense. He is the Glyndebourne singer from Austria, Hans-Peter Vilans, nicknamed by Charles Hart H. P. Sauce in consideration partly of his initials and partly of the gossipy supposition that he has already taken advantage of his landlady.

Marian admitted us and introduced us to Hans-Peter, who is thirtyish, bearded, stout, hearty, and, as Foxy confided in Gem the other day, huggable. He makes jokes that are fey and facetious in mangled English.

Upstairs in the first-floor sitting-room adjacent to the Hookes', the charge of huggability seemed to be proven. Hans-Peter slumped in a chair, while Marian was handsomer than ever with burnished hair and luminous complexion, and her glistening shaded eyes must have been set in her face by the smutty finger of sexual satisfaction. And she laughed loudly at Hans-Peter's witticisms, the best of which was his presumption that Gem and I were a Mr and Mrs Love-

238

us from Pope Cottage and representatives of the Roman Catholic Church.

We had to ask him to our party, too.

Incidentally, although I do not approve of George Drewett's slanderous and jealous joke, I could not help remembering it with secret amusement. George said that Marian always sleeps with her operatic lodgers and that she and the opera house come into season together.

We then knocked with some trepidation on Betsy Hooke's door. We had not seen Betsy since her dramatic arrival at the Cads' wedding reception − like the Messenger in a classical Greek play − bearing the bad news that Brian had deserted her to elope with Tracy Wilkins; but word of her eccentric behaviour had reached our ears.

In the fullness of time she opened the door a crack; said 'Oh it's you' without audible pleasure; and unfastened the chain, but stood her ground in the doorway, barring entry.

I enquired: 'How are you, Betsy?'

'That should be obvious.'

It was: she was grey all over − hair, face, cardigan, skirt and clumsy trainers. And the lenses of her glasses were so grubby as to look grey.

Gem told her about the party.

'Who else are you asking?'

We named names.

'Patels? Who are the Patels?'

'They're the people from the paper shop.'

'Oh yes − but why do you want them in your house?'

Hypocrite, I thought, recalling the anti-racist posters in the window of her ground-floor front room.

I also thought and would have liked to say: you preach free love, yet when your husband loves freely and publicly you go more to pieces than Wendy Aylward, whom you criticise for feeling sad in the same situation.

'Have you told everyone that you've invited your newsagents?' she demanded.

'We have,' I replied.

'What did the Cads say – and the Drewetts?'

'They were delighted.'

I felt my exaggeration was legitimised by her prejudice.

'Oh well!' She sulked for a second or two. 'Is Octavia coming?'

We hoped so.

She burst out: 'Sorry to be choosy! But I'm getting the message that Brian's either having or has had affairs with most of the women for miles around. I'd rather not think of what's been going on, and I don't know where I stand or who to trust. Octavia's the one person I can rely on absolutely. Maybe I'll come to your party with Octavia.'

We made encouraging noises, which were not altogether sincere, then asked her to pass on an invitation to Jeremiah.

'Jeremiah!' she repeated or exclaimed with a sob in her voice. 'He's gone as crazy as his father. Now he wears suits, and he's trying to get a job in a stockbroker's office in London. He wants to leave home and make money. I don't know what the world's coming to. He used to be my friend and ally. All right – yes – if he should condescend to talk to me I'll tell him. And thanks – sorry – goodbye!' And she slammed the door in our faces.

Betsy has joined not only the Injured Wives Association, but the I.M.C. to boot, the Injured Mothers Club.

ON THE twenty-fourth of May Gem rang Rachel and suggested a day trip to Boltbridge on the following day. Rachel said yes, possibly because she was surprised by the shortness of the notice and could think of no excuse. Thus they planned my birthday treat – or birthday trial.

Gem was unrepentant when I wondered if she had done the right thing. She said she had taken matters into her own hands since ours, Rachel's and mine, seemed to be tied by our contrary reluctance to cause or be caused excessive emotion. She said she loved Rachel, was tired of talking to her on the telephone, and determined to see her even if I was not. And why regard the reunion as a trial? Reality is often less bad to experience than to imagine, she philosophised; and she hoped I would feel none the worse for having had a cup of tea with my sister.

It took four and half hours' driving to get there, and I grew increasingly agitated. For Rachel to have to give us tea, and a birthday tea at that, might be the last straw. And she had been saddled with the difficulty of getting rid of her husband for the afternoon: she would not want one of my happy returns to be a quarrel with my brother-in-law.

We arrived at five o'clock. The front door was unlocked as usual, and we walked in. Rachel was asleep on the sofa in the sitting-room.

It was an awful shock. It was so untypical of her high-strung temperament and hospitable instincts to sleep when she expected visitors. Her thinness – hands like birds' feet – was also shocking. A tray-table covered with a white cloth stood by the sofa.

She woke, smiled up at us, stifled a yawn and said that one of her pills was sleepifying. We all embraced, and she removed the cloth from the tray-table, revealing a plate of my favourite sandwiches and an iced birthday cake, and we trooped into the kitchen to brew the tea.

Back in the sitting-room, perhaps unaccountably, I ate more than my share of the sandwiches, which seemed especially delicious, made of new brown bread and chopped hard-boiled egg and mayonnaise and mustard and cress. The cake too was perfection, sponge with soft shiny coffee icing.

Rachel was much changed, but, so far as I could see now she was awake, to a lesser extent physically than in other ways – emotionally or spiritually, I suppose I mean.

The unwontedness of her behaviour was not confined to her cat-nap. She had woken calmly. She had neither leapt to her feet at the sight of us, nor accused herself with multiple apologies of heinous social crime; and I could not believe that her calmness was wholly chemical.

No – she was relaxed – released. For some reason she was more relaxed than she had been to my knowledge since falling ill: the confusion, panic and misery, which had grated against my nerves and sympathies, were no more.

She wished me the happiest birthday; she was so pleased we had come; and were we really going to live in Lewes; and how was I getting on with my book?

Her wide blue eyes were receptive, and her attention did not wander. I was not struggling against the undertow of her semi-suppressed preoccupations. It was as if we were children again, undamaged by time, buoyed up by confidence and curiosity. The westerly sun poured into the sitting-room with its vases of fresh spring flowers. Her new mood was infectious: for the moment I forgot to be afraid. We sat there chatting and laughing, and the alternative to ever doing so again was unthinkable.

Just before six o'clock she offered to show us her garden, and I wondered if a miracle was indeed occurring, and could and would occur.

But in the embrasure of the french window she stumbled, nearly collapsed, and, when I rushed to the rescue and was helping her to recover herself, she said: 'Oh Huge!' – in a tone of disturbingly rueful resignation.

'Can I hang on to you?' she asked, linking her bony arm in mine. 'My feebleness is funny.'

Somewhere, while we were in the garden, a clock chimed six. It reminded us of a game we played when we were young: walking to the point on the main road equidistant from Boltbridge and East Boltbridge, and trying to hear the church clocks of both places striking the hour. Windy days were no good, likewise rain, mist or a heavy atmosphere. Late afternoons or early evenings in spring were best, dry still evenings such as this one, after the farmworkers had gone home to tea and before the songbirds began their serenade.

Rachel mentioned the young vicar who had recently arrived to minister to the two Boltbridge congregations. She told us his name, Victor Holt.

'Victor's been kind to me.'

'Do you see much of him?'

'No. But I like his sermons. And he's driven me round, so that I can show him the lie of the land.'

'Is he married?'

'Courting – he's engaged to a good girl called Fay. He's brought her to lunch here a couple of times. They're very happy – it's touching.'

'Is Victor as kind to you as you've obviously been to him, feeding him and tucking him under your wing?'

She laughed.

'What happens to Jim when Victor brings Fay to lunch?'

'Jim goes racing or plays golf on most days.'

'Where is he today?'

'Racing.'

'How kind has he been, Rach?'

'Not unkind – he's trying to help – he's had a lot to put up with. Don't worry. There's nothing to worry about, that's the point.'

As she discussed the flowers in the garden with Gem, particularly the roses we gave her last Christmas, I reflected that our roles were again reversed. She was comforting me. She was making me feel that I was the younger one. Was she teaching me the lesson she had been taught in the likeable sermons of Victor Holt: that whether or not we survive is not our business? My fugitive hopes were superficial. The whole point was to cease to fret, to be thankful we were alive and together, and have faith in the future.

Rachel had surely won the ultimate game with clocks, for she seemed to be hearing the chimes of a sort of eleventh hour from this world and the next.

243

'Shall we go in?' she suggested.

Gem said: 'We ought to leave you. How do you manage in the evenings, cooking supper – and getting breakfast for that matter?'

Rachel explained that Mrs Haddon looked after everything: 'I'm so lucky.'

She added: 'You've a long drive home, haven't you?'

She did not attempt to detain us. No doubt she was tired, and dreading the strain of an encounter between her brother and her husband. But I think she was being unselfish.

We kissed goodbye.

I enquired: 'Are your headaches better?' I could not go without showing any interest in her welfare.

'I'm all right,' she replied, looking straight in my eyes. 'Honestly!'

The telephone rang and we parted.

Now, in spite of the reassurance and the ambiguities, I keep on asking myself: how can she be so gallant? How is she, how are we, to bear our fate? How did six million Jews and sixty-six million Russians bear theirs? How are we not to cower paralytically before tyranny and death?

JUNE

GEM TOOK her courage in her hands and bought me a tie for my birthday.

She bought it some time ago, back in March, a day or two after Peter Cadwallader's wedding, from Caleb Hocking, where she was surprised by the smiling service and general joviality of the proprietors, notwithstanding the fact that Brian Hooke, who is married and middle-aged and so on, had just run off with their daughter in the Sabine sense.

We had to agree with Bertha that Naomi and Bert Wilkins were pleased to apply the criteria of shopkeepers rather than the ethics of average parents to the romantic adventure.

Anyway, needless to say, at least to say to men, I decided I would not be seen dead in the tie selected by my dear one, and returned to Caleb Hocking to exchange it yesterday afternoon.

Once more an atmosphere of uncommercial gloom pervaded the shop. Bert displayed his range of ties with resentment, and Naomi, scowling behind the till in her glass compartment, was so unlike herself as to make a mistake in my favour over money.

I told Gem and together we wondered: what catastrophe so much more serious than getting embroiled with Brian Hooke could now have befallen their beautiful daughter and beloved only child?

Bertha put a stopper on speculation by telling us this morning that Tracy has come home – and in one piece: by which she meant, as country folk do, not in two pieces, herself plus baby.

We suppose that Naomi and Bert are contrarily gloomy because they do not like to have goods returned under any circumstances.

Whether or not the vile seducer has followed his victim's example, where he has slunk to, and what effect the end of the affair will have on Betsy and Jeremiah, and on our party, remains to be seen.

Preparations for the party gather momentum day by day: I have signed cheque after cheque to prove it. Bertha spends extra hours here. The cottage is chock-a-block with hired chairs and tables, napery, cutlery, china and glasses. A dipsomaniac could not ask for more booze than we have stocked up with. The number of guests seems to be twenty or so, not counting Hookes.

My Uncle has refused: but refusal is far too harsh a description of his abstruse indication that he and his family would not be joining us. He reverted to the subject, as I had broached it, amongst those pornographic magazines. He stood and spoke with extreme delicacy in front of glossy photos of the private parts of lewd females.

'So thankful for your very kind invitation, Mr Loftus. Please to say thank you to Mrs Loftus, sir. My family is most excited to hear you have asked us into your home. We have all thought how jolly we will be in your company. It is unlucky that Jahendra's second child is studying for examinations. His father and mother help with homework, you see, sir. We all help one another. Everything is better that way. I hope you will understand and accept our gratitude.'

Jahendra was more direct: 'Truly sorry we can't make it. But thanks a lot.'

Gem's regret was tempered with relief that she did not have to cater for an unknown quantity of Patels of all ages, even if they are about to become Loftuses.

She is nonetheless suffering qualms, which are catching,

mainly on account of the weather. If we have to have our party indoors, she declares in the accents of quiet desperation, we shall be done for: Hope Cottage simply cannot accommodate a score and more of guests – they would not pack into the ground floor like sardines, let alone as persons requiring and trying to get at the food and drink. Her plan is – or was – to have three tables seating four apiece in the backyard, one in the sitting-room and another in the hall, and to serve edibles and liquid refreshments in the kitchen. A dry night is therefore of the essence – and rain has fallen almost uninterruptedly for the last ten days. Flaming June, we swear at each other as we watch the drain in River Road for the first sign of flooding.

But the weather still has thirty-six hours in which to relent. Besides, should it decide not to, all is far from lost in my opinion, since a social gathering is nothing if it is not a scrum.

Actually I feel we are threatened by a situation more embarrassing than meteorology, although Gem is inclined to giggle at it. Octavia Pritchett has put us in a position that is already bad and could become much worse. She rang last night to tell us about Brian Hooke – that she has been harbouring him and proposes to bring him to the party.

I answered the telephone and the conversation ran roughly as follows.

'Hullo! Octavia here. Can you keep a secret?'

I ought not to have boasted that I could.

'Well, I've had Brian in residence for a week.'

An exclamation of surprise escaped me, which clearly annoyed her. I expect she has a sexual inferiority complex, and suspected me of assuming that her couch must be chaste.

She grated: 'Brian's a very old friend of mine.'

'Of course – naturally – yes!'

Thus I hurriedly withdrew the modern insult of hinting that a woman is unlikely to be an adulteress.

'Well,' she pursued, 'he is included in your do, isn't he?'

I explained my hesitation: 'I was just thinking of Betsy, Octavia.'

'What about Betsy?'

'The other day she told us that you're the one person she trusts. In fact she was hoping to be escorted to our party by yourself. Isn't she going to be surprised if you turn up with her husband instead? Won't she be shocked to discover he's been hiding in your house, not to mention the shock of suddenly seeing him again after weeks of separation? Shouldn't they get together in private?'

Octavia cut in sharply: 'And instead of asking questions, shouldn't you answer mine?'

I lost my head and had to enquire: 'Sorry – forgive me – but what was your question?'

'You won't raise objections to having Brian in your home, will you?'

'No –'

'Fair enough,' she interrupted me and rang off.

Gem takes a fatalistic view of things to come in the context above. She is sure that exhibitionistic Brian will want to arrive at our party as it were with the extra scalp of Octavia in hand; and equally sure that Octavia will not want to miss her probably last chance to prove to the whole little world of Lewes, as to us, that she has had a man in her bed – and where else would Brian sleep in her doll's house?

Tonight is the night; and in typically British style we are more worried by the weather than by sex – I refer to the rain and the Pritchett-Hooke imbroglio.

Over breakfast we pondered the problem of Cindy's refuge from the revels. We had hoped to settle her in my study; but if people are packed together too tightly on the ground floor they will be forced upstairs, and will open doors, my study's for instance, releasing the dog to run downstairs and out of the house and into the road and under the proverbial bus.

Bertha's proposed solution was to take Cinders along to her cottage for the duration.

'But she'll eat your Minnie and your Winnie, Bertha – thanks all the same,' Gem said.

'No, she won't,' Bertha replied. 'My Minnie's safe in heaven. She was very old and she was ailing, she always was a sickly thing, so I put her out of her misery. I love animals, and they know it, that's why they love me.'

'What do you mean, Bertha – did you personally put her out of her misery? What did you do to her?'

'No – it was the vet – but I paid him. I used the money you've given me for helping with this party – that's what I had Minnie done with.'

'Oh.' Gem was nonplussed by the charge that she had financed the execution. 'When did it happen? Why didn't you tell us?'

'Least said soonest mended,' Bertha returned, and aggravated the offence of her sententiousness by tapping her forehead and adding: 'Empty vessels make most noise' – a boast about the extent of her own grey matter.

'Yes, but when?'

'Last Saturday, before I went Old Tyme Dancing.'

'I'm so sorry.'

'Well, I'm not downhearted – I never let anything get me down. I must have been born under a happy star,' Bertha simpered.

'At any rate,' Gem commented briskly, 'you've still got Winnie – although you might not have her if she was shut in with Cindy for four or five hours.'

'Winnie's gone too.'

'What?'

'Winnie's with Minnie.'

'But Winnie was quite young and in a good state of health.'

249

'Minnie and Winnie were such close friends I didn't like to part them. It cost me extra to persuade the vet I was right. In the end he came round to seeing things my way. People usually do. And I'm grateful to you for making it possible for me to pay the double vet's bill. And I haven't missed the dogs one little bit. No – I feel ever so free without them.'

What could we say? Disapproval was pointless. If wise saws were the order of the day, the one applicable would have been: Too late, too late, the rabbit's on the plate.

The happy hard-heartedness of the mistress of the dear departed was gruesomely funny; and we had to present a united front to the advancing horde of our guests.

It stopped raining and the sun shone from midday onwards. The evening was perfect: air and light washed clean, high cloudless sky of a greenish-pink hue, no wind, and warm enough to sit and eat out of doors. Flowers, wearing pearls of moisture, held up their heads and began to look their crepuscular best. Swallows and house-martins celebrated above, and swifts shrilled and swooped through the improved aerial conditions.

We shut Cindy in my study after all, and were ready for the fray by eight o'clock.

Wendy Aylward was the first to arrive, and not the last to say we were lucky with the weather.

She asked us if Graham Phipps-Hullett was definitely expected, and remarked with a wounded giggle that he had recently been playing hard to get. Privately I guessed he was still wondering if she had tried to poison him with seaweed and suspect oysters.

Wendy wore a little black dress with girlish frills and a lot of white face-powder. She really is a good sort, and would be more attractive if only she could forget she was born a Wilson-Firth and remember that belly-aching was never part of the sirens' song.

The ecumenical trio of the Reverend Crispin Peterson and his reproductive rib, and Father Byrne, came next. The mother of the Peterson progeny is called Rosalie: in the course of the evening I managed to address her as Rosemary, Rosalind and Rosa. She raised no objections. She is not objectionable in any sense. The Peterson's marriage looks as if it was made in heaven not only because of his godly calling, but also because they so complement each other physically. He is lean and keen, she is plump and passive – he is the knife and she the butter; she is a sweet slob, a marshmallow, blessed for the poorness of her spirit, blessed at least with increase.

Father Byrne refused wine and asked for whisky with which to wet his pre-prandial whistle. Was he sticking to the rule about a hair of the dog that had already bitten him? While he showed none of the symptoms of intoxication, the breath he exhaled had considerable alcoholic content. I assumed he had been at some sort of cocktail party, or that he had shared a loving cup with Mrs Samson.

But as if to excuse his request for strong liquor he announced: 'I've been administering the last rites to a parishioner.'

Again it struck me that Father Byrne, his vows of celibacy notwithstanding, is on better terms with the flesh and the devil than Crispin Peterson, who begets a baby a year. Another surprising thing about him is the combination of his ugliness, pig eyes, purple nose, black and broken teeth, and his humorous charm.

The Petersons were draining their second glasses of wine by the time I had fetched the first glass of whisky. They are hungry and thirsty guests, whence their local nickname, the Hoovers. Possibly for religious, but probably for financial reasons, they practise strict asceticism at home: Wendy, who was once invited in for a meal, returned to tell horror-stories of bowls of rice posing as risotto and tap-water to wash it down.

Graham Phipps-Hullett oddly enough in flasher's mack-intosh, and equipped with a telescopic umbrella in a slip-case, had to bend almost double in order not to bump his head on our low doorways and ceilings.

Father Byrne quoted at him, indicating the umbrella: 'O thou of little faith!'

He received the pedantic rejoinder: 'I'm temperamentally more inclined to be safe than sorry, Father.'

'But there's no safety in this world, my son.'

Graham divested himself and hastened dutifully to kiss the cheek of Wendy; beamed at Gem – 'What a splendid occasion!'; greeted the Petersons – 'I trust your little ones flourish!'; and when I had handed him a glass of red wine, thanked me for blushful hippocrene.

Glyndebourne as usual bobbed up in the conversation. Graham paid Wendy the compliment of hoping the institution would not collapse utterly without her support. Rosalie Peterson emerged from her maternal lethargy to observe: 'Oh I do love opera.' Crispin Peterson said he was trying to get a Glyndebourne singer to perform free of charge on behalf of some quixotic charity – Peace Studies in the Middle East, I think it was. Father Byrne made a clerical pleasantry to the effect that his prayer for a seat for *Figaro* had never been heard.

At this point the Drewett gang, Madge, George, Reggie, and Monica and Peter Cadwallader, also Foxy and Guy of that ilk, breezed in – or should I say squeezed? The presence of so many people in our front hall verged on immorality.

'Come out,' Gem pleaded. 'Come into the garden!'

The Drewetts had broken the journey of five hundred yards from Downscene to Hope Cottage at Cadwallader Place.

Reggie flashed his eyes like lighthouses at us and explained: 'We stopped off at the watering-hole in Wharf Road,' and George corrected him with his hamster-like grin: 'There's water, water everywhere in the vicinity of Wharf

Road and not a drop in the drinks at Cads' Pad.'

Madge drawled more emphatically than ever: 'Har are the gangsters, dar,' and Foxy played fast and loose with her teeth.

Guy bowed low for a joke and had a rush of blood to the head and reeled around: which tickled everyone. Peter smirked and silently mouthed bonhomous greetings, and Monica used her unborn baby as a battering-ram to force a passage through the crowd.

Bertha served more wines and spirits to gangsters in the kitchen, and the doorbell rang again.

Gregory Leplay in a floor-length off-white kaftan, and Charles Hart in a black suit striped with silver foil, stood on the doorstep.

Their costumes were good for the customary laugh. Reggie salaamed to the kaftan. Foxy lifted it to peep underneath and objected: 'Not fair, Gregwah, you've got trousers on!' Guy said to him: 'I don't half care for your parlez-vous,' and Madge, pretending to think he had said something vulgar as well as inane, proclaimed in what was more a drool than a drawl: 'They're dirty old gangsters, dar – I told you so!'

Out in the garden Madge caught sight of Father Byrne and vice versa. She drooled: 'My Dadda!' He responded: 'Child of mine!' And they embraced in a clownishly abandoned fashion.

Then Father Byrne went a bit far by asking: 'Gregory, is that a shroud you've got on you? And are you the undertaker, Charles? Well, here's the very man to finish the job' – patting the head anointed with hair-oil of Crispin Peterson, who joined in the general laughter indecisively, no doubt wondering whether or not he was being ensnared in some devious Popish plot.

Father Byrne went further still by comparing Charles in his suit with its shiny metallic stripes to a printed circuit.

Charles blushed a redder shade of red and spat at him

under his breath: 'Delilah!' – an epithet new to me and amusingly inapposite, alluding, as was explained to me later, to the hairlessness of Father Byrne's housekeeper and companion Mrs Samson.

Bertha showed three more arrivals through the kitchen french window: Marian Travers and her nextdoor neighbour Betsy Hooke and her lodger Hans-Peter Vilans.

Marian, dressed in suitably scarlet satin, looked as good as Betsy looked bad.

The latter's dress seemed to be made literally of sackcloth, and she was the colour of ashes from top to toe. She cast a perceptible blight on the proceedings, not least by informing us loudly and sourly: 'Jeremiah's cried off – he couldn't stand it here – he'd feel like Daniel in a den of pensioners.'

But Hans-Peter cheered things up again with his comical English and Germanic humour. He knew everybody, and has clearly become a pet of the Drewett gang: he called Madge Midge, and was publicly called by George and Reggie The Viennese Villain. His great voice boomed in our backyard, and he flirted with the ladies, kissing the work-worn hand of Rosalie Peterson, describing Monica as a ripe woman, and embracing Wendy because she represented Glyndebourne which he was crazy in love with.

By now it was getting on for nine o'clock, and I began to hope that no one else could be coming. I was actually telling Gem that we should soon be able to sit down and eat when the doorbell rang once more.

Octavia Pritchett crossed the Rubicon of our threshold, followed by Brian Hooke.

IN THE front hall Octavia grated in my ear: 'Betsy needn't know how long Brian's been at Beggar's Roost,' while he examined the walls of Hope Cottage and informed me they were mostly made of manure.

I led the way into the garden, where Gem's cheek was

routinely pecked, and, as silence fell, Brian approached his wife.

'Good evening, Betsy.'

He was unabashed, unfeeling probably, and spoke with a satirical intonation in his voice, mocking her or himself.

She concealed her surprise pretty well, just paused, flickered a glance at the curious spectators, and asked: 'Where have you sprung from?'

'Home is the hunter, home from the hill,' he recited complacently, smiling and turning to say hullo to Madge Drewett and Guy Cad.

Guy, oblivious of the melodrama being enacted before his eyes, and incapable of taking anything seriously, extended two fingers of his right hand and said with a silly titter: 'How d'ye do?'

Madge kissed Brian and scolded: 'You wicked old boy!' She then drawled generally: 'You're all wicked old boys!' – but laid a beringed and somewhat humiliating hand on the concave chest of Graham Phipps-Hullett as if to acquit him of the charge. 'They're wicked, that's our problem, isn't it, dar?' she enquired of Betsy.

Wendy put her oar in here, agreeing feebly: 'It is indeed,' and directing a lovelorn glance at Graham.

Betsy shrugged her shoulders and tossed her lank greasy hair and found herself face to face with Octavia.

She was obviously the angrier because George and Reggie and others were now treating Brian like the prodigal son, clustering round and even congratulating him on his coming or his going: and she emptied the vials of her accumulated ill-temper on the available head.

'Did you bring Brian here?'

Octavia bristled and admitted: 'I did.'

'Thanks for nothing!'

I interrupted this skirmish by handing Octavia a glass of wine and suggesting that we might help ourselves to food in the kitchen. My aim was pacific. Everybody else was talking; and if I could separate the ladies without delay, war between them might never be declared. But I was ignored.

Betsy resumed her interrogation of Octavia: 'What was he doing with you?'

'Strange to relate, some men want to see me sometimes,' Octavia retorted.

'How long was he with you?'

'What's the difference?'

'But you must answer my question.'

'Must I?'

Octavia uttered a provocative sound, half incredulous sniff and half obstinate chortle.

Betsy rounded on me: 'You were expecting Brian, weren't you?'

I was caught out and hummed and hawed, vaguely affirmative.

'Octavia warned you – she told you to expect him – how long ago were you told to expect him?'

Again I hesitated; and suddenly, and luckily only verbally, the two ladies were at each other's jugulars.

'I see.' Betsy had turned mauve with fury, and meant that she had recognised yet another rival and enemy in the shape of her trusted friend. 'You've been at it too. Wonders will never cease! What next for Brian? Talk of switching from the sublime to the ridiculous!'

Octavia almost simultaneously was jeering and shouting: 'I'll have him back if you like. I'll hang on to him if you're not careful. Who says I couldn't? I probably could have long ago. You've never been grateful enough to me!'

And just as two equally strong and ferocious boxers have been known to exchange knock-out blows and measure their respective lengths on the canvas, so now, first to my horror, then to that of Gem and all but one of our guests, Betsy doubled up and began to boohoo, and Octavia followed suit, her facial distortions and her tears reminding me irresistibly of the squeezing of a lemon.

In the ensuing commotion the priests tried to do their professional duty in different ways.

Father Byrne enquired paternally: 'Dear dear, what's this, what's the trouble, is it that bad?'

Crispin Peterson asked with a formality eager and discouraging: 'Can I be of assistance?'

Hans-Peter was the hero of the hour. He rushed in where shyer fools feared to tread. He threw his arms round heaving shoulders, rubbed backs better, stroked necks, somehow bounced or dandled Betsy and Octavia up and down like children, and cried or rather roared: 'Oh, oh, oh, oh' – comforting, chaffing, commiserating with and calming them. His mispronunciations helped to turn their tears into hiccupy laughter.

'Poor Bitsy, poor Octave! Bitsy needs honkie now – who has honkie for Bitsy's nose? And Octave will go to the lavabo – who is taking Octave to wash herself?'

Gem volunteered. The combatants, separated in one sense and reunited in another by embarrassment, followed her towards the french window, patting their dishevelled hair and dabbing at their stained faces with wet handkerchiefs.

Brian, the cause of the quarrel who alone appeared to be impervious to the consequences of it, complimented his wife as she passed by: 'Betsy, my dear, I must say you're looking extraordinarily attractive this evening.'

Murmurs of disbelief and disapproval greeted this tasteless and churlish jibe.

Betsy mumbled something that sounded like 'Swine!' – or perhaps it was 'Brian!'

But then, as women will when men behave outrageously, she giggled.

Her amusement, even at her own expense, and the possibility that she might pardon her erring spouse and not completely wreck our evening, revived a semblance of party spirit.

Octavia emitted a semi-strangulated crow indicative of

victory by her standards. She moved indoors, and Madge drawled as if after an air-raid: 'All clar, dars!' Charles Hart remarked: 'Definitely better than TV,' and Hans-Peter boomed with only slightly counter-productive enthusiasm: 'Let us be jolly!'

As Guy Cad queried bemusedly, 'Am I right in thinking we've had a spot of bother?' – my sleeve was plucked by Bertha, asking the question that strikes terror in the heart of every employer: 'Can I have a word?'

In the kitchen she provided me with a perfect example of the unfairness of the fair sex.

'Poor Mr Hooke,' she said. 'It's that Betsy, isn't it, letting him down in public and holding up his dinner?'

Her real worry was also mine: when, at this rate, were we going to eat and get to bed – it was already nine-thirty.

I soothed her savage breast in a manner of speaking, then was beckoned into the hall by George Drewett, who had taken refuge there with Reggie.

He explained: 'I cannot abide women scrapping and cater-wauling.'

I doled out wine and comfortable words, and was told a joke.

'You heard Brian saying he was home from the hill?' Reggie reminded me. 'Well – the only hill he's home from is the mons veneris.'

I WAS seated between Foxy and Madge, with Gregory opposite, at one of the three tables in the garden in the twilight; and hoped to eat my chicken salad and strawberries and cream in peace.

While Madge was gassing to Grégoire, Foxy asked me if I would like to buy a load of Regency furniture. Owing to her imminent departure from Cadwallader Place, she was going to have to dismantle her so-called Prince Regent's Room even before the public had paid to be fooled by it.

'I'd sell it to you for roughly what I gave for it, and you could pass it on for a fat profit if we guaranteed that it came from our ancestral home and was used by the Prince Regent.'

I jogged her memory, recalling her own admission that she herself had bought the furniture from Henry's, and made her laugh by asking her to define the term 'roughly'.

She said, taking a perverse pride in the sharpness of her practice: 'Foxy is as Foxy does, that's what they used to tell me.' She nodded and rolled an eye in the direction of Madge, and added: 'But some of us are foxier than others.'

I put a covert finger to my lips, fearful of more rows.

She shook her head and – almost – the teeth out of it, as if to show she did not care.

'Our trouble is that it's Gulliver's Travels for us. We were too small for Cadwallader Place, and we're too big for Friars' Dene: that's the name of the hovel in Grey Friars Twitten we're being crammed into. What is a Dene? Do you know what Dene's meant to mean? Friars' Den, it should be called. George's workmen had to take the roof off to get our double bed into the bedroom – we're not ready for twins just yet. How Guy's going to manage, I can't imagine – there's no space for him to lay out his hairbrushes and nail-clippers. And what sort of Black Bogy party can we have next Christmas? We'll only be able to play with one other couple. We'll be lucky in the future if our grandchild can slide in for a slice of chocolate cake at teatime. Some people tell us we'll like cuddling up together better than rattling round in the dear old barracks. Some people not a million miles away tell us we should be counting our blessings. I do see that we couldn't afford to dig in our toes. And now I'm willing, as we girls were instructed not to be when we were young – willing to move. But George's merry men are not doing their stuff at Friars' Dene – they're all at Cads' Pad. Our new home's a deserted building site, and our old one's crawling with builders and decorators and surveyors and architects – I discovered five strangers of the opposite sex in my bedroom yesterday morning – and they wanted to measure everything except me! And we're for ever being badgered to remove our belongings, furniture and what's in cupboards, to make room for you-know-who. They can't wait to take possession, Her Nibs and His Nibs, although they're in no hurry to stick to their side of the bargain and re-settle us as quick as poss. It might be different if they were paying for the pleasure of kicking us out. But they're nothing more than caretakers for our Peter and their Monica, they're only borrowing Cads' Pad to supervise the work of modernising it and putting it in order, and once it's ship-shape they're due to hand it back to our descendants: that was the deal, believe it or not. Well, I adore them. We all do, don't we? And Peter may benefit in the long run from what they're up to. I just keep remembering that money isn't made by giving it to friends and relations. They've got the best bargain, something for nothing – and are they sticking to it! They're behaving as if they owned Cadwallader Place. And it's crossed my nasty little mind that the denizens of Downscene have gone and done it again – done it to me – and I've been out-foxed.'

My next course was sweet and sour: the sweet part was the strawberries, the sour was poured into my other ear by Madge, more in sorrow than anger.

'Several large pinches of salt, dar, I hope you've been taking them,' she began. 'Don't bother to tell me what our friend was telling you. I can guess – and set the record straighter. Friars' Dene, dar: George is letting it to the Cads for tuppence farthing and giving them a free hand to re-furbish it. But they're turning a cottage into a miniature palace at his expense, building on a laundry and a bathroom above with gold taps, and hanging one wallpaper on top of another because they change their minds daily. Giving them a pound of our flesh would have been cheaper, dar. We've tried not to hurry them, or seem to be pushing them out of their home; but how to stop them spending our money,

260

that's the question; and they've been so slow, they've taken so long to decide things at Friars' Dene, that we've had to re-deploy our workmen for the time being. Too awkward! Cads' Pad's a wreck, of course, rotting, and filthy with it. George wants to set to work before it falls down, and I'm itching to wield my scrubbing-brush; and at our age we can't hang about if we're ever to enjoy ourselves there. All the same I sometimes lie awake at night and wonder what we've bitten off and if we can chew it. George is such a romantic – and I'm not talking only about the twinkle in his wicked old eye. He's always had this weakness for Cadwallader Place, and a yen to be lord of the manor. But he's had no experience of doing business with a ladyship. I know people think George's heart is as hard as his nose. But he's soft and innocent – not to mention honesty – compared with our lady-friend. It's not surprising the upper crust stays on top – no offence intended, dar! We're being taken to the cleaners and back again – and called names for coughing up. I'm not sure George's pocket's deep enough to please himself now she's got her hand in it.'

I used the excuse of an irresistible desire for biscuits and cheese to retreat to the kitchen, where Maurice and the young Cads, Peter and Monica, were scrounging second helpings of food and drink.

Reggie drew me aside and said: 'Listen – the aged parents are going stately in their dotage. They're sneaking in to Cads' Pad under Monica's skirt, if you catch my meaning. And they're leaving behind yours truly. I'm about to be the proud owner, or at least the occupier, of that shack by the stream known as Downscene. Now the point is, old boy, I'm young, chaste and clean-living, I shall therefore be lonely in my home-life, and short not only of company but also of ready money after paying my own expenses. I'll be an orphan, financially speaking – with no one around to touch or be touched by me. However, rumour has it that you're about to shake the chalky dust of Sussex from your feet –

can it be true? Would anyone wish to leave Lewes and be exiled from the hub of the universe? My unsolicited advice is: abandon us not, render unto the Whitakers the things which are the Whitakers', and share Downscene with Reginald. You can have half the house with every mod. con. and a laughable rent. You give the go-ahead and I'll make you an offer you can't refuse – in return for cash with no questions asked, natch!'

Peter Cad then buttonholed me, and winking, blinking, grimacing and straining his vocal chords to the limit, proposed another scheme, which was ungrateful, dishonourable, certain to fail, and probably characteristic. He seemed to say that he was not going to be relegated to a few upstairs rooms in his own home: he would let George and Madge do up Cadwallader Place – he was owed a handsome dowry after all – he would shut his mouth and lie low while the work was in progress – but when it was complete and his baby was born he would show the Drewetts the door – re-possess the property in its entirety – and let the upstairs flat to us at a price.

AT THIS stage of the proceedings I decided I would rather not spend my declining years in Lewes, representatives of which had forgathered under our roof merely to quarrel, blub, backbite and whine at our expense, or try to sell us a white elephant or a pup.

I had been appreciative of the neighbourliness of our guests, and derived enjoyment from observing their lives and loves, customs, scandals and so on. But at my age the name of the game is detachment, not attachment. After less than twelve months in Eastover, I could not pretend that friendly acquaintanceship with a few of its residents was the pre-condition of my continued existence, nor that I would pine to death elsewhere.

Soon Gem and I would again swap with the Whitakers,

and vacate Hope Cottage and reclaim Thamesview Mansions: which might be no bad thing, I reflected. There was not a house in Lewes for us to live in; and renting bits of Downscene or Cads' Pad with illegal cash from amateur con men could well be worse than homelessness.

And experience suggested that I was as likely or unlikely to write my book in London.

Besides, we had another circle of friends and acquaintances there.

My doubts about the desirability of settling and giving more parties in Lewes were exacerbated by Bertha telling me it was nearly midnight and she was going home, and then by Gem, who had discovered that the kitchen looked like a bomb-site and the red wine was running out.

Our party seemed to have been a flop for all concerned, and I was sorry to have given it. I thought of Rachel, and for a moment ached to be anywhere except at a noisy pointless social bash in our temporary habitat in the tamed wilderness of Sussex.

But a humming sound – a tuneful hum – began to hush the chatter and scrape of chairs on the bricks of our backyard. Gem and I were standing in the french window, and the guests who had dined indoors were coming out to collect husbands and wives and say goodbye. The garden was dark by this time, apart from the glow of the risen moon behind a small cloud, the light from candles in glass jars on the three tables, and the shaft of illumination from the kitchen.

The hum emanated from Hans-Peter Vilans. He was really singing quietly, and gazing at Marian Travers, who, with golden head averted, stared into the middle distance, slightly smiling. Every picture tells a story, as they say. Marian's chair was pushed back, and she was sitting at a right angle to the man serenading her. That she never once glanced in his direction, and smiled so tautly throughout, gave the show away. One could almost hear, like an accompaniment to his song or a secret obbligato, the thumping and thrilling of her heart.

Hans-Peter sang a little louder, enunciating the words of some foreign language, but still softly and smoothly, as if his larynx were well-oiled; and his voice blended naturally into the night, like the buzz of insects and the twittering of birds on a summer's day. I may mean that he sang in a professional manner; but what captivated everyone was the perfect taste of his performance – no exaggeration, no affected flourishes. It was strange: that buffoon, that clumsy Central European heavyweight, lounging in his chair, now commanded rapt attention and respect. Through his scarcely open bearded lips poured the eloquent music of his passion for his landlady.

Guests edged from the kitchen into the garden to listen to him. He sang louder and with a sharper stronger melancholy vibrancy: Russian peasant songs, I heard later. Two people emerged on to the balcony of the block of flats overlooking Hope Cottage. When Hans-Peter paused, everyone except Marian applauded; and cries of encouragement and for more rang out, Foxy's 'Oncor!' and Gregory's 'Bis!' Madge drawled: 'I love it, dar!' Crispin Peterson declared: 'Capital!' – while Father Byrne had recourse to religion: 'For God's sake keep going!' The moon parted company with its cloud and suffused the scene with a silver-blue radiance.

Too soon Hans-Peter finished, laughing and half-breaking the spell he had cast over us. Marian immediately rose to her feet and said it was late, they must go, and, her eyes glistening under languorous eyelids, she hurried her lodger home – no doubt to prove her gratitude for his musical tribute.

The Petersons left to relieve their baby-sitter. Crispin was truly thankful for what he had received; but Rosalie, sedated by food and wine and music as well as maternity, mumbled her goodbyes with a vacant smile.

Father Byrne blessed us for asking him and returned to

Mrs Samson: he is certainly a Delilah with a difference, just as she differs from her biblical namesake, except in a trichological sense.

Gregory and Charles took their leave. I was afraid that Gregory, like me, might have had a surfeit of Foxy and Madge at dinner; but he was excited by Hans–Peter and reiterated with dogmatic ambiguity: 'The man's a dream!'

Charles was also excited, but by the quarrel between Octavia and Betsy: 'Quel melo! I wouldn't have missed it for all the T in I Tatti.' Gem informed me afterwards that I Tatti was the name of the house in Italy of the defunct arbiter of arts, Bernard Berenson. 'Quel melo – and with the cabaret thrown in – thanks two mill!' He mentioned Martin, the designing colleague from Australia, who was staying at Wares House and working at Glyndebourne: 'I'll give him a graphic and watch him go green.'

The Wendy who said goodnight was in better shape than the Wendy who had said good evening. She was to be escorted the few yards to her front door by Graham, and her countenance once more shone with false hopes.

Graham exclaimed: 'What treats! What a superb song-ster!' – while Wendy moderated his impetuosity with a fond indulgent smile and the expert opinion of a Glyndebourne usher: 'Hans–Peter's head–notes are poetic.'

Octavia and Betsy, and Betsy and Brian too, were quite reconciled. The Hookes were going to give Octavia a lift home to Beggar's Roost, where, apparently, a couple of suitcases packed with the detritus of Brian's romantic esca-pade would be picked up.

Reggie, who was standing near me, whispered in my ear: 'What about re-naming the Pritchett-Hooke love-nest Booggar's Rest?'

Brian surpassed himself on the subject of the suitcases: 'They're full of dirty linen – which has already been washed in public – and now has to be scrubbed and ironed privately by darling Betsy.'

265

Neither wife nor mistress could suppress a smile at this insolent sally.

Betsy said to Octavia: 'I'd like to cut his tongue out,' and Octavia to Betsy: 'Why stop there?'

They were grateful to us for the party and everything, and departed laughing.

Monica Cadwallader aimed her swelling stomach at me.

She asked: 'Has Peter been on to you about our marital home?'

The Drewett gang, Cads included, were gathered together in the front hall.

Monica bared her protruding teeth and – metaphorically – sunk them into her husband with forceful good humour: 'He's always planning to sell the roof over my head, he's always trying to cash in on Cads' Pad,' she broadcast, her repetitiveness an ominous reminder that, as daughters do, she was growing more like her mother.

Guy feigned alarm: 'Cash it in? Pop the ancestral? Steady on!'

Foxy confessed: 'Peter's a chip off my block. He's a popper, I'm a popper. He should have been christened Nebuchadnezzar – he'd sell his wife for a pair of shoes – sorry, Monica!' And she addressed the hulking man in question as if he were a lapdog: 'Bad boy!'

Peter pulled guilty faces and shook with mute amusement; Foxy and Guy laughed as heartily as their dentures allowed; Monica asserted with confidence and good humour that she was neither for sale, nor for the time being saleable; whereupon Reggie commiserated with his brother-in-law thus: 'I'm sorry to say it's happy ever after for you, old cock!'

Madge summed up.

'It's happy ever after this party, dars, for all of us.'

Hugs and kisses were exchanged, and hands shaken.

'We're happy to have been here,' Madge resumed. 'We're happy to have such lovely friends. We're happy gangsters, aren't we, dars? And Hans-Peter's not a villain — he made everyone happy, didn't he?'

Gem and I agreed, and, gratifyingly, were asked, told, instructed and implored never, ever or on any account to leave Lewes.

George Drewett's parting shot on the doorstep was to say to me in an undertone: 'I've learnt a lesson tonight — if you're looking for love, learn to sing.'

A WEEK has passed since our party, which ended better than it began; and fortune seems to have decided to do us other favours.

In the envelope containing notes of thanks from Gregory and Charles were two complimentary tickets for *Figaro* at Glyndebourne next month, courtesy of Martin, our unknown and apparently unknowable benefactor, since he has already left Lewes for the Antipodes — and of course thanks to the generosity of our mutual friends.

The next day, three days after the party, at seven in the evening, to be precise, someone knocked on the door of Hope Cottage. I opened it and saw a rough stocky middle-aged man with a stubble of beard and a hangdog expression, whom I mistook in turn for a gipsy, beggar, criminal and escaped lunatic. But he appeared to be harmless.

'I'm Albert,' he murmured. As I must have made it clear that the name meant nothing to me, he repeated in an aggrieved and irritable tone: 'Albert, Albert!' — pointing along Rickman's Lane and adding obscurely: 'It's Mother.'

He was Mrs Spedding's son, the one who in her partisan opinion had a brain and knew how to use it.

Gem was with me, she had identified Albert before I did, and she now asked anxiously if Mrs Spedding was all right.

Albert replied that she only wanted to see us, and he led the way round the corner and through the unlocked front door and into her presence.

Mrs Spedding's greeting was a good example of British phlegm: 'We've got tragedy in this house.'

What had happened, what was it?

'Timmy's flown over,' she replied, white-faced but dry-eyed.

I said: 'Flown off?' – checking that she meant the budgerigar was on the loose and she wished us to try to catch it.

'No, dear, passed, flown over to the other side – he's dead,' she explained anti-climactically.

We sympathised and enquired into the circumstances of his demise.

Albert volunteered gruffly: 'Trod on.'

But Mrs Spedding would be denied neither her drama nor her revenge: 'Tim was on the floor, pecking up my crumbs. He was specially bright this evening too. Albert marches in and puts a great flat foot right on top of him. I heard his little bones crunch. You heard his little bones crunch, didn't you, Albert? He crunched right where you're standing, dear,' she said, pointing to a wettish patch on the carpet under my shoes. 'Well,' she continued, coming to the point so far as we were concerned: 'I can't stay here without his company. Albert agrees – and he's got a brain, though you might not credit it. Timmy was like a husband to me – mate, I suppose I should say – and I know what I'm talking about, because I've had more than my fair share of mates – and now I'm too old to have another, thank goodness! You'll buy this house, won't you, dear? You buy it – then you won't have to leave Lewes and we won't have to wave goodbye. You'd like it, wouldn't you? I'll be glad to get into a comfy Eventide Home, to tell the truth, and to think of you two with Tim.'

We were excited. The fact that Mrs Spedding's house would suit better than Hope Cottage in several respects had not escaped us. But we managed to keep our heads to the extent of saying we would have to ponder her kind offer.

And I requested clarification of her last statement: 'How is it that we'd be with Tim if we were here, Mrs Spedding?'

'Well, in spirit you would be, because this was his home and it is his resting-place.'

'Do you mean he's buried in the garden?'

'No – Albert wanted to put him out there – the bits and bobs of him that were left – but I wouldn't have it – you'd disturb him every time you stuck in a bulb.'

'Where is he at the moment?'

'We dropped him in the Liftalu. He'll dissolve in the acid, and Albert'll be able to pour him down the drain in the street. You're not worried, are you, dear? Tim wouldn't ever worry you. He's got his reasons now, just like me, to be grateful to you for that beautiful present of yours. Besides, most of him should be in the other world now. And I hope to join the little sweetheart before too long.' She concluded in her stoical jolly way: 'That's it, dear – we'll soon be together again, and then we won't worry anyone or have anything more to worry about.'

Fortune's third favour is that Rachel survives, and still seems serene.

But I would not write a word or even entertain a thought that might tempt it to do more harm to its hostage.

The day before yesterday I ran into Jeremiah Hooke in Rickman's Lane. He was wearing not a suit, but that other uniform of sinister politics in the eyes of some, for instance Betsy: grey flannels and a tweed jacket. His greeting was respectfully friendly, and he professed to be sorry not to have made it to our party.

I replied that his mother had conveyed apologies on his behalf, and that I understood his reluctance to attempt to bridge the generation gap.

He blushed and burst out: 'Is that what she told you? It's not true! I was spending the night in London, trying to find somewhere to live when I start working there – I'd have loved to come otherwise. My mother's cut up because I don't dye my hair any more, or pretend I'm part of the alternative society – she thinks it's romantic to draw the dole. She doesn't want me to be poor, or to earn my living. She wants everybody to be unconventional, except herself. She's schizophrenic – I mean she fights for pacifism – and she's a socialist socialite – and she makes bad blood with her good causes. All that hypocrisy, it's no longer acceptable. Well – I'm leaving home. I'll be working for a stockbroker, you know, and hoping to become rich and powerful. Will you explain things to Mrs Loftus, please, and give her my regards? Will you pat Cinders for me? Perhaps I shouldn't speak ill of my parents. But my mother ought to be pleased that I'm rebelling against her influence and feeling much better, and my father hasn't any right to disapprove.'

Twenty-four hours later, yesterday, I paraphrased the above for the benefit of Bertha.

But Bertha had arrived at Hope Cottage with a puppy clasped in her arms: male, ten weeks old, nondescript, enchanting, called either Pop or Pup or both, which monopolised everyone's attention and raised awkward ethical questions.

These were twofold. First: although Bertha may have been justified in signing the death warrant of Minnie, who was geriatric, had she done in Winnie, who was younger and healthier and indeed in her prime, for the sake of Pop? Secondly: had our filthy lucre paid not only for the double execution but also for the dead dogs' replacement – possibly more cuckoo in the nest than canine?

Bertha justified herself by saying she was so fond of dogs and dogs were so fond of her that she just had to have this one. And she had no time to waste in mourning and moping.

After we had swallowed our scruples, and been introduced to Pop or Pup, and Cindy had taken a shine to him and was bowling him over in the backyard, Bertha reverted to the subject of the Hookes with the announcement: 'Jeremiah's gone to town with Tracy Wilkins.'

We were duly astonished.

Bertha expatiated: 'She'll be a fashion model and share his flat in London. None of the Hookes are on speaking terms. The son was jealous of the father, now the father's jealous of the son; and the mother says she'd like to boil the girl in oil. It's not surprising Jeremiah's turned against his people – he's grown up sensible. And Tracy's modern: she's not inclined to hang her head in Lewes because she had a bit of a holiday with Mr Hooke, when she could hold it high elsewhere. Her parents, Naomi and Bert, they're in favour of her being Jeremiah's flatmate. They're shopkeepers, they're all for turnover, even when it comes to their daughter's boyfriends. And they like to think of Tracy being in their line of business in the rag-trade.'

Gem asked: was there no love in the story?

'Well,' Bertha replied, 'Tracy's too young to be married happily, and too pretty to make a husband happy – and men won't let her be good for many a long year. She says she's just friends with Jeremiah, although he's said something different ever since he was a boy. But she's not likely to need a warm puppy to cuddle yet – and then there's rent to pay. When they're alone together in the big city, they'll help to keep the world turning, I shouldn't wonder.'

JULY

WE GO to Glyndebourne this evening.

We hope the weather is only playing a practical joke on us, as it did before our party. In the last few days it has rained, hailed and blown wintry winds. It is raining again this morning – drizzling – and threatens our night at the opera. The worst, which we try not to fear, would include – according to Wendy and other cognoscenti – clothes soaked between carpark and theatre, no tour of the garden and grounds, cancellation of picnic out of doors, and our car probably stuck in the mud when we tried to drive it home. People keep on sympathising with us in advance for missing half the point of the entertainment – that is, the summery scene.

My ignorance of opera used to be blissful: no inkling of operatic opportunities wasted ever troubled my mind. Ignorant I remain, regrettably, notwithstanding Gem's efforts as it were to cultivate the ground, till the barren soil, in preparation for the seminal experience. A week ago she bought me a cassette of *Highlights from Figaro* and a translation of Da Ponte's libretto; and I have dutifully listened and read. But I cannot claim to have mastered the masterpiece in a matter of seven days.

I trust that, in a musical as in a meteorological sense, it will be all right on the night. At any rate I count on perhaps extraneous pleasures, enjoying Gem's enjoyment and seeing the famous place, provided the climate permits us to see it.

My better half refuses to kowtow to the elements: she

spent a day in Brighton, shopping for the right frock for the occasion. And I have disinterred my dinner jacket that was laid to rest after the Black Bogy party, and tried to revive it with clothes brush and iron.

Voices have been raised in my hearing against the custom of donning formal attire to sit and watch opera in a country house in the depths of the Sussex Downs on summer afternoons. People say that things were different in 1934, when John Christie and his wife built the theatre in their garden and staged the first Festival: in those days members of the establishment, even the artistic establishment, theatre-goers and opera-lovers in particular, were hardly ever out of their tiaras and black or white bow-ties. Now, they say, evening dress is as quaint as powdered hair; also embarrassing for those who come and go by British Rail, and have to run the gauntlet of the commuting crowd at Victoria Station and rough types on the trains; and desecrates a temple of culture with snobbery, sartorial snobbery at least, and reinforces the charge based upon the high price of tickets that Glyndebourne is incorrigibly elitist.

Yet everybody who is anybody, from savages to sophisticates and back again in all the ages of history, has known that social activities are more fun, or more bearable, if the participants have made efforts to look their best. The principle of the dinner jacket never will be superseded; and who or what has ever stopped women dressing up? The levellers and puritans and killjoys and lazybones who would like the Glyndebourne audience to wear everyday clothes remind me of the Simple Simons who tried to convince us that so-called kitchen-sink drama was as entertaining as that in which great kings and beautiful queens laugh and cry.

Moreover the word elitist, perhaps because of being half-caste – Anglicised French – is much abused. To egalitarians and inverted snobs and prigs, its meaning is pejorative, and it comes in handy for Sneerwells and mischief-makers. Yet elitist actually refers to what is superior, excellent, caviare to

274

the general and bread and butter to the happy few – to what sets and raises standards and never comes cheap.

John Christie of Glyndebourne was not elitist in the disparaging sense of today's trendy jargon. Wendy Aylward and Octavia Pritchett remember him well, and the senior Cads were extremely fond of him. Evidently he was an eccentric as well as the scion of an ancient family: his own evening dress in his older age included a starched shirt and tennis shoes. He called the restaurants for patrons Nether, Middle and Upper Wallop: real place names somehow connected with his Wallop relations. He was responsible not only for persuading people to pay heavily for changing their clothes and travelling more or less far and often getting wet and cold in order to see and hear an operatic show in Sussex, but also, largely, for another Festival in Edinburgh. He loved pug-dogs and was always attended by one.

Three historic facts contributed to the immediate success of the almost crazily idealistic venture: the talent as singer and actress of Audrey Mildmay, John's wife; their rule that nothing but the best would do; and the refugees of genius from Hitler's Europe who were engaged to help to get things going.

Christies still preside over the Glyndebourne Festival after half a century. By all accounts John and Audrey's descendants have managed to maintain the quality of the five or six annual productions; and the atmosphere they create is a considerable part of the charm of the Glyndebourne experience. The family continues to inhabit the old house, and to farm the land surrounding it; and in winter, when the Festival is finished and the Touring Opera is doing its round of provincial cities, normal country life is resumed – eight hundred persons in full fig do not knock on the front door every evening, expecting to be entertained operatically.

THE RAIN stopped at midday, and then the sun seemed to

reproach me for doubting it by seeing off the clouds and shining hot and strong.

Figaro was due to begin at five o'clock: the early start meant a fairly early finish, which would enable the farther-flung members of the audience to get home at a reasonable hour.

We left Hope Cottage at three, and a mile out of Lewes drove into the Downs in the steamy sunshine, between fields of ripening corn, past the farmstead called Little Heaven, and parked our car with a hundred and fifty others in a sloping field behind the complex of buildings: we were by no means the first members of the audience to arrive.

There was a marquee at one end of the carpark, and through its entrance we could see tables and benches: probably the place for picnics in foul weather. Now in the sun the tent with pennants fluttering imparted an air of garden party or fairground to the scene. The paintwork and chrome of cars reflected dazzling rays of light. Unlikely figures, women in diaphanous dresses and silver sandals and diamonds, men in black dinner jackets and white tuxedos, lugged picnic baskets, folding chairs, bottles of wine, rugs, over the tussocky turf and drying mud. Uninterested sheep grazed on the hillside, and wood pigeons cooed amorously in the leafy shelter of trees.

We followed in the footsteps of other people, carrying our picnic things. We passed a tennis court, where a game of mixed doubles was in progress, and found, in one direction, a pretty walled garden and the celebrated Covered Way, a sort of stone patio on various levels with a bar and doors into the theatre; then, in the other direction, beyond rehearsal stages and stage-doors, the herbaceous borders, lawns, and lakes or ponds we had heard about.

The mathematics of Glyndebourne greenery are impressive: height and circumference of trees, length and breadth of areas of mown grass. And almost every flower is six feet tall and part of a giant bunch or clump. The main lawn is protected from a herd of cattle in the adjoining field by a ha-ha, a ditch and sunken wall invisible from a distance. Another mellower elevation of the house looks out over this lawn, likewise the Organ Room and the Green Room and the line of Dressing-rooms built on by John Christie.

The Organ Room was his first shot at creating a place for singers and musicians to perform in. The story goes that he asked a firm of organ-builders to make him a particular kind of organ for it. Impossible, he was told; whereupon he bought the firm and got what he wanted.

We spread our rug and dumped our picnic in the shade of a ten-feet-high yew hedge flanking the aforesaid lawn, and strolled down to and round the top lake. The multi-coloured flowers of water-lilies almost covering its surface were still opened to the sun. Occasional may-trees growing beside the path found favour in my eyes in their rough countrified way even without the blossoms of spring. Ducks quacked or rather grunted with anxious contentment as they watched over ducklings looking like animated powder-puffs and walking on the water. Moorhens cried weirdly and dragonflies flitted.

In the verdant dell we had to cross in order to return to the garden proper we were surprised to find a white-clothed table sporting a silver candlestick and laid with cutlery, china, glass and napkins for four, plus bottles of wine in patent coolers, a hamper and chairs. The absence of those who would partake of the feast testified either to the honesty of opera-lovers or a foolhardy faith in human nature.

The cooling of liquid refreshment is obviously a problem for picnickers. Some people were solving it by sinking bottles in the lake and tethering them with string to the branches of trees. The partial solution put forward by others was not to allow wine to get hotter and hotter until the dinner interval, but to drink it without delay.

The time was now a quarter past four, more people were in the garden, corks popped, and glasses were being filled, raised and emptied to an accompaniment of the drifting sounds of laughter out of doors.

We observed the passing show on the big lawn. Brian and Betsy Hooke are down on Glyndebourne because, they grumble, it allocates too many tickets to its financial sponsors, and, generally, because it attracts too many rich philistines more interested in being seen there than in seeing and hearing opera. But then the Hookes cannot forgive Glyndebourne for its independence from the state, for neither having to beg for taxpayers' money nor letting itself be blackmailed by bureaucrats. And they are dead against any individual who is richer than they are. If they really loved art, if they loved art as much as politics, and were less confused by the common old collectivist pipe-dream of art for the masses, they would surely and simply be glad that Glyndebourne is supported.

Besides, we could hardly believe that superannuated patrons, ladies with buns and walking sticks in outmoded gowns of faded flowered material, and gentlemen halt and lame in moth-eaten velvet suits, were present for the sake of keeping in the social swim; and the same applied to self-absorbed young couples promenading hand-in-hand.

Singers of both sexes were warbling and warming up in the Dressing-rooms we passed. Indoors, in the Organ Room, Gem admired the pictures, Dutch portraits and sea pieces, while I checked for the umpteenth time that I had not lost our tickets; and in due course we took our seats.

The walls of the auditorium are oak-panelled and the bracket lights must have been old-fashioned when they were installed half a century ago. We were sitting at the back of the stalls: boxes were behind us and the balcony above the boxes. Ushers stood by to help; but Wendy was not on duty. The ushers wore round their necks medallions on red ribbon, badges of office invented by John Christie. The theatre gradually filled, and the unseen orchestral musicians tuned their instruments, and the chatter increased in volume.

At length the lights dimmed, a sudden hush fell, clapping broke out, the spotlit head of the conductor materialised above the barrier between stalls and pit, and he bowed and turned towards the orchestra and the stage with baton raised.

ONCE UPON a time I went to the theatre a lot, though not to opera. I was in the army then, stationed within reach of London, young and impressionable. My leanings were already more literary than military; and I would be gripped, spellbound, enthralled, from the first word of some drama to the final curtain – I ran the gamut of every state of mind known to enthusiasm,.

But age is said to blunt the edge of sensibility: which is ground to dust between the upper and nether millstones of boredom and indifference.

Alas, I now have to allow that such reflections on senior citizenship are not altogether wide of the mark.

And notwithstanding the restorative and rejuvenating effects of Sussex by the sea, and the stimulus of new surroundings and associations in this last year, and the enlivening interest of writing this journal if not my book, and looking forward to *Figaro* almost as eagerly as to the pantomime in Bristol when I was a boy, I did not make much of the first two Acts. The story resembled that of many other comedies which it either pre-dated or imitated, and the music was reminiscent of musical boxes – or so it seemed to me. I did not forget that the opera is considered to be amongst the greatest works of human genius by many highly qualified judges, and possibly I tried too hard not to miss a word or a note. Anyway, somehow, I arrived at the conclusion that it was a disappointment – or at least that I was disappointed.

When the curtain came down I therefore applauded for all I was worth, wishing neither to betray my controversial opinion nor spoil the sport of Gem – although, to my surprise, her applause was actually less enthusiastic than mine.

But her eyes shone, her cheeks were pink with pleasure, and she murmured in explanation of her response to the performance as we trooped out of the theatre: 'I was too carried away to clap.'

It was about seven o'clock. The shadows of trees in a wild bit of the garden divided the lawn: we sat on our rug on the shady side, not talking much. Cows congregated by the ha-ha, staring and chewing their cud, as we picnickers munched our tasty morsels. The interval lasted for an hour and a quarter. Partly to escape the midges and gnats we packed up and carried our paraphernalia back to the car, and made another circuit of the lake, which was mirroring the roseate colours of sunset. Festive human cries mingled with those of the water-birds and the hooting of an owl.

We returned to our seats and the second half of the opera began.

And at a certain moment the Countess sang the words: 'E Susanna non vien.'

The Countess is the heroine of the two famous plays by Beaumarchais that were set to music. She is first the Rosina of Rossini's *Barber of Seville*, in which she is courted by and elopes with Count Almaviva. In the sequel, Mozart's *The Marriage of Figaro*, she is saddened by the roving eye of her husband, the same Count Almaviva who used to adore her. He is now trying to exercise his right as lord and master to make love to her maid, Susanna, engaged to be married to his steward, Figaro: he is claiming his feudal droit de seigneur. But the Countess and Susanna unite with Figaro to frustrate his lustful machinations.

In the Act following the interval the Countess enters, expecting to meet Susanna, who is late, and voices the phrase in question. It is not an aria, not part of the song she sings later on, but the introductory sentence of a piece of recitative, the operatic form of dialogue and soliloquy that is half speech and half singing. So far as I know and have been able to discover, pundits do not single it out for special attention.

Nevertheless, unexpectedly, that phrase broke down my resistance to the opera. The words and the music blended so perfectly: between them they enticed me into sharing the emotions of the character on the stage.

'And Susanna's not here!'

The Countess is complaining with sweet fretfulness and sorrow that on top of everything, to cap all, her maid and friend and ally has not arrived, has perhaps also let her down, and she is alone, lonely, and in love with a man who no longer loves her.

Luckily such sentiments are not applicable to my situation. I suppose I can only explain to my own satisfaction why they moved me by referring to the mystery of art.

The same sort of thing happened when Barbarina, Susanna's kittenish cousin, sings, referring to a pin that figures in the plot: 'I have lost it . . . I can't find it . . . Poor little me!' – six short lines of poetry in the Italian original with even less bearing on my life, or on life itself, or death, or the hereafter. But I believe the unearthly beauty of the music was responsible for the lump in my throat.

Finally, after the unravelling of the drama, the pleading for pardon, the forgiveness and the reconciliations, the whole cast sings in unison: 'Questo giorno di tormenti, Di capricci e di follia, In contenti e in allegria Solo amor può terminar' – or, in English, roughly: 'Only love can turn today's trials and tribulations, fibs and follies, into laughter and happiness.' I had read those words in translation in the libretto. They were more cogent as climax of the performance than they had been in print.

We clapped until our hands hurt, then joined the queue for the exit. But Gem, when I headed for the Covered Way, directed me into the stream of people returning to the garden for picnic baskets and so on.

Night had fallen, but a moon shone, looking as if it was leaning back against the sky, and rectangles of light were projected onto the lawn from the windows of the Dressing-

281

rooms and the house. The excited voices of the performers, celebrating, practising bits of the opera, were audible; also those of shadowy patrons, standing and sinking one for the road before packing up.

Once more we circled the lake. We were not alone on the path beside the luminous wild flowers and the shimmer of black water between the lily leaves. Young lovers whispered and kissed, and couples not so young plodded round, arms linked affectionately. The setting was more romantic than any we had seen on the stage: the genuine moonlight, the real hills and trees and blue-black distance and starry firmament. Sheep bleated, cows lowed, waterfowl splashed, the birds of the night cried and hunted. The air was scented, redolent of flowers, vegetation, animals, ordure, decay – in a word, nature: it was worth the hay fever it would give me in the morning.

People still lingered in the carpark. They were like us in not wanting to leave the place. But we thought of Cindy, and drove home to Hope Cottage.

AND ANOTHER departure draws near: we are due to leave Lewes in a fortnight. Toby and Jane Whitaker will be repossessing themselves of their property, and we shall have to return to ours in London, even if we do decide to sell it and buy Mrs Spedding's house.

Yesterday we drove up to Firle Beacon and walked along the South Downs Way. We wanted to arrive at some decision in respect of our future and to give Cinders and indeed ourselves a treat. The weather beckoned – it has continued fine since our visit to Glyndebourne.

We started from a point opposite to, and across the valley from, the brow of Mount Caburn, where last summer we sat in the sun and surveyed the landscape. I was full of my literary project on that day: which has not come to fruition. I have missed my chance to write my book, the single book that everyone is supposed to have in him or in her: incidentally, the greatest example of which was the effusion of a fellow-soldier by profession – *Les Liaisons Dangereuses* by Choderlos de Laclos.

But there is never a negative without a positive; and I think I can see the positive side of this unproductive year. At any rate I have reached the iconoclastic conclusion that what I wanted to write, or why I wanted to write it, was a mistake.

Perhaps my book refused to be written because it was not right, and it was not right because too concerned with and circumscribed by pain.

Granted, some people count on books – on art – to make them cry. Tears take them out of themselves, just as laughter performs a similar service for most of us, especially when we are older and sadder.

Granted, again, romantic and sundry other artists often seem to be preoccupied exclusively with storm and stress, sickness, unhappiness, murder, suicide and death.

I agree that the alchemy of art is capable of transmuting dross into gold; also that pain can drive the artist to please at least himself or herself by the creation of a work of art.

Yet pleasure for everyone involved, however arrived at, is nonetheless and unavoidably the object of the exercise.

And speaking personally, coming down to earth with a humble bump, I now feel inclined to build my literary monument, if any, not on a scrap of paper with a horrible message scrawled across it by a moron, but on a more pleasurable foundation.

Admittedly I would have linked that moron, who did his communist duty by killing a class enemy I happened to care for, with the spy, liar and cheat Philby, whose communist convictions were his excuse for betraying his compatriots and getting his colleagues killed, and so with Lenin and Stalin, who, in the name of Communism and the greater good of the masses, killed sixty-six million Russians in cold blood. I hoped to strike a blow at the politics and poses which have ruined and injured me and mine, and harassed every beneficiary of achievement throughout this century, and butchered and butchered for the best of reasons – to wit, to gain or retain power. I wished to pray in print for the souls of the hundreds of millions of international victims of twentieth century Collectivism and the reactions it has provoked, and speak up for – or rather against – the unapologetic intellectuals, the eternally discontented clever fools washing their hands in the background, who bear the ultimate responsibility for its crimes.

Crusades are all very well. But crusading books need to be timed correctly, and postponement has with luck rendered mine superfluous. Dead horses should never be flogged – and the spectacle of an aspiring author of advanced years flogging one would not edify. Nobody believes in Collectivism any more, except a few savages, a mad millionaire or two, and the odd Anglican bishop.

That is not to say I have changed my mind about it. I have certainly not changed my mind about its battle-cry: the class struggle. Deciding who should be struggled against is reminiscent of the test of witchcraft in the dark ages: if a woman thrown into water did not drown she was a witch and would be burned at the stake, if she did drown she was not. Even in theory, and as communist practice has amply demonstrated, no one is safe from the assaults of envy, malice, revenge, ambition, paranoia etc, authorised and legitimised by reference to the class struggle. It has justified the blood-lust of revolution, it has excused the bloodthirstiness of tyrants. It is the catch-all booby-trap of modern oppression.

For the term is, and probably always was, indefinable. In Russia virtually every original member of the Bolshevik Party, which shot the Tsar and his children, was later and in turn arraigned as a class enemy and done to death. And in this country nowadays, the rousing summons 'Death to the aristos!' rings pretty hollow when a penniless tramp can inherit some ancient title, and life-peerages are the reward for public service in socialist organisations, for instance, or the trade unions. For that matter the equally archaic 'Up the workers!' is null and void of meaning, since almost every citizen, barring the old, the ill and the unemployable, either works or would work if he or she could. Is it money that separates one class from another? But the dividing line between rich and poor can be drawn anywhere. As a rule wealth, for the politician who would re-distribute it, begins where his or her resources end. And although a millionaire is richer than an Englishman on the dole, to a beggar in Calcutta there would not seem to be much difference between them. Stalin ruled that extremely poor Ukrainians were capitalists and therefore deserved death by starvation.

But the lower class must struggle against the upper for social justice and equality of opportunity, Collectivists insist. They cannot mean justice as practised in the collectivist Jerusalem built by Lenin and Stalin in the Soviet Union: too few of the sixty-six million class enemies who died of it were present at their trials – and recent Soviet leaders have condemned it. Nor can the Soviet Union boast of creating equality of opportunity after seventy years of Marxism: members of the establishment and their offspring enjoy extraordinary advantages – Stalin's daughter was as privileged as any poor little rich girl.

It is always the same sad story. Revolt, we are told again and again: throw off your chains! Seize what belongs to others but is rightfully yours!

So we seize it; and are apt to kill to keep it; and would assuage our guilt by urging everyone else to do as we have done; and our revolutionary meddling and bellicosity cause other nations to arm and fight; and there is still more killing – they are killed, we are killed; and the cup of unkindness overflows.

I mourn the legions cut down in peace and war by the

worshippers of false gods, not to mention true ones. I mourn the fact that great civilisations are founded on conquest and slavery. I cringe before the conditions of existence and the draconian laws of nature. I weep for my sister.

But I have changed my mind inasmuch as I have ceased to believe that wailing and gnashing of teeth is the most constructive attitude to literature and life.

How is Rachel able to stay serene, maintain her poise, and even comfort others?

How is the unbearable to be borne?

Masochists are the lucky ones.

Children in general tell tales, if tacitly. Children dread pain, change, the unknown: they are the staunchest conservatives. How are grown-ups to grow out of their childish apprehensiveness?

Perhaps I was a more cowardly child than most in not loving my visits to the dentist, not pleading to be punctured by hypodermic syringes, not laughing at the prospect of corporal punishment. I was always relieved to see that Mama and Boltbridge Manor had not disappeared during my absence. Yet at school I was regarded or treated as normal enough; and I did not join the army because of receiving white feathers through the post. How are average people like me to be unafraid of the offences committed against them by criminals, the state and nature?

Courage is finite. Observation, for instance of soldiers in action, suggests that courage is a wasting asset and simply runs out. Although bravery cannot be detracted from, the bravest are only those who can be brave for the longest period, or, after recuperative intervals, repeatedly.

If or when courage fails, we should forget to remember pain and death. But living reminds us of pain: or is it the point of pain to remind us that we are alive? And then life does its damnedest to bring death to our attention: our parents and dear ones, our friends and pets, and even occasionally our enemies die. And on top of everything politics may take against us publicly and decree that our innocence is guilt.

How are we calmly to await the capital punishment in store for all of us? How are we to ignore nature's existential threats, which too often prove not to have been empty? How are we to stand up against the menaces of tyranny, and its new instruments of policy supplied by science, chemical torture, nuclear weapons? How are we to exist in a country swarming with paid informers and false witnesses, confined there, denied freedom to travel and free speech, subject to constant surveillance by a secret police force, and random purges, and genocide and organised famine, without the benefit of law, but containing a man-made purgatory in its archipelago of concentration camps, which are probably a short cut to heaven for the majority of inmates?

The easy answer to such questions is by being or becoming a hero and a saint.

Seriously, is there any other solution to the problem of pain?

Death is a different matter, or it can be. I mean that reason can alter our attitude to dying, whereas pain is ultimately beyond the help of reasoning. Everybody, each of us, has some defences, built-in or available, in these deathly regions.

The first is free will. It may be possible sometimes, before nature in morbid mood or the secret police get hold of us, to exercise the freedom of our healthy adult will and choose either to live or not to live. We do not always have to leave the manner of our death to disease, accident, conflict or the executioner.

Secondly we can choose to believe in resurrection. Disbelievers, atheists, put their faith in the power of their presumptuous brains. What evidence is there to prove mundane materialism is erroneous, they ask. And they mock with their awkward questions and pitying smiles: in what part of

287

the body is the soul located? Where does God live, where is heaven, and in what form are we going to ascend into it, or descend into hell? Are rats and worms resurrected too?

Perhaps people who argue that death is the end of everything are more soulless than they know, in that, right or wrong, they have no solace for the poor or the old or the ill or the disadvantaged. And perhaps because their humanism is misunderstood, they are deeply implicated in the inhumanity of this God-forsaken century: for their philosophy of life, offering no second chance, no consolation prize or compensation, has fostered demands for instant wealth, health and happiness which prudent government cannot satisfy, and has led to unrest, strife and oppression.

Moreover irreligion is even worse than religion at answering awkward questions. Atheism is unable to give any explanation whatsoever of the creation of the universe. Since it admits that it does not know – has no idea – where we came from, why should it know better than anyone where we are going or not going?

Whatever lies beyond the grave is the subject of guesswork. At least religion is able to claim the support of nature for its guesses. For nature, notwithstanding its prodigality in another sense, wastes nothing. Fair exchange, not robbery, is its habit. And considering it would not waste our bodies, which as corpses are intended to enrich the earth and feed the creatures that dwell therein and thereon, why should it waste our souls?

Certainly living souls are elusive. But experience, friendship, love and even science acknowledge that under our typical skins, out of reach of physiology and psychology, differing somehow from personality and character, and tainted neither by tribulations nor age, is an essence or spark peculiar to ourselves.

Whether to call it our metabolism or our soul, whether to guess it survives or does not survive death, and whether or not to accept the teachings of every religion I have come across in respect of an afterlife, is part of everyone's birthright of choice.

Just supposing we choose to make the requisite act of faith, and allow ourselves to be convinced that we shall rise from the dead, the prospect before us brightens considerably. Although I have heard cynics say that they dread the reunion with forgotten spouses and former lovers and discarded mistresses and so on, most of us are relieved to believe the promises of religion. We anticipate death with unwonted equanimity. A few even look forward to it.

Thus our lives are to some extent liberated from the natural, economic, social and political ills they may be heir to. A tyrant can still hurt us; but the threat to kill us will have lost its compulsive force. Tyrants wield less power over those who are less afraid to die.

Religion is resurrection; and religion is the opium of the people, according to Marx. Yet Marxism has by now been proved to be a mere drug, keeping the masses quiet temporarily, but none of its promises about dictatorship withering away, or liberty, equality and fraternity; while the charge against religion is not proven.

And speaking for myself as one of the masses, I would far rather be kept quiet by hope, the hope of justice, peace and plenty, and liberation from terror and oppression in the next heavenly world, than by despair in this one, despairing of protecting my individuality from the dogma, incompetence and essential elementary cruelty of Marxism.

Is it religion that has – up to a point – and via the sermons of her new reverend friend Victor Holt – come to the rescue of Rachel?

Rescue is a relative term. A man removed from a house on fire, who then expires, was rescued. If ever I write about people in the process of rescuing themselves from Collectivism, I must qualify any reference to a silver lining. The exceptional sufferings of Russia under the heel of Marxism may in the long long run have a redemptive

289

effect. And the exemplary and horrifying fiasco of Marxism-Leninism-Stalinism may have persuaded other countries, including my own, not to embrace a similar fate. But does Communism learn from its mistakes? Will the vast bureaucracy of the USSR agree to its abolition? Do secret police forces purge themselves?

Who dares to be complacent?

Nevertheless, now that our year in Lewes is nearly over, I can claim that it has not been completely barren. Optimism would say it has rescued me from pessimism. I have lived to witness my sister's moral victory in the battle with her illness, which she may have lost.

THE MARRIAGE OF FIGARO taught me other lessons.

People are ridiculed for saying: 'I don't know much about art, but I do know what I like' – in fact the most perceptive comment it is possible to make on the subject. Rules of art, immutable criteria, do not exist. The greatest art means the most fashionable at a particular time: though never for ever, as proved by the rise and fall and fall and rise of the arts of ancient Greece, revived in the Italian Renaissance and now again out of favour; by the reputation of Spohr, who was considered to be at least the equal of Beethoven; by Mozart's burial in the paupers' grave, and van Gogh's failure to sell a single picture in his lifetime, and best-selling authors sinking into oblivion, and so on.

Fortunately for me, *Figaro* is in fashion. And I know I liked it. And the best explanation of its effect is probably the witty paradox which states that nothing but music and silence tell us the truth.

That evening at Glyndebourne, a sort of climax of our sojourn here, reminded me of my courting days.

I was not too happy when I met Gem. My youth had been squandered conscientiously, soldiering, looking after my mother and her property, trying to make ends meet and do my best for family retainers, and waiting to come into the little that was eventually left of my inheritance. But a young man does not live by the bread of good intentions only. In my case the wise saw could be abbreviated thus: a young man does not live alone. My saving grace, which persuaded me to put up with the army and filial duties and other frustrations, was the love of a good woman.

Mama and Rachel were against it and her: my friends at Boltbridge ditto. They regretted my lack of marriage, children, heirs. They never acknowledged the debt they all owed. For if I had been a husband and father I would not have had so much free time to lavish on looking after them. Besides, I never craved children; and at the end of the day what would mine have inherited?

The idea of attachment is outmoded. The permissiveness of the post-pill and pre-AIDS era laughed it to scorn. Yet there really is a love, a secular love as well as a religious one, that will not let you go.

In my experience and hers, against our expectations and almost against our wills, the weeks and months and years of our association mounted up. When things were not as good as they had been, strain and easing it preoccupied us to the exclusion of keeping an eye on the clock. And the hands of the clock are like scissors that snip away at irregular unions.

We kept on agreeing we ought to part, but could not. It was too soon to detach ourselves, then too late. The last of many last goodbyes was a dreadful wrench.

And I loathed my loveless wasted stupid life. Diversion was not consolation. More precious time sped by.

One Sunday morning in summer I walked from Boltbridge Manor across the fields to Rachel's house for lunch: Mama drove there. It was the finest weather. Rachel was entertaining neighbours, a couple called Kendall, and their weekend guest, feminine, fair-haired and unmarried, Gemma by name.

After lunch and a short tour of the garden I departed with

291

Mama, who observed in the car that Gemma was charming and I ought to try to see her again.

'What I ought to do is marry her,' I returned.

I loved Gem at first sight for her beauty, as distinguished as it was seductive, her gentleness, responsiveness, high–class ease of manner, laughter; and felt an indefinable affinity for or with her or between us.

In the garden, standing near her amongst the flowers in the sunlight, my belief in happiness had ever so tentatively revived, and I suggested a further meeting in London, having already discovered that she too lived there.

'Yes – how kind – how nice – thank you,' she said, or agreeable unspoilt words to that effect.

But in London I could get no reply from her telephone number, and the same applied to the postcard and then the brief letter I wrote her. Six weeks passed. I drew the fairly obvious conclusion that wonderful young women were not waiting on their marks to sprint to the altar with depressed middle-aged men.

I rang once more. She answered – she told me she had been away. I invited her out to lunch, and to dinner on another day, on the neutral ground of restaurants. Both occasions were delightful so far as I was concerned; and she seemed to enjoy them. After we had dined together, I drove her home, parked outside the block of flats and declared myself.

She said she was already involved – she was sorry – it was difficult to explain – she hoped I did or would understand.

Oh yes, I assured her, I understood perfectly, and it was for me to apologise; and I got out of the car and opened the passenger door and bade her good night and drove off.

Time elapsed, four or five days – it was the nadir of my life.

Chances such as Gem represented, I realised, are offered to no one twice. I loved her the more for knowing her, even if she loved me less. Sexual chemistry apart, I admired her cheerful yet sympathetic temperament, her values, her clothes, the interior decoration of her flat, the work she did for charitable organisations, her dog – another Cairn terrier, called Sadie, the predecessor of Cinders. Communication with her was or had been addictive. We would communicate no more. The parallel lines of our acquaintanceship would never touch. I must go and bury myself at Boltbridge, and settle for the solitary and disappointing destiny evidently reserved for me.

But queries as it were shook rebellious fists at my acquiescence. What had Gem thought she was doing, letting me get fond of her, if she belonged to my rival? I could not believe she had been flirting and teasing: could I therefore have misunderstood her – she had said her situation was difficult to explain? Could it be that the admission of her tie to another implied a wish to be untied?

I would find out. I would put my cards on the table: the point was that I trusted her. She would be at least discreet – and I had nothing more to lose.

I invited her to dinner in the flat where I then resided.

She accepted; and I thought or hoped that I detected in her voice on the telephone a note of relief at hearing from me again.

WE GREETED each other and chatted with remarkably little constraint, though I noticed that her appetite for food was no better than mine.

As soon as dinner was done I said my piece, bared my soul, hardly permitting her to interrupt for half an hour or more.

At the end she confessed that she also had been unhappy – miserable – fearing all was over between us because of her inaccurate or incomplete disclosure in respect of her emotional situation.

Thereupon, as in a rare movie in good taste, the picture dissolves.

We began to live – or I did – happily ever after: we were married some three weeks later.

Our meeting was miraculous. And I could love no other woman as I love my wife. But, if honesty is the best policy, and despite my doubts that it is, I would have to admit that I cannot go every inch of the way with traditional Western romanticism. I do not believe that each of us is the half of a whole, and must scour the planet to find our missing segment and unify ourselves. Statistics back up my incredulity: although in one sense too many marriages are unhappy, in another sense there are too many happy ones – miracles are not all that uncommon.

The above is by no means to say that our courtship did lack, and our marriage has lacked, romance: on the contrary.

And in passing I would wag a finger at that aberration of feminism: opposition to the married state. Every lover, everyone capable of love, knows that he or she would bind the beloved object to himself or herself by matrimony, law, custom, private methods and hoops of steel.

But the encouraging old story that I would like to tell, or corroborate, fraught with more romance in my view than the exclusive uncertainty of strict romanticism, is that there are always loving opportunities, opportunities to love and even to be loved and happy, whatever diffidence, fastidiousness, disillusion and despondency may suggest.

The risks Gem and I took, as we contemplate them retrospectively and recall the thirty-three per cent of marriages ending in divorce in this country, make our flesh creep. We scarcely knew each other: we had met seven times, and spent perhaps twenty-four hours together, when I proposed to marry her and she agreed to be married. I could have turned out to be a sadist or drug-addict or bi-sexual or criminal, impatient to persecute my wife. She might have become a promiscuous spendthrift irresponsible unpunctual shrew.

Yet both of us, without hesitation, cast native caution aside.

Cynics will believe they can spell the reason for our recklessness with three letters of the alphabet: S and E and X. Marxism would bawl that Gem and I joined forces the better to exploit the working-class. But exploitation has done us no material good that we are aware of; and the sort of sex that explains everything is sick.

No – I knew I wanted to wed Gem as soon as I set eyes on her; and she has admitted that she felt more or less the same, although inhibited by a previous partial commitment. We were compatible; and time has put its authority behind the idea of our compatibility. Where are such marriages made, if not in heaven? How is good luck to be accounted for, except by reference to nature, fate, destiny, fortune – to supernatural regulation, which reserves the right to be nice to us as well as nasty?

To love anyone is to give a hostage to fortune. Tyranny, the Marxist-Leninist-Stalinist version in particular, is well aware of that alarming adage. Tyranny impersonates fortune in a criminal sense, and blackmails its prisoners by tormenting their dear ones even to death. A citizen of our benign democracy has no more to fear from fortune but that it will visit accident or disease, not to mention old age, on the head of the beloved.

My anxiety, my concern for Gem, in case something should happen to her, as the tactful Anglo-Saxon euphemism describes it, are alleviated on reflection by virtue of the soul. Her pain would be no less difficult to bear. Having impotently to observe and imagine the pain borne by those we love is bound to be painful. I think of Rachel. I flinch from the possibility that Gem will be equally unwell, and that I will. And death overshadows all. But I resolutely refuse to believe, I do not have the courage to believe, that death is final, the fullstop, nothingness, that thrifty nature would waste us, and that the unique brave particle, recognised as the soul in the very dawn of language, will not survive.

It will no doubt change, mutate. The so-called next world will surely resemble this one, this universe, in being utterly beyond our comprehension. Still, experience and religion combine to reassure me that our end must be a beginning. Not only the representatives of our species with the biggest and best brains have arrived at the same conclusion as yours truly; Mrs Spedding who expects to be reunited with her budgerigar Tim on the other side, and Bertha Prior who killed her living dog in the firm conviction that she was thus re-uniting it with her dead one, also support me. And Mrs Spedding and Bertha are country types, country sparrows, which, as they say, are not fooled by chaff.

Gem has rendered me services over and above revealing the availability of happiness through love, and the necessity and benefits of faith in our resurrection.

She inspired me, after the dinner we could neither of us eat, to speak my mind as never before, and she crowned my suit with success.

I cannot claim that my record ever since has been a brilliant reversal of my tendency to fail. I have not made my name or any careerist mark. Yet even at this late stage of my life I am not too uneasy to find myself with so little to show for it. I remember that other self, summoned from nowhere by my future wife, which in a matter of minutes transformed failure into success, and might materialise again.

My book is not written.

And now I want to write it not about cruel political creeds and deeds, nor spies, traitors, disloyalty, ingratitude, wickedness.

The pain and the grief that move and motivate can be, and somehow should be, transmuted into pleasure.

Think of *The Marriage of Figaro*: the music says everything. Death does not figure: for me it is nonetheless reckoned with, accepted and, in Biblical terminology, conquered. The deathlessness of the art drops telling hints on the subject of mortality and immortality. And the last song confirms that

296

at least the aching of soft hearts is curable: for 'love can turn trials and tribulations into laughter and happiness.'

To drag Mozart into the argument about my writing is impertinent. But what is the art of genius for, if not enjoyment and, in context, comparison?

Nothing is certain, whether or not I write, what I write, where we live, if we live – nothing. Unpredictability is the redeeming feature of living and dying. Rachel may survive me. We must not forget that a moment can make all the difference: my sorrows became joys momentarily.

Perhaps it would be easier to give negative examples of the unpredictability of life and death. But this century, more than any other, has had its fill of calamity and the imminence thereof.

As for books, long ones are written in a short time.

In the meanwhile – never mind!